MEASURED AIR LEAKAGE OF BUILDINGS

A symposium
sponsored by
ASTM Committee E-6
on Performance of
Building Constructions
Philadelphia, PA, 2–3 April 1984

ASTM SPECIAL TECHNICAL PUBLICATION 904
Heinz R. Trechsel, H. R. Trechsel Associates,
and Peter L. Lagus, S-Cubed, editors

ASTM Publication Code Number (PCN)
04-904000-10

 1916 Race Street, Philadelphia, PA 19103

Library of Congress Cataloging in Publication Data

Measured air leakage of buildings.

(ASTM special technical publication; 904)
"ASTM publication code number (PCN) 04-904000-10."
Includes bibliographies and index.
1. Buildings—Airtightness—Measurement—Congresses.
I. Trechsel, Heinz R.   II. Lagus, Peter L.   III. ASTM
Committee E-6 on Performance of Building Construction.
IV. Series.
TH6025.M42   1986   697.9   86-10953
ISBN 0-8031-0469-3

NOTE

The Society is not responsible, as a body,
for the statements and opinions
advanced in this publication.

Printed in Ann Arbor, MI
August 1986

Foreword

This publication, Measured Air Leakage of Buildings, contains papers presented at the symposium on Measured Air Leakage Performance of Buildings, which was held at the Philadelphia Centre Hotel, Philadelphia, PA, 2–3 April 1984. The symposium was sponsored by ASTM Committee E-6 on Performance of Building Constructions. H. R. Trechsel, R. A. Grot, M. H. Sherman, D. T. Harrje, and P. L. Lagus presided as symposium chairmen and H. R. Trechsel and P. L. Lagus were editors of this publication.

Related
ASTM Publications

Building Air Change Rate and Infiltration Measurements, STP 719 (1980), 04-719000-10

Building Seals and Sealants, STP 606 (1976), 04-606000-10

A Note of Appreciation
to Reviewers

The quality of the papers that appear in this publication reflects not only the obvious efforts of the authors but also the unheralded, though essential, work of the reviewers. On behalf of ASTM we acknowledge with appreciation their dedication to high professional standards and their sacrifice of time and effort.

ASTM Committee on Publications

ASTM Editorial Staff

Contents

Introduction

On 12 March 1978, ASTM Subcommittee E06.41 on Infiltration Performances sponsored a symposium in Washington, D.C., on Air Change Rate and Infiltration Measurements. At that symposium, the first two standard test methods for determining air infiltration in buildings developed by the subcommittee were presented together with papers dealing with related topics such as field studies, indoor air pollution, air infiltration reduction, energy implications, and innovative measurement methods then not yet considered for standardization. The results of that symposium were published in Building Air Change Rate and Infiltration Measurements, ASTM STP 719.

In discussions of the 1978 symposium, the question about required, or desirable, air infiltration rates was raised. However, as stated in the final discussion at that symposium, "The question of how tight is tight enough has not been answered, nor was it the purpose of this symposium to provide this answer." In 1984, that answer was still not available.

However, designers, builders, regulators, owners, and those involved with the design and application of equipment to heat and cool buildings do need such answers. Innumerable telephone calls as well as written requests were received from persons who all essentially said, "Now that we know how to measure air infiltration and air change rates in buildings, how do we know what results we should expect or demand? In other words, what are acceptable performance levels?"

While we still do not have final answers, many studies have been completed that do indicate what infiltration rates were measured in actual buildings. These rates, together with calculated rates, do give at least some guidance to those needing to know the levels of infiltration performance that can be expected and that are achievable. Thus, it was felt it would be useful to bring together practitioners and researchers; the 1984 symposium on Measured Air Leakage Performance of Buildings was organized for this reason.

The symposium not only uncovered a wealth of data on measured infiltration rates in various building types and climates but also provided an opportunity to discuss related issues of mathematical modeling and prediction of air infiltration rates, methods for infiltration reduction and their effectiveness, and new proposed methods of measuring infiltration. It is hoped that this publication, which contains most of the papers presented, will be useful to both researchers and those engaged in designing and regulating the design of buildings and their equipment by providing data on measured air changes and infiltration rates achieved in existing buildings and by documenting some of the more widely used models and infiltration reduction methods.

Heinz R. Trechsel

Heinz R. Trechsel Associates, Germantown, MD 20874; symposium cochairman and coeditor

P. L. Lagus

S-Cubed, La Jolla, CA 92038; symposium co-chairman and coeditor

Residential

Peter L. Lagus[1] and John C. King[2]

Air Leakage and Fan Pressurization Measurements in Selected Naval Housing

REFERENCE: Lagus, P. L. and King. J. C., **"Air Leakage and Fan Pressurization Measurements in Selected Naval Housing,"** *Measured Air Leakage of Buildings, ASTM STP 904,* H. R. Trechsel and P. L. Lagus, Eds., American Society for Testing and Materials, Philadelphia, 1986, pp. 5-16.

ABSTRACT: Data from detailed tracer concentration decay and induced pressurization measurements were obtained in tests of duplex and row apartments at Norfolk, Virginia and Pensacola, Florida to accurately determine air leakage characteristics of selected naval housing. Local meteorological information also was collected to facilitate comparison of predicted versus measured air leakage rates. For the Norfolk data, the 4-Pa leakage areas inferred from pressurization/depressurization measurements are uniformly lower than those calculated from the measured tracer dilution air leakage rate via the Sherman air leakage model.

Considerable tracer dilution testing was performed on a single unit of duplex housing at Pensacola. Air leakage testing within rooms of this unit disclosed a uniformly low air leakage rate. The data also illustrated the directional nature of air leakage in a duplex. Of particular additional interest were two measurements taken over a 24-h period utilizing a single tracer injection followed by monitoring of dilution decay. Samples were taken by the container method and analyzed.

KEY WORDS: infiltration, tracer dilution method, fan pressurization, air leakage, sulfur hexafluoride, automated air leakage measurement, leakage area

This paper presents induced pressurization and tracer concentration decay measurements performed in naval housing at Norfolk, Virginia and Pensacola, Florida. In both locations, air leakage or air infiltration data or both were required to fulfill a need by the local naval civil engineering center. In the case of the Norfolk data, measurements were undertaken to understand whether addition of insulation to uninsulated or poorly insulated structures would reduce air leakage [1-3]. In the case of the Pensacola data, the mea-

[1]Manager, Applied Science Program, S-CUBED, La Jolla, CA 92038.
[2]Mechanical engineer, Naval Civil Engineering Laboratory, Port Hueneme, CA 93043.

surements were undertaken to accurately characterize air leakage rates within selected structures in order to assist an ongoing research program into the causes of moisture damage within housing in and around Naval Air Station (NAS) Pensacola [4]. During these studies, a quantity of tracer dilution and induced pressurization data were collected, along with attendant meteorological information. These data are presented and discussed in this paper.

Air leakage measurements by the tracer dilution method were performed as per ASTM Method for Determining Air Leakage Rate by Tracer Dilution Test (E 741-83). Tracer dilution data were obtained using an S-CUBED Model 215AUP Envirometer portable tracer gas monitor or the Model 215ACA/ARM automated infiltration monitoring system. Both of these units are owned by the Naval Civil Engineering Laboratory. Indoor temperatures were obtained using the thermometers on individual housing unit thermostats. Outdoor temperatures and wind speeds were obtained from meteorological data routinely taken at NAS Pensacola, or by means of a Meteorology Research, Inc. mechanical weather station at Norfolk. In addition, induced pressurization measurements were performed as per ASTM Method for Determining Air Leakage Rate by Fan Pressurization Test (E 779-81) using Gadzco blower door assemblies.

Norfolk Data

Air leakage measurements in 24 separate three-bedroom apartment units of enlisted personnel housing in the Willoughby Bay area of the Norfolk Naval Base were performed during winter and summer of 1978. These 24 units were segregated into four sixplexes, differentiated only by degree of insulation and orientation.

Sulfur hexafluoride (SF_6) was introduced into the structure through the heating, ventilating, and air-conditioning (HVAC) ducting from outside the structure. The HVAC system was allowed to run for 45 min prior to the onset of measurement. This mixing time provided reasonably homogeneous SF_6 concentrations within the structures. The HVAC blower operated continuously during the testing. Concentration decay was monitored by drawing a sample from the duct and analyzing it with the portable gas chromatograph. Samples were drawn from the ventilation duct using disposable 12-cm^3 polypropylene syringes.

A plot plan of the sixplexes is shown on Fig. 1. Living units are identified by street addresses on O'Connor Crescent. Note that wind directions around 360 and 180° tend to impinge all apartments equally, while winds from 90 to 270° directly impinge only one apartment in each sixplex.

Individual apartment units were nominally identical, two-story, slab-on-grade, three-bedroom apartments, having roughly 102 m^2 of living space. They were clad with continuous aluminum siding. A typical floor plan is shown on Fig. 2. Gas-fired forced air provided heating, and electric air-condi-

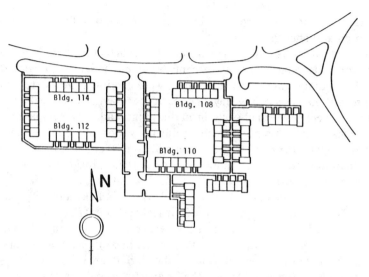

FIG. 1—*Willoughby Bay housing units.*

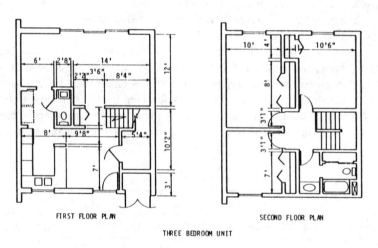

FIRST FLOOR PLAN   SECOND FLOOR PLAN

THREE BEDROOM UNIT

FIG. 2—*Floor plan of typical three bedroom apartments measured during this study.*

tioning provided cooling. Heating and cooling were accomplished through a common ducting system. The gas-fired heater, as well as the HVAC blower, were accessible from an external utility room.

Separate measurements in four apartments similar to those under study showed that two units exhibited no change in the measured infiltration rate due to duct leakage, and two units exhibited a 25% increase in measured infiltration rate due to duct leakage. These data were obtained by performing two tracer dilution measurements in succession, one with the HVAC blower system on and one with it off.

On successive days, one apartment unit from each of the buildings was selected for measurement. The apartments occupied the same relative position in each building with respect to ambient wind conditions and were sequentially measured on successive days. For each apartment, two air leakage measurements were performed—one in midmorning and one in midafternoon. These measurements were performed during winter and summer time periods. The winter period provided higher wind speeds and temperature differences than did the summer data. These data, then, provide four nominally independent measurements of infiltration. Raw data are summarized in Tables 1 through 4, which provide wind speed (W_2), wind direction (Θ), temperature differences (ΔT), and measured air leakage rates (I).

Some of the infiltration rates measured are considerably higher than might first be expected. Note, however, that the winter measurements were obtained during a period of near-record winds in the Norfolk area.

It should be emphasized that in the 24 apartment units tested no attempt was made to block or modify obvious sources of leakage such as bathroom vents, kitchen blowers, etc. All of the apartments were occupied during testing. The residents were asked to minimize ingress and egress. All data were taken, otherwise, on an "as available" basis.

In the summer of 1980, pressurization measurements were performed in all of these apartments as per ASTM Standard E 779-81. Pressurization and evacuation measurements were performed using either two or three blowers simultaneously, with flow measurements obtained in the apartment of interest. Adjacent blowers served to equalize pressures within adjacent apartments, eliminating or at least minimizing cross-apartment leakage. Blowers

TABLE 1—*Data from Building 108.*

Unit/Time	Winter Data				Summer Data			
	$\Delta T,°C$	W_s, m/s	Θ, °	I, ACH	ΔT, °C	W_s, m/s	Θ, °	I, ACH
8118/a.m.	24	2.5	345	1.03	3	2.2	255	0.52
8118/p.m.	22	2.1	290	0.85	7	1.7	360	0.76
8119/a.m.	24	1.5	. . .[a]	1.09	1	3.0	030	0.92
8119/p.m.	23	3.0	290	0.84	3	2.5	050	0.81
8120/a.m.	27	4.1	320	1.02	2	3.5	010	1.49
8120/p.m.	24	4.8	285	0.96	0	3.6	025	1.29
8121/a.m.	19	9.1	255	1.96	2	2.3	010	0.62
8121/p.m.	15	8.7	260	1.35	0	2.5	025	0.58
8122/a.m.	9	10.5	240	2.41	2	2.3	060	0.64
8122/p.m.	10	10.4	240	2.50	5	2.5	040	0.78
8123/a.m.	9	4.3	140	0.94	6	1.7	260	0.60
8123/p.m.	4	6.4	180	1.65	10	1.9	260	0.52

[a]Wind shift of 65° during test—from 75° during first half to 10° during second half.

TABLE 2—*Data from Building 114.*

Unit/Time	Winter Data				Summer Data			
	ΔT,°C	W_s, m/s	Θ, °	I, ACH	ΔT, °C	W_s, m/s	Θ, °	I, ACH
8160/a.m.	24	2.5	345	1.23	7	2.2	255	0.60
8160/p.m.	22	2.1	290	1.11	10	1.7	360	0.79
8161/a.m.	21	1.5	...[a]	1.06	6	3.0	030	0.83
8161/p.m.	20	3.0	290	0.96	8	2.5	050	0.63
8162/a.m.	26	4.1	320	1.63	3	3.5	010	1.10
8162/p.m.	23	4.8	285	1.28	0	3.6	025	1.36
8163/a.m.	22	9.1	255	1.62	1	2.3	010	0.99
8163/p.m.	18	8.7	260	1.51	2	2.5	025	0.88
8164/a.m.	15	10.5	240	2.53	1	2.3	060	0.61
8164/p.m.	16	10.4	240	2.73	4	2.5	040	0.67
8165/a.m.	8	4.8	140	0.78	5	1.7	260	0.68
8165/p.m.	3	6.4	180	1.40	9	1.9	260	0.52

[a]Wind shift of 65° during test—from 75° during first half to 10° during second half.

TABLE 3—*Data from Building 110.*

Unit/Time	Winter Data				Summer Data			
	ΔT,°C	W_s, m/s	Θ, °	I, ACH	ΔT, °C	W_s, m/s	Θ, °	I, ACH
8130/a.m.	9	4.8	140	0.68	4	1.7	260	0.51
8130/p.m.	4	6.4	180	1.16	8	1.9	260	0.62
8131/a.m.	14	10.5	240	2.35	1	2.3	060	0.56
8131/p.m.	15	10.4	240	2.34	4	2.5	040	0.75
8132/a.m.	23	9.1	255	1.91	2	3.5	010	0.99
8132/p.m.	19	8.7	260	1.58	0	3.6	025	1.04
8133/a.m.	26	4.1	320	0.85	2	3.5	010	0.85
8133/p.m.	23	4.8	285	0.82	0	3.6	025	1.25
8134/a.m.	24	1.5	...[a]	1.05	6	3.0	030	0.76
8134/p.m.	23	3.0	290	0.94	8	2.5	050	0.87
8135/a.m.	29	2.5	345	0.81	2	2.2	255	0.51
8135/p.m.	22	2.1	290	0.77	6	1.7	360	0.58

[a]Wind shift of 65° during test—from 75° during first half to 10° during second half.

were standard blower-door units obtained from Gadzco, Inc. of Princeton, New Jersey. Pressurization and evacuation tests were performed in each of the 24 apartments at positive and negative pressures of 25, 50, and 75 Pa. For these 24 apartments, the cross-apartment leakage at 50 Pa averaged 14% of the single blower flow rate and varied from a low of 7% to a high of 24%.

The Sherman air leakage model [5–7] allows calculation of infiltration rates in a structure under specified wind and temperature conditions. The model requires a measure of the 4-Pa leakage area. This is normally obtained from the least squares fit to induced pressurization data. Sherman and co-

TABLE 4—*Data from Building 112.*

Unit/Time	Winter Data				Summer Data			
	ΔT,°C	W_s, m/s	Θ, °	I, ACH	ΔT, °C	W_s, m/s	Θ, °	I, ACH
8148/a.m.	10	4.8	140	0.85	6	1.7	260	0.60
8148/p.m.	6	6.4	180	1.70	10	1.9	260	0.47
8149/a.m.	14	10.5	240	2.77	1	2.3	060	0.51
8149/p.m.	16	10.4	240	2.44	2	2.5	040	0.66
8150/a.m.	21	9.1	255	3.73	6	3.5	010	0.87
8150/p.m.	17	8.7	260	2.00	3	3.6	025	1.26
8151/a.m.	24	4.1	320	0.97	2	3.5	010	1.02
8151/p.m.	22	4.8	285	0.84	0	3.6	025	1.05
8152/a.m.	23	1.5	...^{a}	1.01	5	3.6	030	0.67
8152/p.m.	23	3.0	290	0.86	7	2.5	050	0.70
8153/a.m.	29	2.5	345	0.98	7	2.2	255	0.30
8153/p.m.	26	2.1	290	1.06	10	1.7	360	0.55

^{a}Wind shift of 65° during test—from 75° during first half to 10° during second half.

workers [7] also point out that it is possible to use tracer dilution data to force a fit with the Sherman air leakage model and thereby calculate an equivalent leakage area as sensed by a tracer dilution measurement. The 4-Pa leakage area, as determined by the average leakage area under both pressurization and evacuation, is presented in Table 5. Also included is a calculation of the leakage area by forcing a fit to the tracer dilution infiltration rate. Infiltration values used in obtaining the equivalent leakage area were obtained by averaging the four infiltration measurements provided in Tables 1 through 4. This value, along with an estimate of building volume (249 m³), allows calculation of the tracer infiltration "sensed" leakage area.

Note that, for these particular data, the tracer dilution measurement is consistent with a leakage area two to three times larger than that predicted from the pressurization data. A major source of uncertainty in calculating leakage areas from the tracer dilution data for these units is in the assumption of averaging overall wind directions implicit in the Sherman air leakage model. At least some of this difference may be attributable to directional effects. While wind direction data are provided, no attempt at incorporating these data into the analyses was made. Agreements of factors of two or three, however, are extremely useful in an engineering sense and illustrate that it is possible to utilize tracer measurements to obtain leakage areas for the purposes of comparison or for further model calculation.

Measurements at Pensacola, Florida

Measurements in selected naval housing at Pensacola, Florida were performed during the summer, winter, fall, and spring of 1982/1983. Data were required to characterize air leakage rates in selected structures in order to

TABLE 5—*Leakage area[a] calculated from pressurization/evacuation and tracer dilution data.*

Apartment Number	A_O, Pressurization/ Evacuation	A_O, Tracer[b]
8165	0.038	0.065
8164	0.048	0.074
8163	0.042	0.089
8162	0.038	0.088
8161	0.049	0.073
8160	0.039	0.080
8135	0.036	0.063
8134	0.033	0.074
8133	0.047	0.065
8132	0.046	0.069
8131	0.048	0.071
8130	0.036	0.058
8153	0.036	0.058
8152	0.062	0.067
8151	0.039	0.067
8150	0.039	0.087
8149	0.055	0.072
8148	0.038	0.066
8123	0.040	0.066
8122	0.036	0.075
8121	0.026	0.063
8120	0.053	0.083
8119	0.030	0.081
8118	0.044	0.073

[a]Area units are in m^2.

[b]Calculated from the Sherman air leakage model, assuming: (1) Sherman Class II terrain parameters; (2) Sherman Class III shielding coefficients; (3) Sherman model parameters of $R = 0.3$, $x = 0$, and $h = 3$; and (4) meterological data taken at a height of 2.6 m.

assist ongoing research into the causes of moisture damage within naval housing in and around Pensacola, Florida [4,8,9].

Many of the measurements were performed in an unoccupied unit of a duplex within the Corey Field housing complex. These units are slab-on-grade, single-story construction with concrete block walls and have very tightly weather-stripped doors and windows. A drawing of a typical floor plan is included on Fig. 3. The HVAC system is contained inside the structure in a separate utility room. The air-conditioning exchange condenser is located on a concrete slab immediately in front of the duplex unit. The floor area of the 2363A unit is approximately 102 m^2.

With the HVAC system running in the Corey unit, it was determined that approximately 30 min were required to obtain a roughly homogeneous SF_6

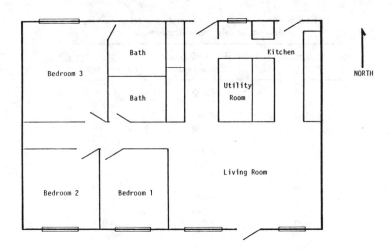

FIG. 3—*Schematic floor plan for 2363A Corey.*

and air mixture. Tracer decay measurements were initiated, therefore, 30 min after SF_6 introduction.

Selected tracer data are presented in Table 6 and discussed in following paragraphs. On 12 Aug. 1982, initial tests were performed with the HVAC system on and off. No change in the leakage rate was noted between the two HVAC states under essentially constant meteorological conditions. Accordingly, for this unit, the contribution to the measured air change with the HVAC system operating appears to be negligible. Air leakage rates with the unit having zero, one, and two doors open under similar meteorological conditions are presented.

Data taken on 13 Aug. 1982 are particularly interesting in that a measurement centered at 1000 h exhibited an infiltration rate of essentially zero. Immediately after that, with meteorological conditions unchanged, the HVAC fan was turned off within the structure, and the kitchen and two bath vent fans were turned on. The air leakage rates within the structure immediately increased to 0.75 air changes per hour (ACH). This 0.75 air change rate is greater than any air change rate measured in the period 12 Aug. 1982 through 28 April 1983. Thus, for this particular structure, the functioning of the kitchen and bathroom vents can assist materially the interchange of inside and outside air.

Data obtained in the 2363A unit on 17 Nov. 1982 and 18 Nov. 1982 under comparable wind speed and temperature differences indicate the magnitude of air leakage within the living room and three bedrooms, respectively. In particular, note that the air leakage in Bedroom No. 1 is noticeably less than the leakage in all other rooms measured. All leakages measured are low when compared to, for instance, air leakage measurements in naval housing at Nor-

TABLE 6—*Selected air leakage data for 2363A Corey.*

Date	Time[a]	I	ΔT, °C	θ, °	V, m/s	Comments
8/12/82	1730	0.19	3	. . .	7.2	all doors closed/HVAC on
	1745	3.2	3	. . .	7.2	front door open/HVAC on
	1750	36	3	. . .	7.2	front back doors open/HVAC on
8/13/82	1000	0.01	7	. . .	3.1	HVAC on
	1010	0.75	7	. . .	3.1	HVAC off/kitchen baths fans on
11/17/82	1400	0.19	3	090	4.1	HVAC on
	1525	0.16	2	090	4.6	HVAC off/in Living room
	1525	0.04	2	090	4.6	HVAC off/Bedroom 1 door open
	1525	0.11	2	090	4.6	HVAC off/Bedroom 2 door open
	1525	0.16	2	090	4.6	HVAC off/Bedroom 3 door open
11/18/82	1045	0.25	3	160	4.6	HVAC off/in Living room
	1045	0.07	3	160	4.6	HVAC off/Bedroom 1 door closed
	1045	0.25	3	160	4.6	HVAC off/Bedroom 2 door closed
	1045	0.22	3	160	4.6	HVAC off/Bedroom 3 door closed

[a]Figures are in military time.

folk, Virginia. These data also demonstrate the direction-dependent nature of air leakage in the duplex. The leakage rate on 18 Nov. 1982 is roughly 75% greater than that measured on 17 Nov. 1982, even though wind speed and temperature differences are roughly identical. However, the wind direction on 17 Nov. 1982 during the measurement period was from the east (90°), while on 18 Nov. 1982 it was from almost due west (160°). Thus, winds on 18 Nov. 1982 impinged on the 2363A duplex directly, while on 17 Nov. 1983 they impinged on its companion unit 2363B, with 2363A being downwind. Note also that the measurements taken with 2363A indicate that Bedroom No. 1 exhibits an extraordinarily low infiltration rate. In fact, the equivalent ventilation rate is less than the 8.5 m³/h (5 ft³/m) per person recommended in ASHRAE Standard 62.

A few additional measurements were performed in several unoccupied units at Lexington Terrace. These units are considerably smaller—averaging approximately 65 m²—and are slab-on-grade construction.

Data were obtained on 18 Nov. 1982 and 19 Nov. 1982 in apartments at 333 and 375 Lexington Terrace. These data are notable in that they represent a 24-h tracer concentration decay measurement due to a single injection of tracer gas. It was not possible to utilize the HVAC in the Lexington Terrace apartments for continual mixing during the entire measurement period as the system could be used only for heating. Accordingly, the heater fan was used during the first hour of measurement to ensure mixing within the structure. After this, the fan was turned off. Subsequent measurements were taken using 60-cm³ polypropylene syringes. Five 10-cm³ samples were taken consecutively in each of five rooms within the structure, yielding a total average 50-cm³ sampler per data point. This sampling procedure is consistent with the container sampling technique contained within ASTM Standard E 741-83. Data are presented graphically in Fig. 4. Average temperature difference and wind speed over 24 h are 6°C and 2.6 m/s, respectively.

Pressurization and evacuation data were obtained for the 2363A Corey structure using both single- and double-blower doors. The average 4-Pa leak-

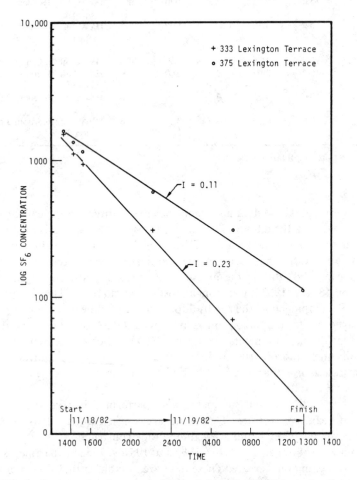

FIG. 4—*Concentration decay over a 24-h period in 333 and 375 Lexington Terrace.*

age area for pressurization and evacuation is 0.050 m². Calculation of infiltration rates, using this leakage area, led to values uniformly higher by factors of two to three than those measured by tracer dilution.

Pressurization and evacuation data, as well as tracer dilution measurements, also were obtained on Apartment 881 Umphill, which is the end unit of a sixplex located on the NAS Pensacola grounds. This unit is similar to the units measured at Norfolk in that it is an approximately 102 m², two-story, slab-on-grade construction. Simultaneous pressurization of 881 Umphill and the apartment immediately adjacent to it was performed so as to eliminate or minimize cross-apartment leakage. Tracer dilution air leakage measurements were performed over a single 24-h period, with samples taken every 10 min using the S-CUBED Model 215ACA/ARM automated infiltration monitoring system. Resultant data were segregated into 1-h blocks and then fit by least squares to an exponential decay in order to determine 1-h average infiltration rates.

Blower door data were notable in that the 4-Pa pressurization leakage area is identical to the 4-Pa depressurization data and in that the single- and double-blower door pressurization and evacuation data were indistinguishable. The 4-Pa leakage area determined for the 881 Umphill apartment was 0.048 m². Calculation of an hourly infiltration rate using this leakage area and the Sherman air leakage model yields values which agree with hourly tracer dilution values to within ±5%. However, the data set was limited to only 24 h of data.

Conclusions

A quantity of tracer dilution and induced pressurization data has been obtained for selected naval housing at Norfolk, Virginia and Pensacola, Florida. For the Norfolk test, pressurization data are consistent with leakage areas somewhat smaller than those calculated from tracer dilution measured infiltration rates and the Sherman air leakage model. On the other hand, pressurization data from the Pensacola structures are consistent with leakage areas somewhat larger than those calculated from measured tracer dilution rates and the Sherman air leakage model. Some of the Pensacola data illustrate the directional nature of the air leakage for row apartments and duplexes.

The tracer dilution air leakage rates for the Norfolk units are significantly higher than those measured in the Pensacola structures. The 4-Pa leakage areas for the units measured in the two locations, however, are comparable.

Summer tracer dilution air leakage rates for the Norfolk units range from 0.5 to 1.4 ACH, while air leakage rates for Pensacola range from less than 0.1 to 0.4 ACH. Winter tracer dilution rates for the Norfolk units range from 0.6 to almost 4.0 ACH, while winter rates for Pensacola range from 0.1 to almost 0.7 ACH.

Acknowledgments

Measurements at Norfolk, Virginia were performed under Contracts N68305-77-C-0045 and N68305-79-C-0034. Data obtained at Pensacola were gathered during performance of Contracts N62583/82M and N62583/83MT140.

References

[1] Lagus, P. L., "Air Leakage in Navy Housing," S-CUBED Report SSS-R-77-3179, prepared for Naval Construction Battalion Center S-CUBED, La Jolla, CA, 1977.

[2] Lagus, P. L., Ellefson, L. D., Broce, R. D., and Talkington, H. A., "Air Leakage Measurements and Energy Consumption Economic Analysis in Navy Housing at Norfolk, Virginia," S-CUBED Report SSS-R-80-4233, prepared for Naval Construction Battalion Center, S-CUBED, La Jolla, CA, Feb. 1980.

[3] Lagus, P. L., "Air Leakage Measurements in Navy Family Housing Units at Norfolk, Virginia," S-CUBED Report SSS-R-82-5288-1, prepared for Naval Construction Battalion Center, S-CUBED, La Jolla, CA, May 1982.

[4] Trechsel, H. R. and Achenbach, P. R., "Field Study on Moisture Problems in Exterior Walls of Family Housing Units at Naval Air Station, Pensacola, Florida," final report on Contract N62583/82 MT145, Naval Civil Engineering Laboratory, Port Hueneme, CA, Aug. 1983.

[5] Sherman, M. H. and Grimsrud, D. T., "Infiltration Pressurization Correlation: Simplified Physical Modeling," *ASHRAE Transactions*, Vol. 86, 1980.

[6] Sherman, M. H., "Air Infiltration in Buildings," Ph.D. thesis, University of California, Berkeley, 1981.

[7] Sherman, M. H. and Grimsrud, D. T., "Measurement of Infiltration Using Fan Pressurization and Weather Data," LBL Report No. 10852, Lawrence Berkeley Laboratory, Berkeley, CA, Oct. 1980.

[8] Lagus, P. L., "Building Air Leakage Tests and Measurements," S-CUBED Report SSS-R-83-6300, prepared for Naval Construction Battalion Center, S-CUBED, La Jolla, CA, Aug. 1983.

[9] Lagus, P. L., "Air Leakage Measurements in Naval Housing at Pensacola, Florida," S-CUBED Report SSS-R-84-6344, prepared for Naval Construction Battalion Center, S-CUBED, La Jolla, CA, Sept. 1983.

DISCUSSION

J. Griffith[1] *(written discussion)*—Was the Norfolk homes' test done with decay tracer?

P. L. Lagus and J. C. King (authors' closure)—Yes, the test was done per ASTM Method for Determining Air Leakage Rate by Tracer Dilution Test (E 741-83), which is specifically for tracer concentration decay.

[1]PSE&G Research Corp., Maplewood, NJ 07040.

Andrew K. Kim¹ and Chia Y. Shaw¹

Seasonal Variation in Airtightness of Two Detached Houses

REFERENCE: Kim, A. K. and Shaw, C. Y., **"Seasonal Variation in Airtightness of Two Detached Houses,"** *Measured Air Leakage of Buildings, ASTM STP 904*, H. R. Trechsel and P. L. Lagus, Eds., American Society for Testing and Materials, Philadelphia, 1986, pp. 17–32.

ABSTRACT: Fan pressurization tests on two unoccupied houses were conducted once every two weeks for a period of a year (May 1982 to July 1983) to determine the seasonal variation in airtightness. Both houses are of insulated wood frame construction. House No. 1 was built with more insulation than is required by the local building code, and a polyethylene vapor barrier was applied with special care to improve its airtightness. House No. 2, a less airtight house, was built with various wall construction features and a polyethylene vapor barrier in only two walls.

Indoor relative humidity, indoor and outdoor air temperatures, and moisture content of the stud and top plates of the wood framing were measured at the time of airtightness testing to determine whether a correlation exists between these factors and house airtightness. The results indicate that air leakage varies throughout the year, with the minimum value in late summer and fall and the maximum value in winter and early spring. The difference is more pronounced in the leakier house. There is also indication of a rough correlation between envelope airtightness and indoor humidity ratio.

KEY WORDS: air leakage, measurement, pressure, fan, weather, residential

A measure of airtightness is given by the amount of air that leaks through a building envelope at a specified pressure difference. Air leakage of houses is generally considered to be constant throughout the year, but a recent study by Warren and Webb [1] indicates that there is seasonal variation on the order of 40% for some houses in the United Kingdom. Persily [2] shows, too, that the air leakage values of some American houses are, on the average, about 22% lower in the summer months than in the winter. The reason for this variation is not yet understood completely, but it is presumed that the contraction and

---

¹Research officers, Division of Building Research, National Research Council, Ottawa, Canada K1A 0R6.

expansion of building materials as a result of changes in relative humidity have some effect on the airtightness of buildings.

To investigate the magnitude of seasonal variations in air leakage of Canadian houses, fan pressurization tests were conducted on two unoccupied houses once every two weeks for a period of a year (May 1982 to July 1983). Indoor relative humidity value, indoor and outdoor air temperatures, and the moisture content of the wood framing were measured at the time of airtightness testing. Specifically, the study was designed to determine (1) the seasonal variation in airtightness of the two houses and (2) the effect of indoor humidity on airtightness.

Test Houses

Both test houses are of insulated wood frame construction. House No. 1 (HUDAC MARK XI project house) [3] is a two-story detached house with a full basement located in a developed residential area in the city of Gloucester, Ontario. The house walls are of standard 38 by 89-mm (2 by 4-in.) wood studs with 38 by 38-mm (2 by 2-in.) horizontal wood furring strips nailed on the inside. To improve airtightness, a 0.10-mm (4-mil) polyethylene sheet was installed between the studs and furring to create an insulated space on the inside of the vapor barrier. Inside this sheet, all the electrical outlets and wiring were installed without cutting through the polyethylene. Special care was taken to seal all joints in the polyethylene sheet. A cross-section of the wall at the intersection with the second floor is shown in Fig. 1.

House No. 2, less air tight, is located in an open field near the Ottawa airport. It was built as an experimental house for studying different wall construction features. For this reason, a polyethylene vapor barrier was included in only two of the wall construction details. A few of the details are shown in Fig. 2.

Table 1 provides a brief description of the two test houses. Neither was occupied during the test period, so that there was no internal moisture generation. The only sources of moisture were, therefore, outdoor moisture carried in by air infiltration and, perhaps, ground moisture entering through basement walls and the floor.

Tests

The air leakage values of the test houses were determined by means of the fan pressurization test method. Two identical apparatuses were used, each consisting of a 40.6-cm-diameter axial fan with a direct-drive d-c motor. The free discharge capacity of the fan is 1200 L/s.

Each apparatus was located inside the test house, with the discharge side of the fan connected by ductwork to an infill panel in an outside window of

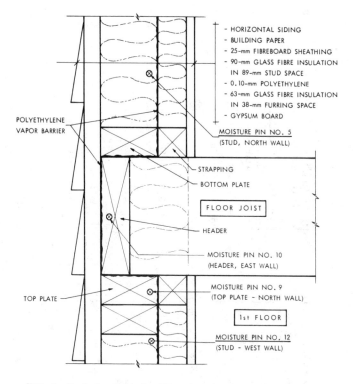

FIG. 1—*Typical wall detail and location of moisture pins, House No. 1.*

House No. 1 and to an infill panel in a patio door of House No. 2. Both the window and the patio door could be closed on completion of the test without moving the apparatus. The flow rate of the fan was measured with a 20.3-cm orifice plate in House No. 1 and with a pair of total pressure averaging tubes in House No. 2 [4].

Inside-to-outside pressure differences were measured using a diaphragm-type pressure transducer (static error band of 5% full scale). Four pressure taps were installed on the outside faces of the four exterior walls. The taps were manifolded before being connected to the pressure transducer in order to provide an average value of outdoor pressure [5].

Each tightness test consisted of measuring the air leakage values at seven or eight pressure differences ranging between 10 and 100 Pa. Measured air leakage values and pressure differences can be correlated by an expression of the form

$$Q = C(\Delta p)^n \tag{1}$$

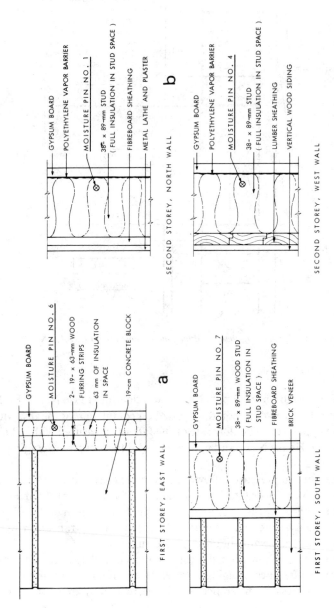

FIG. 2—*Wall details and location of moisture pins, House No. 2: (a) first story; (b) second story.*

TABLE 1—*Description of test houses.*

	House No. 1	House No. 2
Type	single, detached, 2-story	single, detached, 2-story
Floor area, m^2	118	195
Ceiling area, m^2	63.7	97.5
Volume (including basement), m^3	386	520
Outside envelope area, m^2	228	316
Outside wall area, m^2	164	218
Window area, m^2	15.5	17.0
Outside door area, m^2	4.2	5.6
Length of sash crack for window, m	67.6	93.3
Exterior wall finish	brick veneer and aluminum siding	brick veneer, plaster, concrete block and wood siding
Interior wall finish	plaster board	plaster board
Vapor barrier	complete polyethylene vapor barrier	partial polyethylene vapor barrier
Airtightness	tight	leaky
Window	triple-glazed, wood frame, casement	double-glazed, wood frame, removable

where

Q = air leakage value, L/s,
C = flow coefficient for house, L/(s · Pa^n),
Δp = pressure difference across exterior wall, Pa, and
n = flow exponent.

The values of C and n, or the value of leakage at a specific pressure difference, therefore can be used to characterize the airtightness of the house. In this study, the interpolated leakage at a pressure difference of 50 Pa, designated Q_{50}, is used as the indicator of the airtightness of the test houses.

Moisture pins (16 in House No. 1 and 8 in House No. 2) were installed at various locations in the exterior walls of the houses. The detailed locations of a few selected moisture pins are shown in Fig. 1 for House No. 1 and in Fig. 2 for House No. 2. All pins were fixed into wood framing members.

Indoor wet- and dry-bulb temperatures were measured using a sling psychrometer. The daily mean outdoor air and dew-point temperatures on the test date were obtained from the office of Environment Canada. Moisture contents of the wood framing were measured using a moisture meter with an error band of 1% during each air leakage test.

Repeatability Test and Wind Influence

Although all tests were conducted on relatively calm days (wind speed less than 10 km/h), some variation from one test to another was unavoidable. To corroborate the repeatability of the test results and to determine the effect of wind speed on them, a special series of fan pressurization tests were conducted on House No. 1 over a period of seven days. During this time, the air leakage values of the house were determined repeatedly on two calm days, and five air leakage tests were performed on five days when wind speeds ranged from 2 to 24 km/h. The results of the repeatability tests and of the tests with different wind speeds are given in Tables 2 and 3, respectively, in terms of C, n, Q_{50}, and correlation coefficient.

The flow exponent, n, based on the repeatability tests (Table 2), varied between 0.68 and 0.7. To facilitate comparison, values of flow coefficient and leakage were calculated assuming a constant value of $n = 0.69$ (see Table 2). The variation in flow coefficient, C, is less than 0.5%, suggesting excellent repeatability of the pressurization test results.

Wind around and over a house causes variatiohs in pressure; the amount and pattern of pressure depends on wind direction, building shape, and nearby buildings. Pressures are positive on windward sides and negative on leeward sides. Because of this difference, the correct flow equation under windy conditions should take the form

$$Q = \sum_{i=1}^{N} C_i (\Delta p_i)^n \qquad (2)$$

where i is the variable for the various walls.

As it is neither practical to solve for C_i explicitly from the just-mentioned equation nor possible to conduct all pressurization tests under calm conditions, Eq 2 was not used. Thus, the validity of Eq 1 using "average" outside pressure was checked using data measured under various wind speeds and two wind directions. The calculated C and n values for various wind speeds are shown in Table 3 as well as in Fig. 3. The flow exponent, n, varied between 0.69 and 0.7. Again, to facilitate comparison the exponent, n, was assumed to be constant at 0.69, and C and Q_{50} were recalculated. The results indicate that for wind from the exposed side of the house, northwest, the flow coefficient for a wind speed of 16 km/h is about 4% less than that obtained under calm conditions (1.6 km/h). For wind approaching from the shielded side of the house, southwest, the variation in flow coefficient is less than 5% for wind speeds up to 24 km/h. Assuming that the data obtained under a wind speed of 1.6 km/h are correct, Fig. 3 shows that at wind speeds less than 10 km/h the wind effect is negligible.

TABLE 2—*Repeatability test (House No. 1).*

Test	C, L/s(Pa)^n	n	Q_{50},^{a} L/s	Correlation Coefficient	C (n fixed) L/s(Pa)^n	n	Q_{50} (n fixed), L/s	Correlation Coefficient
				(a) WIND SPEED = 4.8 km/h				
1	19.9	0.697	304	0.9999	20.4	0.690	304	0.9999
2	19.7	0.700	303	0.9999	20.4	0.690	303	0.9999
3	20.4	0.692	305	0.9996	20.5	0.690	305	0.9993
				(b) WIND SPEED = 1.6 km/h				
4	21.1	0.688	311	1.000	20.9	0.690	311	0.9999
5	22.0	0.677	311	0.9996	21.0	0.690	312	0.9978
6	22.0	0.678	311	1.000	21.0	0.690	312	0.9994
7	22.0	0.677	311	1.000	21.0	0.690	312	0.9994

$^a Q_{50}$ = air leakage rate at 50 Pa pressure difference.

TABLE 3—*Effect of wind on air leakage value (House No. 1).*

Test	Wind Direction	Wind Speed, km/h	C, L/s(Pa)^n	n	Q_{50} L/s	Correlation Coefficient	C (n fixed), L/s(Pa)^n	n	Q_{50} (n fixed), L/s	Correlation Coefficient
1	NW	1.6	21.1	0.688	311	1.000	21.0	0.690	311	0.9999
2	NW	4.8	20.4	0.692	305	0.9996	20.5	0.690	305	0.9993
3	NW	16.0	20.4	0.689	302	0.9999	20.3	0.690	302	0.9998
4	SW	9.6	21.2	0.686	311	0.9999	20.9	0.690	311	0.9999
5	SW	12.8	20.4	0.695	309	0.9996	20.8	0.690	309	0.9996
6	SW	12.8	20.6	0.693	310	0.9999	20.8	0.690	309	0.9999
7	SW	24.0	19.8	0.693	298	1.000	20.1	0.690	298	0.9999

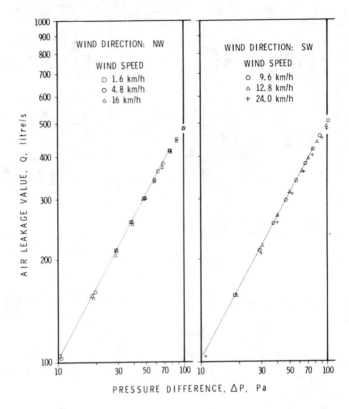

FIG. 3—*Effect of wind on air leakage, House No. 1.*

Results and Discussion

An attempt was made to correlate the seasonal variation of house air leakage with one or other of the parameters (indoor and outdoor humidity ratios, air temperatures, and moisture content of wall framing), which also vary seasonally. In text that follows, the air leakage value at a pressure difference of 50 Pa (Q_{50}) is used to characterize house tightness.

Figures 4 and 5 show the variation of Q_{50}, daily mean outdoor temperature, and indoor and daily mean outdoor humidity ratios with time for Houses Nos. 1 and 2, respectively. The results indicate a seasonal variation in airtightness. The houses were tightest in late summer and fall and leakiest in winter and early spring. In each case the maximum air leakage value was about 20% greater than the minimum value. The results also show that (in general) as the humidity ratios and outdoor temperatures decreased, the air leakage values increased.

Comparing the indoor humidity ratios of the two test houses, it is notewor-

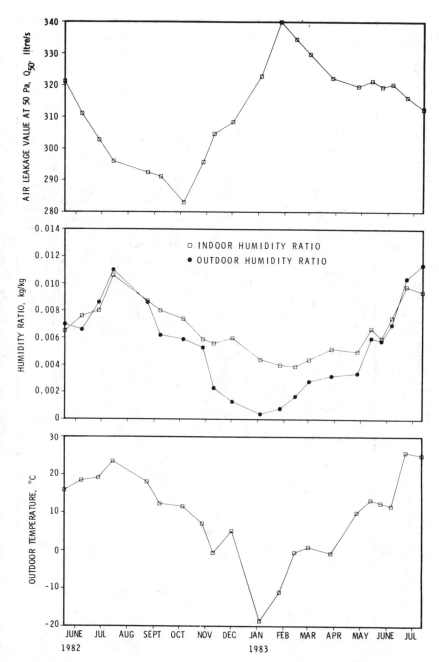

FIG. 4—*Seasonal variation of air leakage, outdoor temperature, and humidity ratio, House No. 1.*

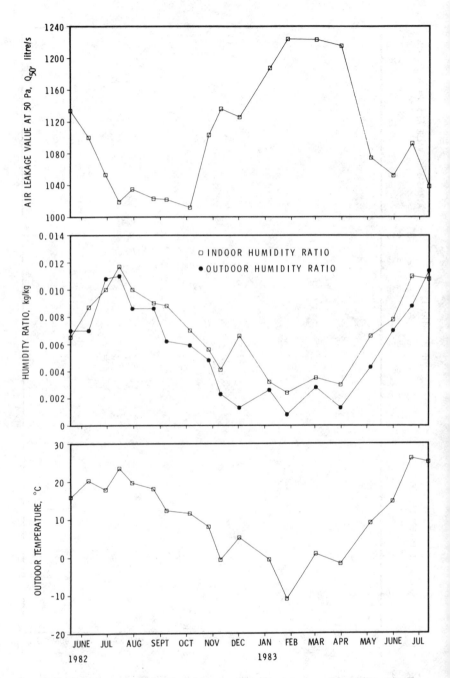

FIG. 5—*Seasonal variation of air leakage, outdoor temperature, and humidity ratio, House No. 2.*

thy that the indoor humidity in House No. 2 was generally lower than that in House No. 1 in winter and higher in summer. This is probably due to differences in both basement moisture gains and airtightness. Because House No. 1 was tighter than House No. 2, its indoor humidity ratio was probably affected less by outdoor conditions.

Figures 6 and 7 show the time variation of moisture content in the wall framing for Houses Nos. 1 and 2, respectively. The air leakage values at 50 Pa also are shown. The moisture readings have been corrected for temperature at the tip of the moisture pin. This was estimated from the thermal resistance values of the wall components and the indoor and outdoor air temperatures. The results indicate that the moisture contents of the walls in both houses were reasonably low (in the range of 8 to 14%), and that a trace of seasonal variation in the moisture content of the wood framing could be detected.

Figure 6 shows that Pin No. 10 measured a higher moisture content than all the other moisture pins, and that its pattern of variation was different from theirs. The reason for this difference is that Pin No. 10 was located on the inside of the polyethylene vapor barrier on the east side of the second floor header, while all other pins were located on the outside of the polyethylene. Moreover, Pin No. 10 was the only one located on the cold side of the wall, as shown in Fig. 1.

Figure 7 shows that Moisture Pins Nos. 6 and 7, located in first-story studs, give slightly higher moisture content values. This could have been due to their

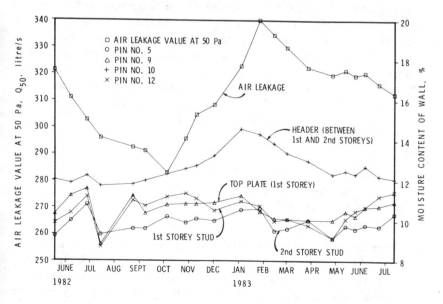

FIG. 6—*Seasonal variation of moisture content of wood framing, House No. 1.*

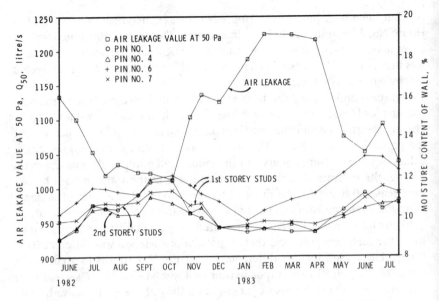

FIG. 7—*Seasonal variation of moisture content of wood framing, House No. 2.*

location (first story versus second story) or, more probably, to the absence of a vapor barrier.

It appears that there is a correlation between airtightness and indoor and daily mean outdoor humidity ratio as well as daily mean outdoor temperature. An attempt was made, therefore, to correlate the air leakage value at 50 Pa with these parameters. Various models were tested. The results shown in Table 4 suggest that the best single-parameter model would be a power law expression relating air leakage value and indoor humidity ratio (Fig. 8).

$$Q_{50} = R \cdot (W_i)^\alpha \qquad (3)$$

where

Q_{50} = air leakage value at 50 Pa, L/s,
R = dimensional constant, L/s,
W_i = indoor humidity ratio, kg/kg, and
α = exponent.

The values of R and α were determined as 182.6 and -0.11 for House No. 1 and 607.4 and -0.12 for House No. 2. The difference in R is the difference in the air leakage characteristics of the two houses. To facilitate comparison, the air leakage values and indoor humidity ratios of each house were

TABLE 4—*Models of air tightness correlation.*[a]

Model	House No. 1					House No. 2				
	R_1	R_2	R_3	R_4	Correlation Coefficient	R_1	R_2	R_3	R_4	Correlation Coefficient
$Q = R_1$	312.6				0.0	1098.0	⋯	⋯	⋯	0.0
$Q = R_1 + R_2(W_i)$	344.4	−4751.0			0.3749	1247.0	-2.08×10^4	⋯	⋯	0.7128
$Q = R_1 + R_2(W_o)$	324.2	−2097.0			0.2161	1195.0	-1.63×10^4	⋯	⋯	0.6018
$Q = R_1 + R_2(T_o)$	486.0	−0.6136			0.2207	2643.0	−5.435	⋯	⋯	0.6099
$Q = R_1 + R_2(\sqrt{T_o})$	657.5	−20.53			0.2220	4184.0	−183.0	⋯	⋯	0.6134
$Q = R_1 \cdot (W_i)^{R_2}$	182.3	−0.1067			0.4211	607.4	−0.1172	⋯	⋯	0.7763
$Q = R_1 \cdot (W_o)^{R_2}$	270.2	-2.64×10^{-2}			0.2400	772.2	-653×10^{-2}	⋯	⋯	0.6467
$Q = R_1 \cdot (T_o)^{R_2}$	6632.0	−0.5415			0.2143	2.54×10^6	−1.372	⋯	⋯	0.6074
$Q = R_1 \cdot e^{R_2 W_i}$	345.5	−15.12			0.3656	1252.0	−18.57	⋯	⋯	0.7074
$Q = R_1 + R_2 \cdot (W_i) + R_3 \cdot (W_o)$	363.7	-1.07×10^4	3676.0		0.4614	1247.0	-2.08×10^4	−1.674	⋯	0.7128
$Q = R_1 + R_2 \cdot (W_i) + R_3 \cdot (\sqrt{T_o})$	190.3	-6.25×10^3	9.77		0.3877	437.3	-2.58×10^4	50.19	⋯	0.7171
$Q = R_1 + R_2 \cdot (W_i) + R_3 \cdot (W_o) + R_4(\sqrt{T_o})$	526.9	-1.06×10^4	4.59×10^3	−10.04	0.4696	246.3	-2.49×10^4	-1.88×10^3	61.82	0.7181

[a] W_i = indoor humidity ratio, kg/kg;
W_o = outdoor humidity ratio, kg/kg;
T_o = outdoor temperature, K.

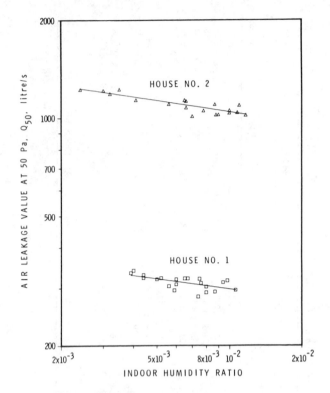

FIG. 8—*Relation between air leakage and humidity ratio, Houses Nos. 1 and 2.*

normalized using seasonal average values. The relation between the normalized air leakage value and the indoor humidity ratio is

$$\frac{Q_{50}}{\bar{Q}_{50}} = K \cdot \left(\frac{W_i}{\bar{W}_i}\right)^{\beta} \qquad (4)$$

where

Q_{50} = air leakage value at 50 Pa, L/s,
$\bar{Q}_{50}$ = seasonal average of the air leakage value at 50 pa, L/s,
K = constant,
W_i = indoor humidity ratio, kg/kg,
$\bar{W}_i$ = seasonal average of indoor humidity ratio, kg/kg, and
β = exponent.

The values of β for Houses Nos. 1 and 2 were found to be -0.11 and -0.12, respectively, and of K were 0.995 and 0.986, respectively. As the β and K values of the two houses were so similar, the data for both houses were

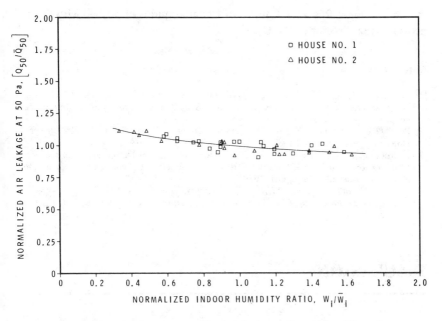

FIG. 9—*Relation between normalized air leakage value and humidity ratio.*

combined in Fig. 9 in estimating the values of β and K applicable to both. The values of β and K were found to be -0.11 and 0.991, respectively.

Summary

1. Air leakage values measured in two unoccupied houses show seasonal variation, being lowest in late summer and fall and highest in winter and early spring. The maximum air leakage value is approximately 20% greater than the minimum value for both houses.

2. The results indicate that there is a strong relation between air leakage value and indoor humidity ratio. For the two unoccupied houses, this relation may be expressed by the equation

$$\frac{Q_{50}}{\bar{Q}_{50}} = 0.991 \left(\frac{W_i}{\bar{W}_i} \right)^{-0.11}$$

Acknowledgment

The authors wish to acknowledge the assistance of D. L. Logan in conducting the tests. This paper is a contribution of the Division of Building Research, National Research Council of Canada, and is published with the approval of the director of the Division.

References

[1] Warren, P. R. and Webb, B. C., "Ventilation Measurements in Housing," CIBS Symposium, Natural Ventilation by Design, London, 1980, Chartered Institution of Building Services, London.

[2] Persily, A., "Understanding Air Infiltration in Homes," Report PU/CEES 129, Princeton University, Princeton, NJ, 1982.

[3] Quirouette, R. L., "The Mark XI Energy Research Project-Design and Construction," Building Research Note 131, National Research Council of Canada, Division of Building Research, Ottawa, Canada, Oct. 1978.

[4] Shaw, C. Y. and Jones, L., ASHRAE Transactions, Vol. 85, Part 1, 1979, pp. 85-95.

[5] Gumley, S. J., Journal of Wind Engineering and Industrial Aerodynamics, Vol. 12, 1983, pp. 189-228.

DISCUSSION

David Saum[1] (written discussion)—What was the 50 Pa air changes per hour (ACH) of the leaky house? What was the percent error in ACH measurements that was not due to seasonal variations?

A. Kim and C. Y. Shaw (authors' closure)—The ACH of the leaky house at 50 Pa was about 8 ACH. The percent error in ACH measurements was less than 2%.

John Shaw[2] (written discussion)—I assume that the house configuration did not change between winter and summer. Therefore, what is the cause of the winter/summer differences that were observed?

A. Kim and C. Y. Shaw (authors' closure)—It seems that the moisture content of the exterior envelope has some effect on the change in house airtightness.

Donald Colliver[3] (written discussion)—It takes a finite amount of time for the materials in the house to pick up/release moisture and therefore to expand or extract. Are your humidity measurements instantaneous measurements or are they an average of prior hours humidity measurements?

A. Kim and C. Y. Shaw (authors' closure)—They are instantaneous measurements.

---

[1]Infiltec, Waynesboro, VA.

[2]U.S. Department of Energy, Environmental Measurements Laboratory, New York, NY 10014.

[3]University of Kentucky, Lexington, KY 40546-0075.

Niren L. Nagda,[1] *David T. Harrje,*[2] *Michael D. Koontz,*[3] *and*
Gary G. Purcell[4]

A Detailed Investigation of the Air Infiltration Characteristics of Two Houses

REFERENCE: Nagda, N. L., Harrje, D. T., Koontz, M. D., and Purcell, G. G., "A Detailed Investigation of the Air Infiltration Characteristics of Two Houses," *Measured Air Leakage of Buildings, ASTM STP 904*, H. R. Trechsel and P. L. Lagus, Eds., American Society for Testing and Materials, Philadelphia, 1986, pp. 33–45.

ABSTRACT: The relationships among energy use, air infiltration, and indoor air quality are being investigated in two detached houses identical in design and wind exposure. One of the two houses was retrofitted to reduce its infiltration rate. Fan pressurization/depressurization measurements taken over twelve months indicated that the air leakage rates for the unretrofitted control house remained unchanged. In the case of the experimental house, a 35% reduction as measured by fan pressurization/depressurization measurements was achieved by retrofitting; this reduction remained constant. The difference in air infiltration rates between the experimental and the control house was 22 to 24% as measured by tracer gas dilution. Infiltration rates were strongly affected by the seasons; infiltration rates obtained in the fall were 50% higher than rates obtained in the summer.

KEY WORDS: energy use, air infiltration, indoor air quality, retrofitting, air-to-air heat exchanger, fan pressurization/depressurization, tracer gas dilution

The rate of air infiltration into a residence affects both energy consumption and indoor air quality. As the rate of air infiltration increases, so does the energy needed for heating or cooling. To improve energy efficiency, the trend in the construction industry has been to build increasingly "tighter" residences, that is, those with relatively low infiltration rates. For existing resi-

[1]Manager, Indoor Environment Program, GEOMET Technologies, Inc., Germantown, MD 20874.
[2]Senior research engineer and lecturer, Princeton University, Engineering Quadrangle, Princeton, NJ 08540.
[3]Research scientist, GEOMET Technologies, Inc., Germantown, MD 20874.
[4]Project manager, Residential and Commercial Applications, Electric Power Research Institute, Palo Alto, CA 94303.

dences, a concurrent practice is to reduce the air infiltration rate through retrofitting. Although a reduced infiltration rate does improve energy efficiency, the reduction can affect adversely the quality of the indoor air.

Quantitative information on how infiltration rates affect energy use and indoor air quality, which can be used for decision-making purposes by consumers, utilities, and the government, is not available. Therefore GEOMET is conducting a study, sponsored by the Electric Power Research Institute, aimed at providing such information. The purpose is to investigate experimentally and analytically the relationships among air exchange, energy consumption, and levels of key indoor pollutants in residential buildings. This paper describes that part of the study concerned with characterizing air infiltration; the results of tracer gas decay and fan pressurization and depressurization tests conducted over a twelve-month period are described.

Study Approach

To meet the study objectives, the following overall strategy was chosen [1]:

1. Use two identical, detached houses, newly constructed but with relatively high air infiltration rates. Retrofit one house to a relatively tight state and equip it with an air-to-air heat exchanger to mechanically manipulate its air exchange rate.

2. Monitor the two houses simultaneously for energy use, infiltration, and indoor air quality parameters over different seasons; quantify the impact of different climatic conditions.

3. Conduct the study under controlled conditions with simulated occupant activities to assess the impact of a variety of occupancy-related factors.

The houses were built during the fall of 1982 in a suburban area near Washington, D.C. This area was chosen because its primary heating and cooling seasons are sufficiently long to permit a relatively large number of measurements. The houses are of identical bilevel/split-style design with integral garages. Both homes face north-northeast on adjacent lots and have relatively homogeneous terrains and similar wind barriers on all sides. Figure 1 shows the floor plans. The upper level of each house has a volume of 215 m³, and the lower level, excluding the garage, has a volume of 113 m³.

The builder[5] was instructed to omit a number of items routinely included to reduce infiltration. These omissions were intended to yield a higher-than-customary rate of air infiltration and thereby to maximize potential pre- and postretrofit differences. The principal omissions were:

1. Sill plate sealer and caulking between masonry and frame wall.
2. Vapor barrier in upper level floor overhang.

[5]Ryan Homes, Inc., 100 Ryan Court, Pittsburgh, PA 15205.

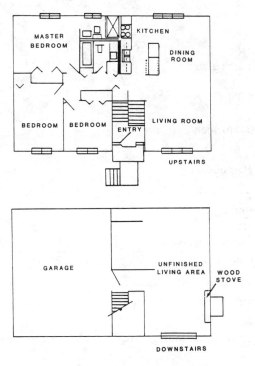

FIG. 1—*Floor plans of the test houses.*

3. Vapor barrier on inside foundation/knee wall.
4. Sealing of electrical outlet and switch boxes.
5. Sealing of pipe and cable penetrations through wall top plates.
6. Caulking of windows.
7. Exterior door adjustments.
8. Weatherstripping of attic access panel.
9. Garage door adjustments.
10. Sealing of wood stove insert plate and mouldings.
11. Adjustment of exhaust fan dampers.

GEOMET's mobile laboratory, located between the two houses, contains instrumentation to measure air exchange, environmental parameters, air pollutants, and energy consumption. The variables measured by the system can be grouped as follows:

Air Pollutants

1. Carbon monoxide.
2. Nitrogen dioxide.

3. Radon.
4. Radon progeny.
5. Formaldehyde.
6. Inhalable particulates.

Tracer Gas

1. Sulfur hexafluoride.

Environmental Parameters

1. Barometric pressure.
2. Relative humidity.
3. Temperature.
4. Wind speed and direction.
5. Solar radiation.

Energy Consumption

1. Total house.
2. Heating and air conditioning: circulation fan, compressor, and heating coil.
3. Electric dryer.
4. Water heater.
5. Refrigerator.
6. Clothes washer.
7. Dishwasher.
8. Heat exchanger.
9. Kitchen exhaust.
10. Bath exhaust.

Both blower door tests and baseline tracer gas studies, which will be described later in this paper, showed that one of the houses consistently had a slightly lower rate of air exchange. To maximize potential differences between the houses, the tighter house was chosen for retrofit. This retrofitted house will be referred to as the *experimental house*. A whole-house air-to-air heat exchanger with a rated capacity of 5.7 m^3/min at a pressure drop of 2.5 mm of water was installed in the experimental house. The other house, left in its original state of construction, will be referred to as the *control house*.

To study air infiltration characteristics, five zones—two per house and one outdoors—are being used for measuring air exchange and most pollutants and environmental factors (Fig. 2). Representative sampling locations within each zone were determined as the measurement system was being completed and tested during the spring of 1983. Sulfur hexafluoride (SF$_6$) is being used

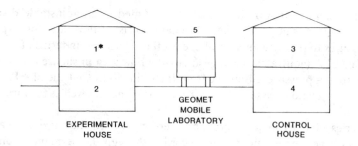

FIG. 2—*Measurement zones: 1. main floor, experimental house; 2. lower level, experimental house; 3. main floor, control house; 4. lower level, control house; 5. outdoors.*

as the tracer gas to measure air exchange. An electron-capture gas chromatograph[6] is used to measure tracer gas concentrations. The sampling strategy for SF_6 was dictated by the 3-min analytical time required by the instrument for each sample. Beginning on the hour, and every 3 min thereafter, an instantaneous sample is taken through a polypropylene sampling line from a fixed location in one of the zones. A valve sequencer controls the order of sampling; consequently, each instantaneous sample for a particular zone is separated in time by exactly 15 min. This strategy enables the calculation of air exchange rates over 15-min periods or multiples thereof. A purge time included in the sampling procedure eliminates the possibility of carryover between successive samples. The integrity of the entire process has been verified by inputting standard concentrations from each sampling location. To accommodate changing environmental conditions, an automated injection system was installed so that either the frequency or volume of an SF_6 injection easily could be varied. The tracer gas is injected directly into the air circulation system; the air circulation fan is programmed to operate continuously for about 30 min when an injection occurs.

   In analyzing the effects of weather on air infiltration and the subsequent influence on indoor air quality, it is necessary to be certain of the building envelope tightness over all seasons. Variations due to weather and moisture effects have been shown in past studies [2,3] to directly influence the building tightness by 20% or more. To provide these data, the pressurization approach is used in a series of visits, usually at 4- to 6-week intervals, that extend across more than a year of testing. These tests consist of pressurizing and depressurizing each house through prescribed pressure steps. Based upon international convention [4], the pressure difference between the house interior and exterior at 50 Pa (5 mm of water) is used to compare building tightness expressed as air changes per hour (ACH) at 50 Pa. A blower door, consisting

[6]Manufactured by S-Cubed, Inc., P.O. Box 1620, La Jolla, CA 92038.

of a flow-calibrated, variable-speed fan mounted in an adjustable door, is used for tightness measurements. The data consist of flow rates for a variety of pressures to produce an air leakage profile. Measured in terms of ACH at 50 Pa or ELA (equivalent leakage area—the flow area in square centimetres based upon a pressure difference from the inside to the outside of 4 Pa), the leakage rate could be assessed for seasonal differences as well as for variations over time.

A series of week-long experiments were conducted during each season. Results of these experiments were recorded through the permanent, on-site measurement system. Throughout each weekly experiment, the air circulation fan and heat exchanger settings remained undisturbed. A number of routine household activities were repeated for each experiment. On Mondays and Wednesdays during each experiment, a gas stove, a dishwasher, a washer, a dryer, and a shower were operated for prescribed lengths of time. On Wednesdays only, a bath fan and a range fan were operated concurrently with the shower and the gas stove. Vacuuming was done on Tuesdays. Thursdays were reserved for maintenance or special experiments. All systems were calibrated on Fridays.

Fan Pressurization/Depressurization Results

The first pressurization/depressurization test of the two houses took place soon after the houses were constructed. Subsequent tests were conducted at intervals of approximately 4 to 6 weeks.

The data for the control and experimental houses (Fig. 3) indicated no sys-

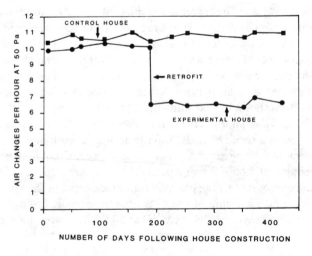

FIG. 3—*Effect of retrofit: Fan pressurization/depressurization measurements expressed in air changes per hour at 50 Pa.*

tematic variation in tightness on a seasonal basis. As shown in Fig. 3, ACH at 50 Pa are the numerical average of ACH under pressurized and depressurized conditions. The air change rate at 50 Pa showed a slight trend over time toward greater leakage (under 3%) for both houses, but within the range of measurement errors. Over a six-month period prior to retrofit, the average air change rates at 50 Pa were 10.6 ± 0.3 ACH for the control house and 10.1 ± 0.2 ACH for the experimental house. The experimental house was 5% tighter on the average as determined by blower door measurements and ranged from 1 to 9% tighter. Over a 6-month period following the retrofit, the control house averaged 10.8 ± 0.1 ACH and the experimental house averaged 6.5 ± 0.3 ACH.

The data scatter (expressed as percent standard deviation) for the ACH values was approximately ±4% in the half year that data were collected after the experimental house was retrofitted. In terms of ELA (Fig. 4), the data scatter was ±5% for the control house and ±8% and ±11% in the experimental house before and after retrofit, respectively.

Retrofits were concentrated on leakage sites at the attic level and the basement or ground floor; the blower door method was used to chart the progress as the large and small openings were sealed. For the experimental house, retrofitting achieved about a 35% reduction in ACH values at 50 Pa and in the magnitude of ELA. Thus, after retrofit the experimental house was about 40% tighter (range of 38 to 43%) than the control house. Leakage reduction of this magnitude is feasible, and the reduced leakage value has held nearly constant in the more than 6-month period of monthly testing following retrofit.

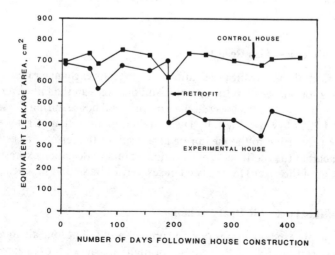

FIG. 4—*Effect of retrofit: Fan pressurization/depressurization measurements extrapolated to compute ELA.*

Preretrofit Tracer Gas Results

Tracer gas dilution measurements were taken during two weekly periods shortly before the retrofit procedure was applied. During the first week, the air circulation fan was operated in the normal, periodic manner in both houses. During the second week, the fan was operated constantly in both houses. During the week with constant fan operation, rates for all four zones were virtually identical (Table 1).

As shown in Table 1, the major environmental driving forces (ΔT and wind speed) for air infiltration were stronger during the first week. In this case, the experimental house had slightly lower average air exchange rates in both the upstairs and downstairs zones. The average rates were almost twice as high downstairs as upstairs for each house. This apparent difference between the two zones could have been due to either the tracer gas migrating upstairs from the downstairs or due to the downstairs being leakier than the upstairs. This issue cannot be easily resolved without multiple tracer measurements, which are planned.

The average whole-house rates for the houses and the percentage differences between these rates are summarized in Table 1. The comparisons shown in this table are based on hours when air exchange rates were calculated for both houses. The rate for the experimental house was 10% lower in one case and virtually identical to that for the control house in the other case. Thus, the range of differences between the houses in the average weekly air exchange rate (0 to 10%) was very similar to the range of differences estimated by the blower door method. In all cases, the experimental house measured as tight or tighter than the control house. The experimental house was retrofitted so that air infiltration differences between the two houses could be maximized.

Postretrofit Tracer Gas Results

The effect of the retrofit procedure on average air exchange rates is shown in Table 2 for one week in the summer and one week in the fall. Average air exchange rates were 24% lower in the experimental house during the summer week and 22% lower in the fall. The variation in air exchange rates was reduced in proportion to the mean rate as a result of the retrofit, as evidenced by the fact that the coefficients of variation (standard deviation expressed as a percentage of the mean) for the two houses were quite similar for each season.

Effect of the Air-to-Air Heat Exchanger

Average air exchange rates during summer and fall at four air-to-air heat exchanger settings (off, low, medium, or high) are shown for the experimental house in Table 3. Corresponding rates for the control house are shown as a

TABLE 1—*Air exchange rates (in ACH) for control and experimental houses during two weekly periods prior to retrofit (spring, 1983).*

Circulation Fan Operation, Dates	Environmental Conditions[a]		Control House[a]			Experimental House[a]			Percent Differences[c]	Number of Paired Hourly Measurements
	Outdoor Temperature	Wind Speed	Upstairs	Downstairs	Whole House[b]	Upstairs	Downstairs	Whole House[b]		
Periodic (May 6–12)	9.7 ± 5.8°C (49.5 ± 10.4°F)	4.6 ± 3.5 mph	0.36 ± 0.13	0.66 ± 0.41	0.41 ± 0.12	0.32 ± 0.10	0.63 ± 0.48	0.37 ± 0.08	10.2	29
Constantly on (May 13–19)	15.5 ± 6.2°C (59.9 ± 11.2°F)	4.1 ± 2.0 mph	0.30 ± 0.12	0.30 ± 0.11	0.30 ± 0.11	0.30 ± 0.12	0.30 ± 0.13	0.30 ± 0.12	0	65

[a]Mean ± standard deviation.
[b]Whole-house average is a volume-weighted average of upstairs and downstairs.
[c][(Control house − experimental house)/control house] × 100.

TABLE 2—*Average air exchange rates for control and experimental houses during two seasons following retrofit.*

| | Air Exchange Rate, ACH | | | Number of Paired Hourly Measurements |
	Control House	Experimental House	Percent Difference[a]	
		SUMMER		
Mean	0.15	0.11	24	74
Standard deviation	0.07	0.05		
CV[b]	45%	43%		
		FALL		
Mean	0.28	0.22	22	79
Standard deviation	0.09	0.08		
CV[b]	33%	37%		

[a][(Control House − Experimental House)/Control House] × 100.
[b]CV = coefficient of variation or the standard deviation expressed as a percentage of the mean.

TABLE 3—*Average air exchange rates (in ACH) for the control house and the experimental house at different heat exchanger settings by season.*

Heat Exchanger Setting	Control House[a] (No Heat Exchanger)	Experimental House[a] (With Heat Exchanger)	Difference[b] (Experimental minus Control)	Number of Paired Hourly Measurements
		SUMMER		
Off	0.15 ± 0.07	0.11 ± 0.05	−0.04 ± 0.04	74
Low	0.20 ± 0.09	0.33 ± 0.08	0.13 ± 0.05	53
Medium	0.19 ± 0.08	0.45 ± 0.09	0.27 ± 0.05	54
High	0.17 ± 0.06	0.57 ± 0.08	0.40 ± 0.08	68
		FALL		
Off	0.28 ± 0.09	0.22 ± 0.08	−0.06 ± 0.06	79
Low	0.23 ± 0.09	0.36 ± 0.09	0.13 ± 0.06	47
Medium	0.29 ± 0.10	0.60 ± 0.09	0.31 ± 0.07	50
High	0.42 ± 0.10	0.76 ± 0.11	0.34 ± 0.13	44

[a]Mean ± standard deviation.
[b]Average difference between the two houses and the standard deviation of the difference.

reference. The experimental house had lower average rates when the heat exchanger was off but higher rates when the heat exchanger was operated. The difference in rates between the two houses increased with higher heat exchanger settings. The differences between average rates for the two houses are statistically significant at the 0.01 level, based on a paired t-test.

Although the heat exchanger increased the air exchange rate substantially, it had little or no effect on the variation in air exchange rates. Only for the high setting during the summer season was there some evidence of an impact on variation. The standard deviation for the experimental house was 0.02 ACH smaller than that for the control house with the heat exchanger off; with the heat exchanger on high, the standard deviation for the experimental house was 0.02 larger than that for the control house.

Figure 5 shows infiltration rates for the upstairs of the two houses over a typical 24-h period with the heat exchanger at the medium setting. The differences between the two houses were relatively constant over time. The trends for the two houses were generally similar but not exactly alike.

Conclusions

Conclusions based on data collected in the first year (through Oct. 1983) are as follows:

Fan Pressurization/Depressurization Measurements—Through the first twelve months after construction of the two houses, the air leakage rates for the control house, as measured by the fan pressurization/depressurization

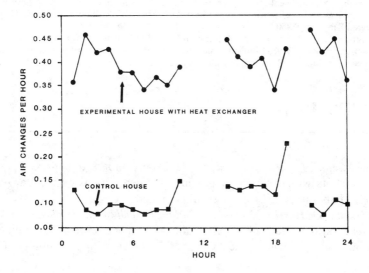

FIG. 5—*Variations in hourly air exchange rates—effect of air-to-air heat exchanger.*

technique, remained essentially unchanged. In the case of the experimental house, a 35% reduction was achieved by retrofitting for tightness. This reduction in leakage rate remained constant for the ensuing 6 months.

Tracer Gas Measurements—Reduction in air infiltration rates due to retrofit, as measured by the tracer gas dilution method, was 22 to 24%. Change in seasons had a strong impact on infiltration rates; summer infiltration rates were lower than fall by about 50% for each house.

Air-to-Air Heat Exchanger—Operation of the air-to-air heat exchanger increased the overall infiltration rates. The increases in infiltration rates were consistent with the heat exchanger setting. The differential increase in the hourly infiltration rates due to the heat exchanger appeared to be relatively constant for the summer and fall, even though the base infiltration rate (that is, without the heat exchanger) varied with ambient conditions.

Acknowledgment

This work is supported by the Electric Power Research Institute under Contract Number RP 2034-1.

References

[1] Nagda, N. L., Koontz, M. D., Rector, H. E., Harrje, D. T., Lannus, A., Patterson, R., and Purcell, G., "Study Design to Relate Residential Energy Use, Air Infiltration, and Indoor Air Quality," Paper 83-29.3 APCA, presented at the 76th Annual Meeting of the APCA, Air Pollution Control Association, Pittsburgh, PA, 1983.
[2] Persily, A. K., "Understanding Air Infiltration in Homes," Ph.D. Thesis, Princeton University, Center for Energy and Environmental Studies, Princeton, NJ, Jan. 1982.
[3] Warren, P. R. and Webb, B. C., "Ventilation Measurements in Housing," in *Natural Ventilation by Design*, CIBS symposium, Chartered Institution of Building Services, London, United Kingdom, 1980.
[4] Elmroth, A. and Levin, P., "Air Infiltration Control in Housing, A Guide to International Practice," Doc. D2:1983, International Energy Agency—Air Infiltration Centre, Swedish Council for Building Research, Stockholm, Sweden, 1983.

DISCUSSION

David Saum[1] (written discussion)—Did you compare your pressurization measurements with your tracer gas measurements by using the Lawrence Berkeley Laboratory's (LBL) infiltration model?

N. Nagda, D. Harrje, M. Koontz, and G. Purcell (authors' closure)—Yes. For our data, the results of the LBL infiltration model were not dissimilar to those obtained by dividing the ACH at 50 Pa by an arbitrary number of 20.

[1]Infiltec, Waynesboro, VA 22980.

We also calculated ELA at 4 Pa. As shown earlier, there was a greater data scatter associated with the estimates of ELA than ACH at 50 Pa.

David Saum[1] (written discussion)—In another paper, Shaw and Kim[2] showed a correlation between humidity and 50 Pa ACH measurements. Did you measure humidity and did it vary significantly during the year that you made door measurements?

N. Nagda, D. Harrje, M. Koontz, and G. Purcell (authors' closure)—We measured relative humidity (RH) in all four indoor zones and outdoors. Indoor RH ranged from 39 to 85% during the summer, 31 to 81% during the fall, and 15 to 39% during the winter. Outdoor RH varied from 26 to 98% during each of these three seasons. Thus, while we saw differences in indoor RH, we did not see any seasonal variations in the leakage rates measured by the blower door method.

Helmut Feustel[3] (written discussion)—How did you measure the infiltration rate of the different rooms by using only one tracer gas?

N. Nagda, D. Harrje, M. Koontz, and G. Purcell (authors' closure)—We did not measure infiltration rates of different rooms.

[2]"Seasonal Variation in Air Tightness of Two Detached Houses," A. Kim and C. Y. Shaw, this publication.

[3]Lawrence Berkeley Laboratory, Berkeley, CA 94720.

Andrew K. Persily[1]

Measurements of Air Infiltration and Airtightness in Passive Solar Homes

REFERENCE: Persily, A. K., **"Measurements of Air Infiltration and Airtightness in Passive Solar Homes,"** *Measured Air Leakage of Buildings, ASTM STP 904*, H. R. Trechsel and P. L. Lagus, Eds., American Society for Testing and Materials, Philadelphia, 1986, pp. 46–60.

ABSTRACT: The airtightness of 82 passive solar homes located throughout the United States was studied using tracer gas measurements of air infiltration and pressurization testing. The air infiltration measurements employed the tracer gas decay technique in a low-cost mode employing air sample bags and off-site infiltration determination. The infiltration rates measured under natural conditions ranged from about 0.05 to almost 2 air changes per hour (ACH). The pressurization test results ranged from 1 to more than 30 ACH at 50 Pa, with an average of about 10 ACH. By comparing the pressurization measurements on these homes to measurements on other homes, the passive solar homes were found to be in general no tighter than other U.S. homes. The air infiltration and pressurization measurements of the Class B homes were compared using existing infiltration models and other empirical relations.

KEY WORDS: air infiltration, air leakage in buildings, airtightness of buildings, building airtightness, blower door tests, passive solar buildings, pressurization testing, tracer gas measurement

The Solar Energy Research Institute (SERI), funded by the Department of Energy, has established programs to evaluate the thermal performance of passive solar residential buildings. The programs, Class A, B, and C, vary in the detail and expense of the monitoring. The homes described in this paper belong to the middle level of monitoring, Class B. The purpose of the Class B program is to determine the thermal performance of different types of passive houses located in different climates by calculating the monthly building energy balance, the solar fraction, and solar savings [1–2].

As part of the Class B monitoring, each home was subjected to pressurization testing [3] to measure the airtightness of the building shell and to a small number of tracer gas decay tests [4] to measure air infiltration rates. This

[1]Mechanical engineer, National Bureau of Standards, Gaithersburg, MD 20899.

paper discusses the techniques used for both measurements and reports on the results obtained. Such a large group of passive solar homes was never subjected to airtightness measurements before. The air leakage rates of this type of home are often assumed to be below average, and these tests reveal the actual performance of these homes.

The two methods of measurements also were compared to one another to assess their accuracy and consistency for evaluating the airtightness of these buildings. Preliminary measurement results for some of these homes have been published previously [5].

Homes

The Class B homes, located throughout the United States, employ several different passive features, including sunspaces, Trombe walls, and green-houses. Most of the homes are occupied, while some serve as models for homebuilders. The homes discussed in this report are divided into five regional groups (Denver, Northeast, South, California, and Mid-America) and one group of "manufactured," or factory-built, homes located throughout the country. All the homes were designed to have thermal envelopes of above average integrity in terms of both insulation levels and airtightness. Eighty-two homes have received at least one pressurization test or infiltration measurement.

Measurements

The Class B homes were subjected to pressurization tests to measure the airtightness of the building shell and to tracer gas measurements of air infiltration rates under natural conditions. Both techniques have been used for several years to evaluate the airtightness of homes.

Pressurization Measurements

In whole house pressurization, a large fan mounted in a door or window induces a large and roughly uniform pressure difference across the building envelope [3]. The leakier the house, the more airflow is necessary to induce a specific pressure difference between inside and outside. The pressurization tests of the Class B homes employed devices called "blower doors," consisting of a variable speed d-c motor and a large fan mounted in a wooden frame of adjustable height and width. The blower doors used in these tests are calibrated to yield the flow rate through the fan as a function of the rate of fan rotation and the inside-outside pressure difference. In conducting the blower door tests, the homes were pressurized and depressurized to pressure differences from 12 to 60 Pa in increments of about 12 Pa. Some of the leakier or larger houses could not be pressurized to all of these levels. During the pressurization tests, all interior doors were open and any flues or vents were in their normal positions. The tests were conducted with sunspace or greenhouse doors open and with these same doors closed, but generally the result with the doors open was used to characterize a house's leakiness.

The pressurization tests were performed by several different subcontractors and SERI, and the data were sent to the National Bureau of Standards (NBS) for analysis and interpretation. Of the many possible ways to convert the pressure difference and airflow data to a measurement of building tightness, we present the flow rate required to maintain an inside-outside pressure difference of 50 Pa. To obtain the 50-Pa flow rate, the flows and pressure differences from the test are fit to an equation of the form

$$Q = C(\Delta p)^n \tag{1}$$

where

Q = flow rate, m^3/h,
Δp = inside-outside pressure difference, Pa, and
C,n = empirical constants from regression analysis.

The equation is fit to data obtained by both pressurizing and depressurizing the house. Equation 1 is used to determine the 50-Pa flow rate in m^3/h, which is then normalized by the house volume (including the basement) to yield the flow rate in house volumes per hour or ACH. The 50-Pa flow rate measurement is accurate within about ±10%. Typically, U.S. homes lie in the range of 10 to 20 ACH but can be tighter or looser [6-7].

Air Infiltration Measurement

Air infiltration rates in buildings have been measured for many years using tracer gas techniques [4, 8-9]. The infiltration rates of the Class B homes were measured using the tracer gas decay or dilution method in which the gas is released all at once and the decay in concentration is monitored. Automated equipment can be used to measure infiltration continuously, but using such equipment in the large number of Class B homes would have been prohibitively expensive. Instead, a low-cost system was used involving on-site sampling of the interior air and off-site measurement of the tracer gas concentration. This "air bag" technique has been used successfully to measure the infiltration rates of a large number of homes with only a single tracer gas concentration measuring device at a central laboratory [7].

The air infiltration rate of a building is strongly influenced by the weather conditions during the measurement, and this rate can vary over a range of 5 to 1 for a single home depending on the weather conditions. Therefore, a single infiltration measurement is only of limited use for characterizing building tightness. The original experimental design was to test each home from five to ten times; however, most of the homes were tested only once or twice.

In each tracer gas test, the experimenter released a small amount of sulfur hexafluoride (SF_6) into the interior of the house. The amount of SF_6 injected was determined according to the house volume, the target concentration being 100 ppb. To increase the uniformity of the gas distribution, the tracer was released slowly as the experimenter walked through the house. Forced air distribution systems and fans were used to mix the interior air more completely. A waiting period of about one-half hour after the tracer gas release further ensured a uniform distribution of tracer gas. At this point a sample bag was filled with interior air while walking through the house. A total of four sample bags were filled at roughly half-hour intervals.

The air sample bags then were shipped to NBS, where the SF_6 concentration in each bag was measured with a gas chromatograph equipped with an electron capture detector. The rate of decay of the SF_6 concentration over time then was used to calculate the infiltration rate. The infiltration rates determined in this manner are accurate within about 0.1 ACH. During each infiltration measurement, the inside and outside temperatures and the wind speed were measured at the site.

Results

Figure 1 is a frequency distribution of the 50-Pa flow rates in ACH for the 74 homes which were pressure tested. The average 50-Pa flow rate for these homes is 10.1 ACH with a standard deviation of 6.1 ACH. Figure 2 is a frequency distribution of the 87 measured infiltration rates in ACH for 54 of the Class B homes. The average measured infiltration rate of the Class B homes is 0.42 ACH with a standard deviation of 0.30. The average weather conditions for these infiltration measurements are a wind speed of 2.1 m/s and an inside-outside temperature difference of 10.6°C.

The average infiltration rate measured in the houses is not representative of the heating season due to the mild weather conditions under which many of

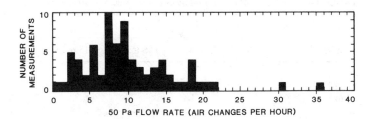

FIG. 1—*Frequency distribution of pressurization test results.*

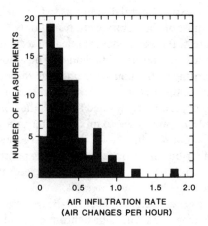

FIG. 2—*Frequency distribution of air infiltration measurements.*

the measurements were made. Table 1 shows the distribution of infiltration measurements with weather conditions. The number in each square is the number of infiltration measurements made under the corresponding conditions of wind and temperature difference. As can be seen in the table, many of the measurements have been made under relatively mild weather conditions: 24 of the 87 infiltration rates were measured with temperature differences of 5°C or less, and 61 of the rates were measured with a temperature difference less than 15°C. Roughly one third of the homes never had their infiltration rates measured for temperature differences greater than 5°C. This preponderance of mild weather infiltration measurements is the result of contractor actions and must be kept in mind when considering the magnitude of the measured infiltration rates. Also, for many of the homes, we have not reliably characterized their heating season infiltration rates.

TABLE 1—*Distribution of infiltration measurements with weather conditions.*

	$\Delta T(°C)$				
u(m/s)	<0	0 to 5	5 to 15	15 to 25	25 to 35
0 to 1	3	6	9	9	1
1 to 3	3	7	20	7	2
3 to 5	0	3	2	2	0
5 to 7	1	0	5	4	1
>7	1	0	1	0	0

NOTE—ΔT = the inside-outside temperature difference; u = the wind speed. Both values are averages over the infiltration measurement period.

Comparison to Other Homes

This data set of airtightness and infiltration measurements on passive solar homes provides an opportunity to compare the tightness of these buildings to other homes. These passive solar buildings, designed to consume relatively low levels of energy for space conditioning, are expected to be more airtight than other homes by builders, designers, and others involved with this proj-

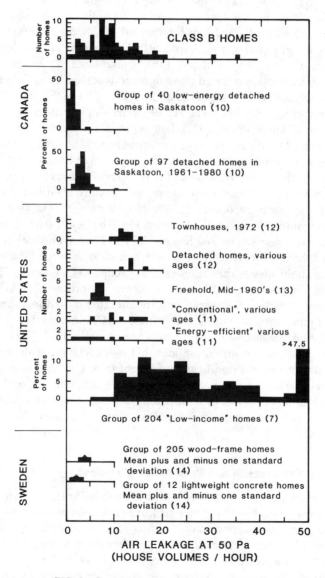

FIG. 3—*Comparison of pressurization test results.*

ect. The data presented in this report do not support this expectation. Figure 3 is a series of frequency distributions comparing the pressurization test results for the Class B homes to other homes. The Class B data are at the top of the figure, followed by two groups of Canadian homes [10], six groups of U.S. homes [7,11–13], and two groups of Swedish homes [14]. The Canadian and Swedish homes are examples of successful construction of tight homes. The recently built, low-energy homes in Saskatoon are tighter than their older counterparts, but the older homes are still quite tight.

The Class B homes are not as tight as the Canadian and Swedish homes, nor are they significantly different from the other U.S. homes, except for the "low-income" group. The fourth and fifth U.S. groups are divided by the researchers who studied the homes into "conventional" and "energy efficient." This distinction is based on design and intended level of energy use, not on the actual performance of the buildings. Similar to the Class B homes, the "energy efficient" homes are not necessarily tighter than the so-called "conventional" homes or other U.S. homes. Thus, the pressurization tests on these passive solar homes show that they are in general no tighter than typical U.S. homes and not as tight as levels being achieved in Canada and Sweden.

Comparing the air infiltration rates of the Class B homes to those in other residences is more difficult than comparing pressurization test results because of the strong dependence of infiltration on weather. The average infiltration rate for the "low-income" homes in Fig. 3 is about 1.0 ACH, averaged over 1000 measurements on 266 homes [7]. The average infiltration rate for the Class B homes is only 0.42 ACH, which is lower than the "low-income" homes and slightly lower than rates generally found in U.S. homes. The very tight homes in Sweden have infiltration rates on the order of 0.1 ACH [15].

As discussed earlier, the average infiltration rate for the Class B homes is somewhat misleading because of the mild weather conditions during most of the infiltration measurements. It is difficult to determine the infiltration rates under less mild temperature conditions, but they certainly would have been larger and probably not significantly different from U.S. homes in general. Empirical relations between pressurization test results, weather, and infiltration, which could be used to generalize infiltration data to weather conditions more representative of the heating season, are discussed in following paragraphs.

Infiltration Measurement and Pressurization Testing

The primary purpose of the pressurization and infiltration measurements on the Class B homes was to gather air leakage data on passive solar homes, but it also presents an opportunity to compare the two evaluation techniques. The relation between pressurization and infiltration has been discussed before, and the data presented here may contribute to our understanding of this relation [6,16–19]. In addition, the consistency of the two measurement techniques can be assessed by comparing the results of both measurements. One must note that the tests were conducted by field personnel of limited experience with the measurement techniques and that the wind data was of variable accuracy. Therefore, this is not a comparison of pressurization and infiltration under ideal experimental conditions, but rather a realistic demonstration of the accuracy and reliability achievable in the field.

At the most basic level, the relation between the 50-Pa flow rate Q_{50} and measured air infiltration rates can be examined. Figure 4 is a plot of measured infiltration I for a house against Q_{50} for the same house, both in ACH. There is indeed significant scatter in the data. A least squares, linear regression of I against Q_{50} yields the following equation

$$I = 0.06 + 0.041\ Q_{50} \tag{2}$$

The standard error of the estimate of this regression is 0.222, which is 52.4% of the mean measured infiltration rate for these homes, and the coefficient of determination r^2 has a value of 0.50. If these same data are regressed without the point in the upper right hand corner, the value of r^2 drops to 0.36. This simple comparison neglects the dependence of infiltration on wind speed and temperature difference. Empirical relations between pressurization and infil-

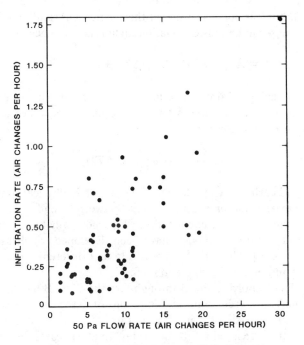

FIG. 4—*Measured infiltration versus 50-Pa flow rates.*

tration that include weather effects, and existing pressurization-infiltration models, are discussed in following paragraphs.

Empirical Relations

It is difficult to relate infiltration to pressurization measurements and weather conditions. The dependence of the infiltration rate of any particular house to wind speed and temperature difference depends on the building dimensions, leakage distribution, and exposure to the wind. In this section, empirical relations between infiltration, pressurization test results, and weather conditions are presented and applied to the data. In these relations, a house's leakiness is characterized by its 50 Pa flow rate Q_{50}. The weather variables include temperature difference ΔT and wind speed u. The first expression has separate terms in wind and temperature along with a product term

$$I = AQ_{50}u + BQ_{50}|\Delta T| + CQ_{50}u|\Delta T| \qquad (3)$$

In Eq 3, Q_{50} serves as a leakage coefficient for the house while A, B, and C characterize two aspects of the pressurization-infiltration relation, the connection between Q_{50} and infiltration and the weather dependence of the house's infiltration rate. The value of A also depends on where the wind speed u is measured. Physically, infiltration should depend on the square of the wind speed, but it is not clear whether this change will result in a better fit to the data. The second empirical relation includes u^2 in place of u in Eq 3

$$I = A'Q_{50}u^2 + B'Q_{50}|\Delta T| + C'Q_{50}u^2|\Delta T| \qquad (4)$$

Instead of having separate terms in wind and temperature difference along with a product of the two, the two weather terms can be added together and their sum raised to a power m

$$I = Q_{50}(\bar{A}u^x + \bar{B}|\Delta T|)^m \qquad (5)$$

As mentioned earlier, x can take on values of 1 or 2. Physical considerations lead one to expect that m will have a value between $1/2$ and 1. Pressurization testing has shown that the exponent n in Eq 1 generally has a value around 0.65. Several infiltration models have been developed which assume m is equal to $1/2$ [18,20]. Thus, Eq 5 is applied in four different forms, x equal to 1.0 and 2.0 and m equal to 0.5 and 0.65.

The results of applying Eqs 3 through 5 to the Class B data are shown in Table 2. The six different empirical equations fit to the data are shown along with results of regressing the infiltration rates calculated using each expression against the measured infiltration rates. In all six cases the value of r^2 is about 0.70, and the standard error of the estimate is about 40% of the mean

TABLE 2a—*Empirical relations between pressurization, weather conditions,
and air infiltration.*

P0: $I = Q_{50}[(1.35\ 10^{-2})u + (3.09 \times 10^{-3})|\Delta T| + (-6.77 \times 10^{-4})u|\Delta T|]$
P1: $I = Q_{50}[(3.12\ 10^{-3})u^2 + (3.24 \times 10^{-3})|\Delta T| + (-1.72 \times 10^{-4})u^2|\Delta T|]$
P2: $I = Q_{50}[(3.17\ 10^{-4})u + (1.60 \times 10^{-4})|\Delta T|]^{0.5}$
P3: $I = Q_{50}[(4.38\ 10^{-5})u^2 + (1.71 \times 10^{-4})|\Delta T|]^{0.5}$
P4: $I = Q_{50}[(1.35\ 10^{-3})u + (5.88 \times 10^{-4})|\Delta T|]^{0.65}$
P5: $I = Q_{50}[(1.80\ 10^{-4})u^2 + (6.45 \times 10^{-4})|\Delta T|]^{0.65}$

TABLE 2b—*Regression Results:* I_P *numbers against* $I_{measurements}$.

Equations	r^2	s_e	$\bar{I}_P$	$s_e/\bar{I}_M$
P0	0.71	0.168	0.386	39.6%
P1	0.68	0.185	0.365	43.6%
P2	0.69	0.160	0.407	37.7%
P3	0.66	0.167	0.389	39.4%
P4	0.70	0.162	0.392	38.2%
P5	0.65	0.174	0.371	41.0%

[a]s_e is the standard error of the regression estimate.

infiltration rate. Most infiltration models have a form similar to one of these
six equations, and therefore these results may serve as a reference for comparing the predictive accuracy of the models. Six corresponding empirical relations can be formed by substituting the 4-Pa flow rate from Eq 1 for the 50-Pa
flow rate in Eqs 3 through 5. The predictive accuracy of the 4-Pa equations is
almost identical to that of the 50-Pa equations.

Model Predictions

This data set of infiltration and pressurization measurements is useful for
checking some existing models of the relation between the two measurement
techniques. Five models have been applied to the Class B data. The first is the
model developed by Sherman and Grimsrud of the Lawrence Berkeley Laboratory [18]. This model is based on a detailed formulation of the phenomena
of air infiltration in homes and characterizes the leakiness of a house through
the 4-Pa flow rate. Its predictive equation is identical in form to Equation P3
in Table 2 if the 4-Pa flow rate is substituted for the 50-Pa flow rate. In applying the Lawrence Berkeley Laboratory (LBL) model to this data set, the required inputs were determined for each house by the people responsible for
testing the house.

The second model, developed by Shaw and Tamura of Canada [17], is
based on empirical relations between pressurization and infiltration derived
from detailed studies of two houses and uses the values of C and n from Eq 1
to characterize a house's leakiness. This model has separate predictive equa-

tions for when wind and temperature difference effects dominate and another equation when both effects are important.

Values of the temperature difference and wind speed, which determine the particular predictive equation which should be used, are given by Shaw and Tamura for the two houses used to develop their model. The specific values of temperature difference and wind speed, which determine the predictive equation that should be used, are house dependent, and we used the same values for the Class B houses that Shaw and Tamura used for their homes. For this reason, we expect that the predictions for this model will be in poor agreement with the measured infiltration rates.

The third model, developed by Kronvall [16], also uses the constants C and n from Eq 1. In Kronvall's model, one predicts the infiltration rate from the equation

$$I = C/V \, (0.026|\Delta T| + 0.010u^2)^n \tag{6}$$

where V is the house volume. The coefficients in front of ΔT and u^2 were derived empirically from pressurization and infiltration measurements on 19 tight Swedish homes. The fourth model uses Eq 3 to predict infiltration rates. The values of the constants A, B, and C are based on averages for several other homes. These values are, of course, different from those obtained from the regression of the Class B data, but in checking the models they are used as if one does not know the actual measured infiltration rates. This is the way the models would be used in practice, and we do not want to take advantage of the fact that we know the measured infiltration rates. The values of A, B, and C used to predict the Class B infiltration rates are 0.0075, 0.0025, and -0.0005, respectively.

Finally, the infiltration rates are predicted with an approximate rule of thumb which states that the infiltration rate under natural conditions is the 50-Pa flow rate in ACH divided by 20. This rule is crude and based on empirical results, not physical effects. It predicts only a single infiltration rate for each house, independent of weather conditions.

The results of the predictions from the five models are summarized in Table 3. The mean measured infiltration rate and the standard deviation of the measurements are given at the top of the table. For each of the models, the mean predicted infiltration rate and the average of the absolute value of the percentage difference between the predictions and measurements are shown. The table gives the results of linear regressions of the predictions against the measurements, including the coefficient of determination r^2 and the standard error of the regression estimate s_e. The ratio of s_e to the mean measured infiltration rate also is given. The values of r^2 are similar for the five models, but the mean predicted infiltration rates and the average percentage errors are variable. Kronvall's mean predicted rate is close to the average of the measured rates, and the average error is low.

TABLE 3—*Results of predictive models of infiltration. Mean Measured Infiltration Rate^a = 0.424. Standard Deviation = 0.312 (73.6% of the mean).*

Model	$\bar{I}_P$	Average Percentage Error	Regression Results		
			r^2	s_e	$s_e/\bar{I}_M$
LBL	0.547	58%	0.60	0.248	58.5%
Shaw-Tamura	1.212	210%	0.59	0.615	145.0%
Kronvall	0.400	39%	0.61	0.188	44.3%
ABC	0.270	41%	0.69	0.128	30.2%
Divide by 20	0.449	60%	0.50	0.192	45.3%

^{a}This mean is calculated only from measurements in those houses which were pressure tested.

The *ABC* predictions are low on average but have a small percentage error. The model of Shaw and Tamura makes some very bad predictions when wind and temperature effects both are significant, and therefore there are large errors for this model. This is because we divided weather conditions into wind and temperature difference dominance according to the same conditions that Shaw and Tamura found appropriate for their two test houses. These distinguishing conditions are house dependent, and the use of the same conditions for all the Class B homes would be expected to cause the significant predictive errors which occurred.

Comparing the model predictions to the empirical fits in Table 2, we see that the value of r^2 for the empirical fits are somewhat higher, about 0.7 compared to 0.6, and that the associated errors are much less. The mean predicted empirical infiltration rates are closer to the mean measured rate, and the standard errors of the estimates are also smaller than for the model predictions.

Conclusions

As part of the SERI Class B study of the thermal performance of passive solar buildings, pressurization and infiltration measurements have been made on about 80 homes. This is the largest set of such air leakage measurements on passive solar homes. Seventy-four homes have been pressure tested to obtain a weather independent measure of envelope tightness. The resulting 50-Pa flow rates range from about 1 to 36 ACH, with an average of 10.1. The infiltration rates of 54 homes have been measured with the tracer gas decay method employing on-site sampling with air bags and off-site analysis of these bags. The average infiltration rate is 0.42 ACH, but the measurements were made under relatively mild weather conditions.

The measurements indicate that the passive solar homes are not significantly tighter than other U.S. homes. Although the Class B homes are designed and constructed for below average energy consumption, they are not exceptionally tight. One must note the important difference between design intentions and actual construction. Although a building may be designed to be airtight or well insulated, the tightness of the resultant building depends on the attention to detail and the quality of the actual construction. The relation between pressurization and infiltration also was studied, and it was found that the correlations developed for other houses were appropriate for these passive solar homes.

Acknowledgments

The analysis work at the National Bureau of Standards was based on work done under Department of Energy Contract No. DE-AI101-76PR06010 as part of a program of technical support to the Department of Energy Passive and Hybrid Solar Energy Division. Andrew Persily's work was done under a National Research Council Postdoctoral Research Associateship at the National Bureau of Standards. The author acknowledges the efforts of the many participants in the air infiltration measurements on the Class B homes, including Blair Hamilton, John Duffy, Don Witt, Dave Gustashaw, George Yeagle, Steve Brant, Sukhbir Mahajan, and Mark McKinstry. Charlene Frith and Steven Schweinfurth of NBS deserve particular recognition for their analysis of the air infiltration and pressurization data.

References

[1] Frey, D. Swisher, J., and Holtz, M., "Class B Performance Monitoring of Passive/Hybrid Solar Buildings," Report SERI/TP-254-1492, presented at ASME 1982 Solar Energy Conference, Albuquerque, New Mexico, Solar Energy Research Institute, Golden, CO, 1981.
[2] Swisher, J. and Cowing, T., "Passive Solar Performance. Summary of 1981–1982 Class B Results," SERI/SP-281-1847, Solar Energy Research Institute, Golden, CO, 1983.
[3] "Method for Determining Air Leakage Rate by Fan-Pressurization Test," ASTM E 779-81, The American Society for Testing and Materials, Philadelphia, 1981.
[4] "Method for Determining Air Leakage Rate by Tracer Dilution Test," ASTM E 741-83, The American Society for Testing and Materials, Philadelphia, 1983.
[5] Persily, A. K. and Grot, R. A., "Air Infiltration and Building Tightness Measurements in Passive Solar Residences," in *Solar Engineering 1983*, L. M. Murphy, Ed., American Society of Mechanical Engineers, New York, 1983.
[6] Persily, A. K., "Understanding Air Infiltration in Homes," Report No. 129, Center for Energy and Environmental Studies, Princeton University, Princeton, NJ, 1982.
[7] Grot, R. A. and Clark, R. E., "Air Leakage Characteristics and Weatherization Techniques for Low-Income Housing," DOE/ASHRAE Conference on Thermal Performance of Exterior Envelopes of Buildings, Orlando, Florida, December, 1979, ASHRAE, Atlanta, GA, 1980.
[8] Hitchin, E. R. and Wilson, C. B., "A Review of Experimental Techniques for the Investigation of Natural Ventilation in Buildings," *Building Science*, Vol. 2, 1967.
[9] Hunt, C. M., "Air Infiltration: A Review of Some Existing Measurement Techniques and Data," in *Building Air Change Rate and Infiltration Measurements, ASTM STP 719*, C. M. Hunt, J. C. King, and H. R. Trechsel, Eds., American Society for Testing and Materials, Philadelphia, 1980.
[10] Dumont, R. S., Orr, H. W., and Figley, D. A., "Air Tightness Measurements of Detached Houses in the Saskatoon Area," Building Research Note No. 178, Division of Building Research, National Research Council of Canada, Ottawa, 1981.

[*11*] Grimsrud, D. T., Sherman, M. H., Blomsterberg, A. K., and Rosenfeld, A. H., "Infiltration and Air Leakage Comparisons: Conventional and Energy Efficient Housing Designs," Report No. 9157, Lawrence Berkeley Laboratory, University of California, Berkeley, 1979.

[*12*] Blomsterberg, A. K. and Harrje, D. T., "Approaches to Evaluation of Air Infiltration Energy Losses in Buildings," *ASHRAE Transactions*, Vol. 85(I), 1979.

[*13*] Persily, A. K. and Linteris, G. T., "A Comparison of Measured and Predicted Infiltration Rates," *ASHRAE Transactions*, Vol. 89(II), 1983.

[*14*] Kronvall, J., "Airtightness—Measurements and Measurement Methods," Report D8, Swedish Council of Building Research, Stockholm, Sweden, 1980.

[*15*] Kronvall, J., "Testing of Homes for Air Leakage Using a Pressure Method," *ASHRAE Transactions*, Vol. 84(I), 1978.

[*16*] Kronvall, J., "Correlating Pressurization and Infiltration Rate Data—Tests of an Heuristic Model," Lund Institute of Technology, Division of Building Technology, Lund, Sweden, 1980.

[*17*] Shaw, C. Y., "A Correlation Between Air Infiltration and Air Tightness for Houses in a Developed Residential Area," *ASHRAE Transactions*, Vol. 87(II), 1981.

[*18*] Sherman, M. H., and Grimsrud, D. T., "Infiltration-Pressurization Correlation: Simplified Physical Modeling," *ASHRAE Transactions*, Vol. 86(II), 1980.

[*19*] Warren, P. R., and Webb, B. C., "The Relationship Between Tracer Gas and Pressurization Techniques in Dwellings," First Symposium of the Air Infiltration Centre, Windsor, England, 1980.

[*20*] Reeves, G., McBride, M., and Sepsey, C., "An Air Infiltration Model for Residences," *ASHRAE Transactions*, Vol. 85(II), 1979.

DISCUSSION

David Saum[1] *(written discussion)*—(1) Did these houses have air-vapor barriers? (2) Do your results suggest that the models that relate infiltration to pressurization measurements are no more accurate than dividing the 50 Pa ACH by 20?

Andrew K. Persily (author's closure)—(1) Some of the houses have air-vapor barriers, and others do not. The construction details of each house are available in SERI publications on the Class B programs. (2) Our results do seem to indicate this, but this is only a small number of houses, and this result will not necessarily apply to other houses.

Terry Brennan[2] *(written discussion)*—Using grab samples of tracer gas taken by homeowners and mailed in to a central lab for processing makes it possible to collect a large number of samples with a small number of field personnel and only one set of processing instrumentation. It also introduces the possibility of a number of errors (timekeeping, container damage, container leaks, container mislabeling) that have happened frequently enough to trained personnel (me, for example) to prompt the following question. Can you give us some idea of the reliability of the data collected by homeowners in the study? As people with experience at making such a data acquisition

[1]Infiltec, Waynesboro, VA.
[2]Red Wing, Rome, NY 13440.

method work perhaps you could give one or two insights that would be helpful to others contemplating using the same method.

Andrew K. Persily (author's closure)—The potential for error due to the causes you mention does exist, but such errors can be minimized if careful instructions are provided and followed. It is very important that field personnel be properly trained and that they closely follow the correct procedures. This is the most important advice we can provide. When the appropriate procedures are applied, the infiltration rates should be accurate within 0.1 ACH and only about 10% of the tests will have to be thrown out due to some unavoidable mishaps (leaks, inappropriate injection volumes).

Richard B. Gammage,[1] *Alan R. Hawthorne,*[1] *and*
D. Allen White[2]

Parameters Affecting Air Infiltration and Airtightness in Thirty-One East Tennessee Homes

REFERENCE: Gammage, R. B., Hawthorne, A. R., and White, D. A., **"Parameters Affecting Air Infiltration and Airtightness in Thirty-One East Tennessee Homes,"** *Measured Air Leakage of Buildings, ASTM STP 904,* H. R. Trechsel and P. L. Lagus, Eds., American Society for Testing and Materials, Philadelphia, 1986, pp. 61–69.

ABSTRACT: A major pathway for loss of conditioned air in east Tennessee homes with externally located heating, ventilation, and air-conditioning (HVAC) systems is leakage in the ductwork. The effect on infiltration rates, as measured by Freon-12 tracer gas dilution, becomes marked if the central duct fan is operating; duct-fan on and duct-fan off measurements of the rate of air exchange gave mean values of 0.78 and 0.44 h^{-1}, respectively, in a total of 31 homes. Specific leakage areas measured by the blower-door, pressurization-depressurization technique are affected to a lesser extent by inclusion of the ductwork volume within the total volume of the house that is being pressurized. A subset of seven of the study homes were measured using this technique; the average increment in the specific leakage area was about 15%. Leaking ductwork in attached garages also causes degradation of the indoor air quality by pulling in pollutants such as gasoline fumes from automobiles and distributing them throughout the house. In dealing with homes that have central HVAC systems, weatherization and energy conservation programs should be cognizant of the seriousness of air and energy losses caused by leaking ductwork as well as possible degradation of the indoor air quality.

KEY WORDS: ductwork leakage, central duct fan, air infiltration, air exchange rate, Freon-12 tracer, blower door, specific leakage area

More so than usual for a study of this nature, serendipity played a major role in guiding the course of the studies. What started as routine measurements of tracer gas air infiltration in support of an indoor air pollution study

[1]Manager, Occupational Health Research Program, and Leader, Measurement Applications Group, respectively, Health and Safety Research Division, Oak Ridge National Laboratory, Oak Ridge, TN 37831.
[2]Graduate student, Chemistry Department, University of Tennessee, Knoxville, TN 37916.

[1,2] became a study focused on the impact on air infiltration of the ductwork and the duct fan of heating, ventilating, and air-conditioning (HVAC) systems. An apparently marked difference in the "natural" air exchange rate was first noted in houses with HVAC systems, dependent on whether or not the central duct fan had been running at the time of the tracer gas measurement. Two rather than one tracer gas measurements were subsequently made with and without the operation of the central duct fan in each house with a central HVAC. The study later was expanded to include blower-door measurements that either included or excluded the ductwork system in the pressurized volume of the house. The objectives were to evaluate quantitatively the impact of central ductwork systems and operating duct fans on air infiltration and air leakage parameters.

Procedure

Natural air infiltration rates were measured as rates of air exchange in 31 different houses by the tracer dilution technique. During the measurement, the exterior doors and windows of a house remained closed while the interior doors between the finished living areas were left open. The tracer gas, Freon-12, was sprayed throughout the house and dispersed with the aid of several portable floor fans that continually circulated air while the concentration decay was being measured. The maximum indoor concentration of Freon-12 was 20 ppm, which is 1/50th of the American Conference of Governmental Industrial Hygienists threshold limit value (TLV) of 1000 ppm. The concentration of Freon was monitored with a Wilks Miran-80, single-beam infrared spectrometer that measured the absorbance at 9.26 μm. A mathematical equation based on a well-mixed, single-compartment mass balance was used to model the data [3]. A least-squares program was used to obtain the best fit of the absorbance versus time data to obtain the rate of air exchange. Two sets of tracer dilution data were obtained sequentially. In one instance, the duct fan of the central HVAC system was operated, and, in the other instance, the fan was left off. The fan-on experiment was generally performed first, followed by the fan-off experiment. Each experiment usually lasted between 1 and 2 h, and the tracer gas was reinjected between experiments.

In a subset of seven houses, the induced pressure method was used to measure airtightness. The blower door [4] was temporarily installed in an exterior door of each house. Inside-outside pressure differences were recorded with a Magnehelic pressure gage calibrated against a water manometer in our laboratory. Both fan-pressurization and fan-depressurization measurements were made by operating the blower fan in a clockwise or anticlockwise direction. Plots of the flow rates versus the inside-outside pressure differences induced by the blower were combined with clockwise and counterclockwise nomographs. This permitted the leakage area, and hence the specific leakage area (square centimetres per square metres of floor space) of a house, to be determined graphically for a pressure differential of 4 Pa [0.406 mm (0.016 in.) of water]. A calibration information packet for the blower door was provided by Harmax Corp. of Los Angeles.

Prior to measuring air leakage, the following openings in the house were covered with plastic and sealed with tape: open fireplaces, air exhausts above kitchen cooking ranges, and exhausts for bathrooms.

Two types of blower-door measurement were made. In one instance, the air entry and exit vents to the duct system were left open. In the other instance, the vents were closed either by shutting the attached louvers or covering them with plastic. Thus, the volume of the duct system was either included or excluded from the total volume being pressurized or depressurized by the blower door. The central duct fan was left in the off position throughout the blower-door experiments.

Results

The rates of air exchange obtained from measurements of tracer gas decay are reproduced in Table 1. The majority of these measurements were made during the spring, summer, and fall of 1982 and generally during the morning. At these times of the year and day, the wind speed was observed to be generally less than 4.5 m/s.

Of the 42 houses that were available for study [1,2], 34 were equipped with central HVAC systems. In 31 of these 34 homes with HVAC, the air exchange rate measurements were made with the central duct fan both on and off. In about half of the homes, the measurements of tracer gas decay were repeated on different days.

Another important measurement involved the additional use of carbon dioxide (CO_2) as the tracer gas on one occasion (House No. 7). Whether the tracer gas was Freon-12 or CO_2, essentially the same result was obtained for the rate of exchange of air. This consistency was preserved when the central duct fan was running.

The mean value of the rate of exchange between outdoor and indoor air in closed-up houses was 0.44 changes per hour (h^{-1}) when the central duct fan was switched off. With the central duct fan running, the mean air exchange rate was nearly doubled at 0.78 h^{-1}.

The results of the induced pressure measurements, made in a subset of seven houses, are shown in Table 2. Each specific leakage area (cm^2/m^2) is the mean of two leakage measurements in which the house was either being pressurized or depressurized.

For House No. 1, pressure differentials were measured in the return duct at a location 3 m in front of the central duct fan. With the duct fan running, a decrement of 25 Pa [2.54 mm (0.10 in.) of water] was measured. At the same point in the ductwork, with the duct fan off but with the blower door depres-

TABLE 1—*Rates of air exchange from tracer gas decay.*

House No.	Date	Rate of Air Exchange, h^{-1}	
		Central Fan Off	Central Fan On
1	14 March 1983	0.36	0.69
2	9 Sept. 1982	0.31	0.65
	13 Dec. 1982	0.48	0.81
3	25 Aug. 1982	0.32	0.73
5	13 Aug. 1982	0.22	0.45
	14 Dec. 1982	0.18	0.42
7	6 April 1982	0.44	0.89
	7 May 1982	0.28	0.85
8	8 July 1982	0.27	0.58
12	12 May 1982	0.46[a]	0.67
14	19 May 1982	0.27	0.81
	16 Dec. 1982	0.39	0.68
15	23 June 1982	0.29	0.69
21	24 June 1982	0.15	0.45
24	17 Jan. 1983	0.96	0.92
	3 Feb. 1983	0.92	1.04
26	26 May 1982	0.24	0.37
29	13 May 1982	0.12	0.14
33	16 July 1982	0.14	0.35
34	17 June 1982	0.47	0.46
36	15 June 1982	0.18[a]	0.90
	15 Dec. 1982	0.73	1.10
41	8 June 1982	0.11	0.70[a]
54	26 Jan. 1983	0.97	0.89
	7 Feb. 1983	0.98	1.21
55	22 June 1982	0.28	0.31
	8 Feb. 1983	0.39	0.51
58	12 Nov. 1982	0.95	1.56
	20 Jan. 1983	0.71	1.27
	2 Feb. 1983	1.08	1.23
61	15 July 1982	0.48	0.86
62	6 May 1982	0.27	1.57
	7 Jan. 1983	0.75	1.69
	27 Jan. 1983	1.28	1.98
64	16 June 1982	0.42	0.83
65	27 May 1982	0.26	0.32
	25 Jan. 1983	0.41	0.96
	11 Feb. 1983	0.31	1.05
68	9 June 1983	0.83	1.34
	10 Feb. 1983	0.40	0.83
75	5 Nov. 1982	0.51	0.78
79	9 July 1982	0.21	0.69
	9 Dec. 1982	1.04	1.32
80	13 July 1982	0.62	0.92
	12 Jan. 1983	0.41	0.64
81	15 Oct. 1982	0.34	0.96
82	10 Nov. 1982	0.24	0.51
	5 Jan. 1983	0.50	0.96
83	5 Nov. 1982	0.60	1.07
	3 Jan. 1983	0.96	1.84
	1 Feb. 1983	0.65	0.96
Mean for 31 houses		0.44	0.78

[a]Noisy data.

TABLE 2—*Specific leakage area.*[a]

| | | Specific Leakage Area, cm^2/m^2 | |
| | | Ductwork | |
House No.	Date	Closed Off	Vents Open
1	15 Dec. 1983	8.4	10.7
3	19 Aug. 1982	5.8	6.3
7	18 Aug. 1982	4.3	4.5
12	19 Aug. 1982	5.1	5.1
36	25 Aug. 1982	4.7	4.9
62	15 Dec. 1983	4.0	5.5
65	15 Dec. 1983	4.0	4.3
Mean for 7 houses		5.1	5.9

[a]Effective specific leak area at a pressure difference of 4 Pa.

surizing the main volume of the house to 25 Pa, the pressure inside the ductwork was also 25 Pa.

Volatile organic compounds were measured with a Photovac 10A10 portable gas chromatograph, into which small air samples could be injected directly. In Fig. 1 are shown chromatograms of the indoor air taken from the bedroom located above the attached garage of House No. 2. The return ductwork of the HVAC system is located inside this attached garage. The HVAC duct fan was running when each of the two air samples was collected. The peaks in the chromatograms are characteristic of the signature of gasoline fumes.

Discussion

The most striking finding was that, for 31 homes with central HVAC, the mean rate of "natural" air exchange was nearly doubled, from 0.44 to 0.78 h^{-1}, when the central duct fan was operating. A duplicate measurement with CO_2 tracer confirmed that the effect was real and not due to loss of Freon-12 tracer by means other than leakage. Portable fans were operated at all times to ensure good mixing.

The dominant driving force for the enhanced air exchange is leakage of air from joints in the central ductwork at locations exterior to the principal living zones. These zones include attached garages, crawlspaces, attics, and in ductwork adjacent to heat pumps located outside the house. These leaks are readily detected by force of draft on the hand or with a smoke stick. In return ducts under negative pressure, such as those often located in garages, the enhanced exchange will be due to ingress, rather than egress, of air (the pressure decrement was 2.54 mm (0.10 in.) of water for House No. 1).

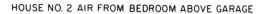

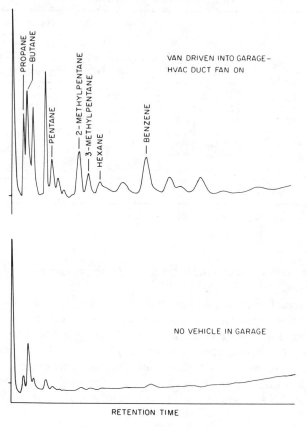

FIG. 1—*Volatile components of gasoline in the bedroom air above the attached garage of House No. 2.*

Ingress of air from the garage also can have a pronounced effect on the indoor air quality of living zones inside a house. The events depicted in Fig. 1 show a dramatically boosted entry of gasoline fumes when a van engine is operated inside the attached garage for a short time. Because of leaks in the return ductwork, uncombusted gasoline in the engine exhausts was drawn into the ducting and then distributed throughout House No. 2. Even in the absence of the van, residual traces of gasoline persisted in the indoor air of House No. 2, as well as in all the other houses that we studied. Likewise, escaping vapors from other garage-stored items, such as paints, cleaners, polishes, and insecticides, will be drawn into the ducting. The residents of these homes who store such items in their garages are mistaken in their belief that any escaping fumes will not permeate the normal living zones.

The rather low mean rate of air exchange without duct fan operation probably reflects the generally benign weather conditions at the time the tracer gas measurements were made rather than tight construction. These east Tennessee homes are less airtight (from induced pressure measurements) than other U.S. homes of more recent construction [5].

It has been recognized before [3] that leaks in central ductwork may produce an increase in the air infiltration rate. To our knowledge, however, the only instance where the effect has been quantified is in a study reported by Prado et al [6]. A single mobile home with owner-installed flexible ductwork was used in that study. He and his coworkers observed an increase in rate of exchange of air from 0.8 h^{-1} with all HVAC systems off to values ranging between 2.3 and 2.7 h^{-1} with the HVAC blower operating. There was, perhaps, some doubt that the effect often would be seen in conventional homes with professionally installed central ductwork. Our findings indicate, however, that air leakage in HVAC ductwork is often a major pathway for air and, therefore, energy loss. The enhanced air exchange will occur intermittently in homes where the duct fan is operated only during active heating or cooling. On the other hand, the enhanced air exchange will be continuous in homes with continually running duct fans, as might be the case where an electrostatic precipitator is incorporated into the HVAC system.

House No. 24 is of special interest. The owner had personally applied sealant to the ductwork joints prior to thermally reinsulating the ductwork. This air leakproofing action proved to be quite effective since there is virtually no difference in the rate of air exchange with the duct fan either on or off.

There is no simple formula for converting blower-door data to natural leakage rates [7]. Any relationship is complicated because blower-door–induced pressures are applied equilaterally to all walls and surfaces, whereas forces due to wind or stack effect are asymmetrical. Also, blower-door–induced rates of air exchange are usually much larger than natural air leakage rates. The present work points out a further complication, that of duct-fan–induced leakage occurring alongside natural air leakage throughout the rest of the house.

The effect of including or excluding the volume of the central duct system from the volume of the house subjected to blower-door pressurization is quite revealing. Exclusion of the ductwork volume causes an average 15% reduction in the specific leakage area. Similar air losses in a duct system have been reported for a California house [8]. Although significant, the magnitude of the effect is much less than the near doubling of the tracer gas air exchange rate brought about by running the central duct fan. A logical explanation is as follows. In a tracer gas measurement with the duct fan running, pressurization of air is greatest within the ductwork, and this is especially so in regions close to the duct fan. Such was the case for House No. 1 with an excess pressure of 25 Pa inside the ductwork. Ductwork leaks thus have a pronounced effect on the overall rate of exchange of air. In these experiments, we made certain that the central fan always was turned off for the blower-door pressurization measurements. The pressurization within the ductwork, therefore, will be the same as or even slightly less than in the more open volumes of the house. During the blower-door measurement in House No. 1, the pressure in the return ductwork was the same as the pressure applied to the living volume. Hence, in such a circumstance, ductwork leaks have no preferential influence on the specific leakage area.

Conclusions

Utility companies in their weatherization programs pay considerable heed to the manner in which the ductwork of HVAC systems should be thermally insulated. Little is generally said about airtightness except that joints should not leak. More attention needs to be devoted to the better leakproofing of ductwork, since leaking ductwork clearly provides a major pathway for loss of conditioned air. Our study showed that on the average in 31 houses in east Tennessee the rate of exchange of air measured by decay of tracer gas was nearly doubled by operation of the central duct fan. Air leakage within ductwork has a less pronounced effect on blower-door pressurization measurements, the specific leakage area increasing by an average of about 15% upon inclusion of the duct volume with the pressurized volume of the house.

There is another disadvantage of leaking ductwork. Escaping and potentially hazardous fumes from a variety of products that homeowners are prone to store in their garages can be sucked into the ductwork and subsequently can permeate the normal living zones.

Acknowledgments

The authors extend their appreciation to G. E. Courville of the Oak Ridge National Laboratory, Energy Division. He provided the blower door and its accessories, instruction in its use, and also instruction on the handling of data. We also thank P. W. Childs for practical help during some initial blower-door installations and measurements. Statistical evaluation of the tracer gas decay data was made by C. S. Dudney of Oak Ridge National Laboratory, Health and Safety Research Division, and is gratefully acknowledged.

References

[1] Hawthorne, A. R., Gammage, R. B., Dudney, C. S., Womack, D. R., Morris, S. A., Westley, R. R., and Gupta, K. C. in *Proceedings*, Measurement and Monitoring of Non-Criteria (Toxic) Contaminants in Air, Air Pollution Control Association, March 1983, pp. 514-526.
[2] Hawthorne, A. R., Gammage, R. B., Dudney, C. S., Womack, D. R., Morris, S. A., Westley, R. R., White, D. A., and Gupta, K. C., "Results of a Forty-Home Indoor Air

Pollutant Monitoring Study," 76th Annual Meeting of the Air Pollution Control Association, Atlanta, 20–24 June 1983.

[3] Lagus, P. L. in *Building Air Change Rate and Infiltration Measurements, ASTM STP 719*, C. M. Hunt, J. C. King, and H. R. Trechsel, Eds., American Society for Testing and Materials, Philadelphia, 1980, pp. 36–49.

[4] Gadsby, K. J., Linteris, G. T., Dutt, G. S., and Harrje, D. T., "The Blower Door," Report PU/CEES 124, Princeton University, Princeton, NJ, Oct. 1981.

[5] Grimsrud, D. T., Sonderegger, R. C., Sherman, M. H., Diamond, R. C., and Blomsterberg, A., "Calculational Infiltration: Implications for a Construction Quality Standard," in *Proceedings*, SP-38, DOE Conference on Thermal Performance of the Exterior Envelope of Buildings, Las Vegas, Dec. 1982, American Society of Heating, Refrigerating, and Air-Conditioning Engineers, New York, pp. 422–452.

[6] Prado, F., Leonard, R. G., and Goldschmidt, V. W., *Transactions*, Vol. 82, Part 2, American Society of Heating, Refrigerating, and Air-Conditioning Engineers, New York, 1976, pp. 151–166.

[7] Hunt, C. M., "Air Infiltration: A Review of Some Existing Measurement Techniques and Data," in *Building Air Change Rate and Infiltration Measurements, ASTM STP 719*, C. M. Hunt, J. C. King, and H. R. Trechsel, Eds., American Society for Testing and Materials, Philadelphia, 1980, pp. 3–23.

[8] Grimsrud, D. T., Sherman, M. H., Diamond, R. C., Cordon, P. E., and Rosenfeld, A. H., "Infiltration-Pressurization Correlations: Detailed Measurements on a California House," Report LBL-7824, Lawrence Berkeley Laboratory, Berkeley, CA, Dec. 1978.

DISCUSSION

P. Lagus[1] *(written discussion)*—I am concerned that such a relatively modest duct leakage could evidence such a large change in measured infiltration. Freon-12, your tracer, is a common refrigerant. Could there have been a source of Freon in the HVAC system? A Freon leakage into the house during times when the HVAC was in operation would yield anomalously low air leakage rates.

R. B. Gammage, A. R. Hawthorne, and D. A. White (authors' closure)— The validity of the Freon-12 measurements was verified using CO_2 as a tracer in one of the houses, as is mentioned in the paper. Some more recent measurements in two houses using sulfur hexafluoride (SF_6) and Freon-12 tracers also showed the same effects.

[1]S-Cubed, Box 1620, La Jolla, CA.

Victor W. Goldschmidt[1]

Average Infiltration Rates in Residences: Comparison of Electric and Combustion Heating Systems

REFERENCE: Goldschmidt, V. W., "Average Infiltration Rates in Residences: Comparison of Electric and Combustion Heating Systems," *Measured Air Leakage of Buildings, ASTM STP 904*, H. R. Trechsel and P. L. Lagus, Eds., American Society for Testing and Materials, Philadelphia, 1986, pp. 70–98.

ABSTRACT: Research and test results presenting measurements of air infiltration rates in residences are reviewed. In particular, comparison of electric and combustion heating shows (on the average) infiltration rates to be 0.1 to 0.25 higher for residences with combustion heating.

KEY WORDS: infiltration, air exchange, electric heating, combustion heating, energy use

Infiltration is that air which enters a residence from the outside environment via cracks, pores, or whatever openings connect the living area with the outdoor environment. Some infiltration always may be desired as it can provide fresh air for the comfort and health of the occupants. However, in most cases a comparison of the required fresh air for health (in accordance with appropriate standards and in the absence of major sources of pollution) and that naturally infiltrating will show the latter to be more than necessary.

Infiltration beyond that required for providing fresh air is not desirable as it imposes an additional load on the heating or cooling equipment. This is because that outside air has to be either heated or cooled from the outdoor to the indoor conditions. Normally (at design conditions), that additional load is estimated at about 25% of the load attributed to temperature differences (and hence conduction through the walls, roofs, etc.), and for the case of cooling is due also to internal heat gains and solar effects. In the case of well-

---

[1]Professor of mechanical engineering, Purdue University, West Lafayette, IN 47907.

insulated residences, the load due to infiltration will be a much higher percentage—in some cases well above 40%.

Infiltration is caused by three phenomena, which are generally coupled together.

The first is the wind. As the wind blows on the outside surface of a building, it causes a pressure difference between the inside and outside and hence a driving pressure gradient across any cracks or pores on the walls, ceilings, or whatever. Generally, the stagnating face (facing upstream) will cause an increase of the outside pressure and hence a pressure difference between the outside and the inside, driving air into the residence. The downstream side, with the predominant wake effects and separation, generally will have a pressure which is lower than the atmospheric pressure and hence a tendency to have air from inside the residence driven to the outside. This is also the case over the roof, where the wind again causes a pressure difference which would drive air from the inside ambient to the outside environment. The pressure distribution across the face of one given surface (that is, roof, wall facing upstream, wall facing downstream, etc.) is essentially uniform due to the bluff geometry of most buildings. This means that the actual distribution of the cracks and openings on a given surface (that is, whether they are all bunched near the edges or all in the midplane) will not affect much the wind-driven infiltration. It is for this reason that fan pressurization or "blower tests" sometimes are used to obtain the "leakage area" of a residence in order to estimate infiltration rates.

A parenthetical comment is in order. Air will not only infiltrate a residence but will also exfiltrate. In the just-cited example, air infiltrates through the windward-facing wall and exfiltrates through the backward-facing wall and roof. The infiltration and exfiltration are such that over time the same mass of air that enters has to leave. Traditionally, volume flow rates have been used as the reference, although strictly speaking mass flow rates should be used. Furthermore, in a purist sense, a more proper expression would be "air exchange rate" (which clearly accounts for both infiltrating and exfiltrating air) rather than simply "infiltration rate."

The second phenomenon driving infiltration is the temperature difference between the inside and outside. It is important, when analyzing this component, to recognize that air is not incompressible. Its density, pressure, and temperature will vary with elevation not only due to "hydrostatic" effects but also due to a "polytropic" process or some similar relationship governing the properties of the air. Different mean temperatures indoors and outdoors then will lead to different pressure distributions with height on the indoor and outdoor faces of the walls (irrespective of the wind effects). These differences can in turn impose a pressure difference across cracks, pores, or whatever openings connect the indoor and outdoor environments. The distribution of these openings along the surface of the wall will obviously affect the infiltration driven by these differences in temperature. The phenomenon is sometimes called the "stack" effect, or the "buoyancy" driven component. The fact that it is so dependent on the location of the openings (not only on the total leakage area) means that it is impossible to quantify the "stack effect" from only a "blower test."

The third phenomenon is an internal-induced phenomenon. Two types are common: the first is induced by a blower with part of its ductwork outside of the living area; the second is a combustion process. Normally, the infiltration rates due to these induced phenomena are treated as additive to the infiltration rates driven by the wind and temperature difference between the indoors and outdoors. A single package heat pump would be a clear example of the first case. Due to cracks in the outside section of the ductwork (as well as in the unit itself), outside air will infiltrate and cause an increase in the inside pressure and hence a balancing increase in the exfiltration—with a net increase in the air changes per hour (ACH). Another example of blower-induced infiltration would be systems with a return or supply ductwork in spaces not directly connected with the living quarters. There, the net effect of unavoidable duct leakage would be a similar change in the indoor pressure and a related increase in the infiltration rate. The second effect would be due to any combustion process whatsoever requiring inside air and having the products of combustion exhausted to the outside. This effect can be substantial. For example, White et al [1] determined that a 23.4-kW (80 000-Btu/h) gas furnace [in a mobile home with an inside volume of about 141 m³ (5000 ft³)] required about 12 L/s (1500 ft³/h) of combustion air while the furnace was on. Had this air been provided from the inside environment, it would have led to a substantial increase of 0.3 ACH to the otherwise natural infiltration rate.

Infiltration is understood to be that uncontrolled exchange of air between the indoors and the outdoors. The controlled exchange (via kitchen and bathroom exhaust fans, make-up air inlets, open windows, etc.) is considered as a ventilation rate and can be called upon as needed to provide health and comfort. As infiltration is reduced, ventilation rate can be increased and hence controlled. Provision of fresh air by controlled ventilation air through controlled inlets (rather than by infiltration through uncontrolled and multiple openings) permits the use of energy-saving devices such as heat recovery exchangers. These devices are not common yet in residential applications, but their availability to homeowners is coming.

It is obvious, then, that any economical and practical scheme to reduce infiltration rates in residences should be considered. Of first and primary concern is defining the actual levels of infiltration for residences of different types. The U.S. Department of Energy in one of its draft documents simply characterizes infiltration rates as 1.0 for "average" construction, 0.7 for "tight" construction, and 0.4 for "very tight" construction. The Department does this with limited backup data and without differentiating between types of heating systems.

The use of a conventional fossil-fuel–fired system, when compared with an electric system will lead to increases in infiltration rates. This will be due to two factors: (1) the increased leakage paths due to the presence of a chimney protruding generally through the roof; (2) the call for combustion air. Any generalization or analysis on the comparative consumption of residences will have to account for these increases.

The use of sealed combustion furnaces is almost universal in mobile homes (and rare in stick-built homes). In the case of sealed combustion systems, the combustion air would not add to the infiltration. However, the stack itself generally will add measurably to the leakage paths.

In some special installations, the furnace might be located completely outside of the living area. When that is done, the benefits of eliminating the leakage paths through the chimney-roof and the lack of effects of combustion air on infiltration are apparent. However, in this case there will be detrimental effects in that the blower and inherent duct leakages will cause an additional infiltration (as well as the leakage paths for the ductwork-wall), while at the same time none of the furnace jacket losses of thermal energy will be gained by the living area (which is not the case with a furnace at least partially in the living area).

There is a considerable shortage of dependable field data on the comparative infiltration rate of residences heated with either electric or fossil-fuel-fired systems. The essential differences between these systems are obvious from the previous discussion. The need for dependable field data is crucial in any estimate of energy consumption, especially when recalling that the load due to infiltration can be in the order of 25% or more of the total load. (Caffey [2] estimates that to be up to 40%; Blomsterberg[2] about 33%, even for tight Swedish homes; Shaw and Tamura [3] estimate 20% for electric-heated homes; Warren [4], 20 to 40%; Lipschutz et al [5] quote a study where infiltration is 25 to 40% of the heating load; Collins [6] refers to a study where well-insulated homes showed 35 to 36% of the energy loss through air infiltration under both heating and cooling and 19 and 27% for heating and cooling modes, respectively, in uninsulated houses; Diamond et al [7], 28%; and Veenhuizen and Lin [8] estimate that 46% of the total heat is lost through infiltration.)

Methods of Measurement

There are two basic test methods employed in the field. One is the blower test, and the other is the tracer gas test.

---

[2]Blomsterberg, A., "Air Tightness vs Air Infiltration for Swedish Homes—Measurements and Modelling," private communication of a manuscript draft, 1983.

Blower Test

The blower test simply consists of pressurizing or depressurizing the residence with a blower introduced through a sealed opening (such as a window or door) until a predetermined pressure difference between the inside and the outside is reached (in the order of 50 Pa). The blower flow rate necessary to maintain that pressure difference then is measured. With that measurement, one of two things is done: either it is related to an expected infiltration rate (via some calibrating coefficient), or an effective leakage area is determined and then used to estimate infiltration rate. Both methods have major and fundamental shortcomings. First, the measurement with the blower test is never done in the complete absence of wind or temperature differences, hence "smearing" the blower test data. Second, the blower test (in principle) induces a uniform pressure difference through all the external surfaces of the building, while the wind always induces positive differences in some surfaces and negative differences in others and is hence dependent on the geometry of the building (which the blower test is not). Third, and most important, the blower test cannot by itself account for the temperature-driven ("stack") effects as these effects depend not only on leakage areas but very strongly on the distribution of the leakage paths. Fourth, the blower test is not capable of directly determining the induced infiltration rates (that is, due to combustion processes, external ducts, etc.).

The blower test has become popular as it is simple and rapid. A number of authors address themselves to its use, and some acknowledge its shortcomings. The major advantage of the blower test is that it is straightforward and readily permits comparison of "leakage areas" for different buildings. In spite of that, its relationship to actual infiltration rates leaves a lot to question—both in practical aspects as well as physical principles. (The limitations of the blower test, or fan pressurization test, while clearly stated in ASTM standards, sometimes are ignored in published literature.)

Gas Decay Rate (Tracer Gas Test)

The basic principle of the decay gas technique is straightforward: to inject a tracer gas, mix it well in the residence, and measure its decay of concentration with time. (A convenient alternative is to continuously measure tracer added in order to maintain a constant concentration.) That decay will be due to the inlet of fresh air (that is, infiltration). The faster the decay, the higher the infiltration. Without recourse to the simple mathematics governing gradient mass transport, it suffices to state that the slope of the natural log of the average concentration of the tracer in the building when plotted against time gives a measure of the infiltration rate in changes per unit of time.

The complications with the decay gas technique are many. First, inasmuch as the infiltration rate is generally a strong function of wind and temperature, its measure requires simultaneous recording of the weather and the indoor temperatures. Furthermore, a single value of infiltration is not what is required but rather a set of values under different weather conditions. At best, a table or expected functional relationship is obtained, but only after considerable test data are taken to average out test uncertainties. A third complication lies in the need for multiple point sampling of concentration in order to obtain an average concentration. It does not suffice to "bag" samples at some arbitrary location in the building at fixed times after injection of the tracer and to hope from that alone to determine infiltration rates. [An ASTM standard, ASTM Method for Determining Air Leakage Rate by Tracer Dilution Test (E 741-83), recommends procedures to follow while conducting tracer gas tests.]

The most applicable field data, then, are those that result from decay gas measurements: (a) taken over sufficiently long time periods, (b) with essentially constant wind and temperatures and (c) with multiple sampling within the residence (or, at least, in the return duct for forced air systems). These data should be looked upon with the highest credibility in the review of the literature.

Field Data

Some of the current and salient publications providing field data on infiltration rates are listed in the bibliography. Of interest are those references that at least (a) compare the effects of different heating systems, (b) present effects of retrofitting or (c) give representative values.

In quoting published literature, the units reported therein are used. For conversion to SI, mph $\times$ 0.447 = m/s, and temperature difference $(DT)(°F)/1.8 = DT(°C)$ and $(°F - 32)/1.8 = °C$.

Different Heating Systems

Of primary interest is the comparison of electric and fossil-fuel–fired heating systems. Among the field data permitting that comparison are the following:

Battelle [9]—Part of this report addresses itself to infiltration data. In particular, it refers to Institute of Gas Technology (IGT) data suggesting an excess infiltration rate, ϕ, due to the fossil-fuel–fired furnace, given by ϕ as about 0.5 and equal to

$$\phi = (I \text{ stack open} - I \text{ stack closed})/\text{Chimney flow rate} \qquad (1)$$

The report also reviews some of the models available for infiltration. The Ohio State University (OSU) model fails to effectively account for the location of the furnace; the linear modified Coblentz-Achenbach equation fails to match quite a bit of the field data; the Lawrence Berkeley Laboratory (LBL) model is suggested as an improvement—it is based on an effective leakage area; the IGT model requires permeability coefficients for each wall type; the National Research Council (NRC) model does include an effect adding 0.38 to 0.40 ACH due to furnace operation (for an extremely limited sample of two homes). Finally, Peterson [10] suggests that simply

$$I = A + B(DT) + C(W) \qquad (2)$$

where $A = 0.10$, $B = 0.006$ to 0.012, and $C = 0.015$ to 0.030; where DT is in °F and wind (W) in mph. In the case of furnaces, A should increase to at least 0.20. For instance, at a 15 mph wind and a DT of 40°F, the value of I then would be between 0.57 and 1.03 for homes without furnaces and 0.67 to 1.13 otherwise.

Cole et al [11]—The report refers to data taken at Canton, Ohio, Princeton, New Jersey, Columbus, Ohio, and Canada (published in other references), as well as intensive data taken in a gas-heated, ranch-style home, as well as in other homes tested by IGT. The data for the ranch test home included a number of runs, some with the furnace on, others with the furnace off (apparently all with the blower on). Comparisons also were made with the stack closed or open. Averaging some of these data:

Wind, mph	DT, °F	Stack Closed	Stack Open	Furnace On
2 to 3	4 to 18	0.17	0.24	0.34
2 to 3	33 to 55	0.33	0.39	0.53
4 to 7	0 to 14	0.20	0.29	0.41
4 to 7	29 to 56	0.31	0.43	0.53
8 to 11	25 to 37	0.30	0.50	0.57
SIMILAR DATA FOR A TEST HOME AND INDOOR FURNACE				
4	58	0.72	0.77	0.86
8 to 9	48 to 52	0.94	0.70	0.92
15	64	1.03	0.97	1.17
FOR A HOME WITH A FURNACE IN THE GARAGE				
7 to 8	34 to 41	0.50	0.45	...
13 to 15	28 to 37	0.48	0.56	...
FOR ANOTHER FOUR HOMES				
8	21	0.29	0.31	0.35
8	58	0.49	0.81	1.0
13	55	0.45	0.66	0.46
15	55	0.59	...	0.72

Cole et al [12]—This is a rather comprehensive report, with reference to considerable field data. In particular, the study presents decay gas data for three "intensive homes" (one ranch and two 2-story homes) and 20 "extensive" homes. The data for the ranch included infiltration under the condition of open doors, as well as the simulation of an "electric" home when the chimney was closed. (The home was actually heated with a gas furnace.) The following data resulted with the door closed:

DT, °F	W, mph	Blower	Burner	Chimney	Infiltration
50	14	on	on	open	0.51
50	14	on	off	open	0.53
50	14	off	off	open	0.42
50	14	on	off	closed	0.31
50	14	off	off	closed	0.21
38	7	on	on	open	0.47
46	8	on	off	open	0.36
45	5	on	off	open	0.44
44	8	off	off	open	0.39

An additional table compares various readings under different modes. Their averages give:

Blower	Burner	Chimney	Infiltration
Off	off	closed	0.26
Off	off	open	0.45
On	off	open	0.46
On	on	open	0.51

Data also are given for a "northern home," a rather modern home with an aerodynamic design roof, passive solar heating, and a pulse-combustion boiler/fan-coil unit. The following were noted:

Wind, mph	DT(°F)	Infiltration	Conditions
21	26	0.81	solarium closed
15	60	0.66	solarium closed
15	59	0.73	solarium open
15	30	0.51	solarium closed
13	62	0.70	solarium closed
13	28	0.81	solarium open
10	40	0.44	solarium closed
9	29	0.31	solarium open
8	34	0.38	solarium closed

A comparison also was made to find the effect of the fireplace being on. For that case, the infiltration increased from 0.31 to 0.48. Data also are given for the MEDII home, a home with a solar collector for hot water, high levels of insulation, and a balanced-flue, direct-vent, hydronic boiler/fan coil unit for space heating. The unit also had an economizer with a damper with substantial leakage. The measured values (with the blower off to not include the damper leakage effects) gave:

Wind, mph	DT(°F)	Infiltration
11.8	14	0.27
8.0	13	0.27
6.9	14	0.32
5.8	15	0.35
5.8	1	0.22

Based on what appears as a pretty good model average heating season, infiltration rates are estimated for five different homes in both Washington, D.C. and Madison, Wisconsin. Four of these homes (two IGT, one OSU, and one Tamura) were gas heated. One, OSU, has electric heat. The averages for these simulated homes are:

	Washington, D.C.	Madison, Wisconsin
Four gas	0.46	0.51
One electric	0.39	0.45

Dale et al [13]—Preliminary data in six uninhabited wood-frame, single-story modules are presented. Although electrically heated, they simulated a "gas-furnace" by venting appropriately (but without including combustion . . .). The six modules modelled different construction possibilities; the "conservation" one included a vapor barrier as well. At an outdoor temperature of −10 to −20°C and winds from 3 to 6 m/s, the following resulted:

Home	Infiltration	Infiltration Flue Blocked
Standard	0.51	. . .
Short Term	0.52	0.22
Conservation	. . .	0.08
Passive Solar	0.33	0.12
Solar Liquid	0.42	. . .
Solar Air	0.42	. . .

Dickinson et al [14]—The results of metering pre- and postretrofit of 20 houses by Pacific Gas and Electric (PG&E) and 18 houses by the Bonneville Power Administration (BPA) are reported. The only check for infiltration was by the blower test. Little relationship was found between the retrofit action and the change in infiltration rate. The 18 houses tested by BPA were all electric and built between 1945 and 1968; the homes tested by PG&E were all heated with forced-air-natural-gas and were built between 1956 and 1969. A heating season infiltration rate was determined following the LBL model based on the blower data and on a total annual energy use estimated, giving the following averages:

Heating	Energy Use, Pre	kW/year, Post	Expected Seasonal Infiltration.	
			Pre Retrofit	Post Retrofit
Electric	18 830	14 980	0.38	0.34
Gas	38 614	34 459	0.49	0.40

Dumont et al [15]—Pressure tests on 176 houses of different types, ages, and contractors are reported. A comparison of the data for different heating systems leads to the following:

Type of Homes	Q/V at 50 Pa
Pre-1945, all gas heat	10.35 (19 home average)
1946 to 1960, all gas heat	4.55 (20 home average)
Post-1960, all gas heat	3.58 (95 home average)
Post-1960, all electric	3.16 (2 home average)
"Low energy," gas heat	1.28 (22 home average)
"Low energy," electric	1.67 (17 home average)
"Low energy," oil	1.88 (1 home average)

NOTE: Q/V = ACH at 50 Pa.

Dumont et al [16]—Measurements on 27 low-energy houses, all equipped with a continuous vapor barrier, are reported. These data include blower tests of airtightness. The pressure test results (in ACH at 50 Pa) gave values as follows:

Heating Type	Range	Average
Electric furnace	1.3 to 4.0	2.2
Electric bunsen burner	0.8 to 3.2	1.9
Gas furnace	0.6 to 3.2	1.9

Two words of caution are in order when comparing the just-cited averages. First, they are not based on actual decay gas data, only on pressurization tests. Second, of the five electric furnace homes tested, all but one had an air-to-air heat exchanger, whereas, of the seven gas-heated homes, five did not have an air-to-air heat exchanger installed. (The average for the two gas homes with an exchanger was 2.0; the average for the five without was 1.8.)

Elkins and Wensman [17]—The infiltration rates in two identical homes, one with electric heat and the other with gas heating, are reported. The data suggest strong dependence on the wind speed and considerably lower values of infiltration rate for the all-electric home. The following table tabulates some of the data:

	Temperature, °F	Wind, mph	Infiltration Rate
Home Gas	71	4.2	0.26
	36	6.9	0.62
	43	7.7	0.52
	30	6.8	0.54
	47	9.8	0.67
	5	12.2	0.83
	4	8.2	0.50
	20	8.7	0.44
	38	6.8	0.62
	70	4.5	0.24
	76	6.0	0.44
	35	6.5	0.52
Electric	73	4.8	0.21
	49	5.2	0.36
	86	8.6	0.36
	96	3.2	0.13
	34	5.6	0.31
	24	6.2	0.41
	76	6.1	0.35
	38	6.8	0.42
	28	10.0	0.33
	28	9.0	0.33

The paper suggests a constancy of the ratio of the infiltration to the wind. Based on such, the infiltration rate for the gas home is, on the average, about 1.5 times larger than that for the electric home.

Janssen et al [18]—The measure of infiltration in two homes located in Minneapolis is reported as well as that for five Denver and Kansas City homes, all with combustion heating systems. A comparison is made of the levels of infiltration with the furnaces on and with the furnaces off. The data in the table at the top of Page 81 suggest that on the average the infiltration rate is about 1.25 times higher when the furnace is on. The infiltration rate when the furnace is off with the stack plugged might be about 15% less than when the furnace is off but the stack is not plugged.

Laschober and Healy [19]—Data for the Institute for Building Research (IBR) hydronic and the warm air–heated test homes (reported in part in Bahnfleth et al [20]) are thoroughly analyzed proposing governing models. In particular, the warm air home is heated in one instance with electric resistance heat (and all flues sealed) and in the other with a gas furnace. Comparison of these data leads to the following values of infiltration measured by the

Type of Home[a]	Wind, m/s	Temperature, °C	Infiltration Rate Furnace On	Infiltration Rate Furnace Off
Tri-level, MN	4 to 6	−6	0.49	0.46[b]
Tri-level, MN	9 to 13	−1	1.07	0.95
Rambler, MN	8 to 14	−8	...	0.30
Rambler, MN	3	6	...	0.24
Two story, Denver	0.7	0	0.95	0.97
Ranch, Denver	1.3	4	0.41	0.44
Tri-level, Denver	1.0	4	0.69	0.58
Tri-level, Denver	0	1	1.19	0.67
Tri-level, Denver	0	5	0.96	0.41
Two story, KC	9 to 13	21	0.48	0.42
Tri-level, KC	1	4	0.47	0.52
Split, KC	0	2	0.74	0.57
Tri-level, KC	0.7	−3	0.75	0.57
Rambler, KC	0.5	1	0.65	0.57

[a]MN = Minnesota; KC = Kansas City.
[b]0.40 with the stack plugged.

decay gas technique at winds between 10 and 17 mph and at outside temperatures between 13 and 38°F:

1. Electric: 0.61, 0.61, 0.47, 0.70, 0.45, 0.54, 0.64 and 0.67.
2. Gas: 1.01, 0.71, 0.53, 0.78, 0.50, 1.44 and 0.47.

The average values are: for electric—0.59 and for gas—0.78 (1.32 times larger).

Peterson [10]—Based on a partial review of the literature, a rather simplistic approach to determine infiltration rates is given. Values from 0.36 (for tight) to 0.86 (for loose) are suggested as representative (at 20°F and 5 mph). The article also recommends adding 0.10 ACH (or 21% more) to the infiltration rate in gas-heated homes when comparing to equivalent electric-heated homes.

Reeves et al [21]—The Ohio State Electric Power Research Institute (EPRI) data included nine homes and the possibility to compare the effects of gas or electric heating in forced air systems. Even with infiltration rates measured only in the living space (somewhat erroneously excluding the basements where the furnaces were located), an additional 12.5% of infiltration was noted as due to combustion heating.

Shaw and Brown [22]—Results are reported of an experimental evaluation of the effect of a chimney on the infiltration of an unoccupied two-story detached house with a forced air system heated by either gas or resistance heat. Data for the gas-fired system were taken with the burner on, off, and cycling. The chimney was capped while data were taken with the electric heating system. The conclusions, based on the decay gas data alone, are that: the infiltration with the burner on continuously is 10% greater, on the average, than with the burner cycling; switching from an electric furnace to a gas furnace results in a 50% increase in air infiltration (for the test house and with calm winds); the infiltration for the gas furnace showed a dominant stack action (even with winds up to 7 m/s). (The infiltration rates measured ranged from 0.17 to 0.4 ACH.)

Tamura [23]—The earlier air leakage measurements (1960–1962) on two single-story houses are recalled. The houses were both five-room, wood-frame homes with a forced air, oil-fired furnace system. The following table presents some of the data, permitting an estimate of the effect of the furnace operating:

House No.	Infiltration	Furnace	Temperature Difference (°C)	Wind, m/s
1	0.22	off	29.4	1.4
	0.24	off	17.8	3.4
	0.25	off	25.0	4.3
	0.38	off-on	41.7	0.2
	0.41	off-on	35.5	3.8
	0.23	on	21.1	1.7
	0.25	on-off	23.3	3.7
	0.16	damper sealed	19.4	3.2
2	0.42	off	14.4	1.2
	0.39	off	22.8	1.1
	0.50	off	16.6	2.6
	0.39	off	18.3	2.7
	0.45	off	21.6	4.1
	0.25	off	3.3	1.9
	0.63	on-off	25.0	4.6
	0.49	on-off	26.6	3.2
	0.55	on-off-on	33.3	4.6
	0.40	off-on-off	17.8	1.9
	0.24	damper sealed	13.9	0.0
	0.59	off—fireplace damper open	10.0	2.5

The values in this table suggest, for House 1, an average infiltration of 0.24 with the furnace off and 0.32 with the furnace on. Sealing the damper lowers that to 0.16 or so. Similarly, for House 2, the furnace operation changes the average from 0.40 to 0.52, while sealing the barometric damper reduced that to 0.24. These values are extremely crude due to the limited data. But they do suggest an increase in infiltration in the order of 30% due to furnace operation and a substantial decrease when the barometric damper is sealed.

Among related studies, adding some insight into the possible effects of ductwork location, chimneys, dampers, furnace operation, etc. are the following:

Bahnfleth et al [20]—Measurements of infiltration rates in two test homes (the IBR and the warm air homes) are reported. Both homes were gas heated, the first by hydronic means and the second by forced air. The homes were not otherwise identical. Some of the representative data gave:

Home	Tout (°F)[a]	Wind, mph	Infiltration
Hydronic	28	4	0.32
	24	8.5	0.38
	25	13	0.35
Warm air	31.4	5	0.52
	32	9	0.56
	32	12	0.60

[a]Tout means outside temperature.

Blomsterberg [24]—Three comparisons of measured infiltration rates are given for a one-story, three-bedroom Swedish home built in 1977. At an outside temperature of 3.0°C and a light wind, the natural infiltration was noted to be 0.11. With an exhaust fan turned on, that value increased to 0.23, while with the addition of opening slightly a few windows that value increased further to 0.41.

Dickerhoff et al [25]—Thirty-four houses were tested (primarily through a blower test) in Atlanta, Reno, and San Francisco in order to estimate the paths of the leakage. The Atlanta homes also had decay gas tests. Fireplaces with dampers accounted for about 13% of the leakage (37% when the damper was left open), while the ductwork in forced air distribution systems accounted for about 9% of the total. The infiltration measured with the decay gas technique was extremely limited in that the winds were all measured as very low (under 1.5 m/s), and the outside temperatures were generally slightly above the indoor values. Under these conditions, the infiltration rates for six homes with the distribution fan on ranged from 0.29 to 0.92. In particular, the values for three homes with the fan on or sealed gave the following:

Home	Fan On	Fan Sealed
6	0.60	0.23
7	0.92	<0.02
8	0.64	0.41

Etheridge and Phillips [26]—Limited data are presented for a two-story home with a fossil-fuel–fired hydronic system. Data for overall infiltration gave:

Wind, m/s	Temperature (°C)	Infiltration	Comments
2.2	1.7	1.15	furnace on
3.05	4.4	0.90	furnace on
3.86	8.6	0.69	furnace on
4.00	11.1	0.75	furnace off

The dependence on wind is quite erratic. However, a simple average of the data gives infiltration rates of about 0.9 with the furnace on (compared with the single value of 0.75 with the furnace off).

Grimsrud et al [27]—Infiltration data for a Walnut Creek natural gas, forced-air–heated house are presented. Interestingly, data with the ductwork sealed exhibit an average infiltration rate about 0.7 times smaller than that with the ductwork unsealed. This suggests considerable leakage through the distribution system. Although not suggested by the authors, this leakage is expected to be mostly up the stack or through the duct in the attic space.

Guillaume et al [28]—Measurements in six houses built in Belgium in 1977 are reported. The homes were apparently designed to be heated with hydronic-gas–fired systems; however, during the tests the homes were heated with electric space heaters, and the openings to the flues were sealed. Although complete data are not given for all the houses, the conclusions are that the natural infiltration of a 4-m/s wind is about 0.4 to 0.5, while the infiltration when the exhaust system was operational gave values considerably in excess of the flow rate through the fan. (The difference corresponded to the natural infiltration rate.)

Hartmann and Muhlebach [29]—Data for the EMPA single-family test home are presented. The infiltration rate is shown to satisfy a relationship of the form:

$$I = a + b\mathrm{DT} + c \text{ (wind squared)}$$

When the temperatures are in °C and the wind in m/s, the coefficients are as follows:

Condition	a	b	c
Chimney sealed	0.1070	0.0090	0.0059
Chimney flap closed	0.0244	0.0264	0.0056

For the case with the chimney always completely sealed, the typical winter day infiltration rates with winds between 1 and 3 m/s are 0.25 to 0.3 ACH.

Hartmann and Muhlebach [30]—This report presents extensive decay gas and pressurization data in a Swiss residence heated with a hydronic oil-fired system. Extensive measurements were taken with and without a chimney being blocked off. At about a 5-m/s wind and a temperature difference between 10 and 15°C, infiltration rates of about 0.23 were measured with the chimney blocked off, and 0.4 otherwise. In general, the data were found to satisfy a relationship of the form:

$$I = a + b(\Delta T)^{0.8} + c(W)^{1.7}$$

with the coefficients unique to the reference home and its configuration.

Lipschutz et al [5]—Pressurization and decay gas data are presented for twelve energy-efficient homes. None had ducts located outside the heated space, nor did any employ fossil-fuel–fired heating systems. All twelve homes had either woodburning stoves or fireplaces with glass doors. All were equipped with external combustion air inlets. Some of the homes used forced air, some resistance heat, others heat pumps, others radiant resistance heat, and others solar. The "heating season" infiltration rates were estimated to be an average of 0.34 (with a lowest of 0.17 and a highest of 0.49, unrelated to type of heating system). The decay gas measurements were limited to one run per home. All houses except for House H were at wind speeds under 2.6 m/s and with DT under $7°C$ and gave measurements of 0.09 to 0.27 L/h. House H was tested at 3 m/s and with a DT of $8°C$ and gave 0.21 ACH. The study also includes the effect of furnace fan operation, estimating the effect of the fan as 0.05 to 0.14 ACH.

Lipschutz et al [31]—Primarily pressurization data for a number of homes are given. In particular, some 59 homes in Rochester, New York, with heating systems identified are compared. For the set of post-1976 homes, the average predicted heating season infiltration rates become: 0.28 for two with electric baseboard heat; 0.37 for eight with electric forced air; 0.47 for five with (central?) heat pump systems, and 0.59 for eleven with gas-fired systems. It must be underscored that the just-mentioned statistics were not based on decay gas data.

Macriss et al [32]—A rather thorough model is presented and verified against a sample of 23 homes. Of interest is the conclusion that on the average the existence of a chimney and furnace burner operation in a home increases infiltration rate losses by almost 20%. The average seasonal air infiltration rates were found to be:

Conditions	Infiltration, Average Seasonal		
	Mean	Min	Max
Burner on	0.67	0.3	1.7
Chimney closed	0.55	0.25	1.25

Sepsy et al [33]—The report is a summary of a long research project. Infiltration models based on data taken in nine different homes are summarized. These models permitted changing the heating systems in two residences from forced-air, gas-heated to electric heating. The changes also were done in the field. The conclusions are that the infiltration rates of the residences were between 12 and 14% higher for gas than for electric heating. These values were obtained without considering the basements in the analysis. In reality, the difference is expected to be more (see also Reeves et al [21]).

Shaw [34]—Fan pressurization and decay gas data are correlated. The data used for the comparison are those reported in Shaw and Tamura [3], as well as data by Tamura and Wilson [35], Kronvall [36], and Dumont [15]. For wind speeds of 3.5 to 10 m/s and temperature differences of 20 to 40°C, the spread in the data suggests: for oil-fired furnaces, means of 0.3 to 0.5, ranging from 0.25 to 0.65; for natural gas heating, means around 0.23; for all electric, values from 0.18 to 0.4; for gas hydronic (but all sealed), values from 0.2 to 0.3.

Treado et al [37]—Air infiltration and blower tests on a three-bedroom townhouse with a forced air, gas-fired furnace are presented. The house was an end unit, two-story house built in 1970. With the burner off, average winter infiltration rates are estimated to be 0.56. Accounting for the burner, this value becomes 0.717. The data suggest that combustion and draft-diverter air accounts for 21.9% of the air leakage and the blower operation for 7.7%.

Warner [38]—Considerable data in (obviously) prewar dwellings are presented. Of relevance might be the comparison between sealed and unsealed flues for gas heaters in two flats. The infiltration rates increased from 0.84 and 0.72 to 1.17 to 2.06 ACH.

Effects of Age, Retrofit, or Other Changes

Various studies have attempted to compare the relationship of building age on infiltration as well as of benefits of retrofit on reduction of infiltration rate.

Bassett [39] presents pressurization studies on 40 different homes. The comparison of air change at 50 Pa is made to building age. In Blomsterberg,[2] pre-1975 Swedish homes are noted to have natural infiltration rates in the order of 0.23; post-1975, 0.16. Conventional U.S. homes are noted to be about three times leakier. Three test homes were analyzed in more detail and their expected natural infiltration rates at summer conditions (16.6°C, 4.0-m/s wind) found to be 0.09, 0.12, and 0.14, whereas at winter conditions (−0.6°C, 5.5-m/s wind) the values were 0.13, 0.15, and 0.18 ACH. Blomsterberg and Harrje [40] give pressurization and tracer gas data for a number of houses. The tracer gas data is limited to four townhouses two stories high, all supposedly exposed to a wind of 4 m/s and a DT of 17°C. The measured infiltration rates were 0.38, 0.31, 0.36, and 0.42. On the other hand, an older detached dwelling heated with "warm air" and under the same wind and temperature is quoted as having a measured infiltration rate of 0.82 (compare with Blomsterberg et al [41]). Coblentz and Achenbach [42] present data for ten houses, five new (as of 1963) and five 20 to 40 years old, which led to the following decay gas data (adjusted to 10-mph wind and a temperature difference of 40°F):

1. New houses: 0.37, 0.48, 0.48, 0.50, and 0.66.
2. Old houses: 0.62, 0.71, 0.75, 0.86, and 0.99.

Collins [6] shows results of 59 metered homes, with supersucker (pressurization) measurements in 29 of these pre- and postretrofit homes. Two houses also included tracer gas testing before and after retrofit. The comparisons for these two homes gave the following data (the *I* levels are estimated for 10-mph wind and 40°F difference).

House No.	Infiltration L/h		Induced Infiltration at 25 Pa	
	Pre	Post	Pre	Post
R-15	0.70	0.50	6.7	3.6
R-10	0.45	0.29	6.7	<2.6
R-15 ducts closed	0.33	0.20	. . .	. . .

The experiment with the R-15 ductwork sealed shows the effect of isolating the crawl space from the living quarters. The lack of a constant ratio between the measured and "induced" infiltration rates shows the uncertainty of the blower-type test. The major part of the retrofit consisted of caulk and tape. Diamond and Grimsrud [43] make reference to measurements (with the blower test) on 50 homes in Rochester, New York (Ryan homes). The average heating season air change was 0.73 for the pre-1976 homes and 0.52 for the post-1976 homes. In Dickinson et al [44], a study is reported based on 18 all-electric homes built between 1943 and 1968. The retrofitting consisted of adding insulation, caulking, and in some cases storm doors and windows. The only infiltration-related testing was through a blower test. The retrofitting was done in two phases, with homes in different "cells" according to the type of retrofit. The following heating season air changes (based on blower tests) were noted:

Cell	Prephase I	Postphase I	Prephase II	Postphase II
1	0.42	0.43	0.44	0.32
2	0.35	0.33	. . .	. . .
3	0.36	0.33	0.35	0.28

Infiltration rates were measured by E+ Energy Consultants [45] in two houses following the decay gas technique, one (A) caulked and the other (B) not. The "bag technique" was used for sampling and analysis. It appears as if both homes were heated with fossil-fuel–fired furnaces. They both had fireplaces—the one in House B was closed 50 min into the test. The average wind during the test was 15 mph with an average ambient of 33°F. The corresponding data for infiltration are quite approximate, in the order of 0.7 for House A and 1.0 to 1.6 for House B. Goldschmidt et al [46] and Goldschmidt et al [47] present measurements for two mobile homes, both with electric resistance heat but one with sheathing and the other not. At the design winter conditions of $-16°C$ and 6.7 m/s, values of 0.83 and 1.53 ACH are found, whereas at the design summer conditions of 32.8°C and 6.7 m/s, values of 0.46 and 0.91 ACH are noted. The infiltration at a gas-heated townhouse when the wind was intercepted by an evergreen windbreak was noted by Mattingly et al [48] to be reduced from 1.13 to 0.66 (for a wind of 12.5 mph and a temperature difference of 32.5°F). The discussion acknowledges that the infiltration rate for electric heating should have been lower.

In Shaw and Tamura [3] data for four detached two-story homes are presented. These data include the measure of infiltration rate for two of the homes, one forced air resistance heat, the other forced air, heat-pump heating. Comparison of blower tests and decay gas tests suggests that these data may be correlated. The monthly averaged infiltration rates for the "standard house" were around 0.25, whereas the "heat pump" house had averages around 0.18 ACH. The "heat pump" house was an upgraded wood frame with additional insulation as well as a vapor barrier. Data taken for the City of Seattle Department of Lighting are presented. These data include blower test and decay gas tests on five pre- and postretrofitting homes. The infiltration data result in a correlation of coefficients as given in the Sepsy et al relationship. For comparison purposes, the values at a 10-mph wind and a zero temperature difference would be about:

Home	Type	Year	Expected Infiltration at 10 mph	
			Pre	Post
1	el. air	49	2.19	1.83
2	baseboard	50	3.03	2.16
3	baseboard	99	1.33	1.14
4	el. air	79	1.25	...
5	el. air	23	0.89	0.67

NOTE: El. air = electric forced air.

Representative Values

In addition to the data already summarized in the preceding sections, data also are presented by the following:

Biggs[3]—Measurements in the Australia Commonwealth Scientific and Industries Research Organization (CSIRO) "Low Energy House" (that is, fully solar) show infiltration rates in the order of 1.0 for winds of about 6 m/s and in the order of 0.5 for winds of 2 m/s. On a separate and ongoing study, infiltration data for two houses and pressurization data for a total of 15

[3]Biggs, K. L., private communication, 1983.

houses, some solar and others supposedly gas heated, are compared. The infiltration data for two homes, both solar, suggest levels in the order of 0.4 for calm winds and 0.8 to 1.0 for winds around 3 m/s.

Blomsterberg et al [41]—The paper refers to earlier infiltration rate measurements taken at Princeton and in California. These values were as follows:

House	Average I	Wind, m/s	DT (°C)	Comments
NJ	0.37	4	17	two-story townhouse basement
NJ	0.4 to 0.6	4	17	detached, 1.5 to 2 stories
Ca-Da1	0.31	2.1	6	one-story, detached taped vents
Ca-Da2	0.64	4.5	9	one-story, detached taped vents
Ca-Ha1	0.18	2.8	13	one-story, detached taped vents
Ca-Ha2	0.17	2.8	9	fireplace and kitchen vents open
Ca-Ha3	0.21	2.0	9	all vents open

Caffey [2]—The "supersucker" is described, and the results of its use in measuring the leakage in some 50 homes are reported. Infiltration rates were estimated as one fourth of the value measured with the blower test. For tighter homes, values in the order of 0.35 to 0.5 are suggested as adequate.

Etheridge et al [49]—Data presented include a measure of the natural infiltration rates in a four-bedroom, 1967 test home. The home has a hydronic heating system with a gas-fired, room-sealed boiler. The natural infiltration rate was measured with and without sealing the doors and windows and found to be essentially unchanged. At wind speeds of 5 m/s, the infiltration rates were about 1.5, whereas at 3 m/s they were closer to 0.8 ACH.

De Gids [50]—The report includes data for three homes; two were two-story dwellings and the third was a flat. The data include the air change rate with windows closed (and for one house with open windows as well) as well as pressure differences and blower test data. The homes were occupied and undetached, and apparently all had flues and were heated with gas-fired boilers. The decay gas data for the single-family houses are similar: infiltration rates in the order of 0.8 to 1.0 at calm winds, in the order of 0.8 to 1.3 at 5 m/s, and 1.0 to 1.8 at 10 m/s. Surprisingly, the flat exhibited little dependence on wind velocity, with an infiltration rate in the order of 0.3.

Goldschmidt and Wilhelm [51]—Measurements in a mobile home are recalled. The home had electric resistance heat and caulking. The measured infiltration (over a 16-month period) is seen to satisfy a relationship of the type

$$I = 0.034 + 599 \ DT/(T_i T_o) + 2.9 \ W/T_o,$$

where the wind is in m/s and the temperatures are in degrees Kelvin. (T_i is the indoor temperature, T_o outdoor, and DT = $|T_i - T_o|$.)

Graham and Sulatisky [52]—Pressurization tests on 24 houses are reported. Four of the houses had electric baseboard heat; all the others had electric forced air. The homes were all bungalows with an average floor area of 100 m². The effective leakage areas were seen to vary from 440 to 750 cm² for houses built by one contractor and from 690 to 1110 cm² for houses built by the other contractors. There was no notable difference between forced air and baseboard heating (when comparing effective leakage areas). It is of interest that a plot of consumption (in terms of kW/DD) showed no correlation to the effective leakage area [even though consumptions varied from 2.1 to 4.4 kW/degree day (DD)].

Grimsrud et al [53]—A survey is made for over 300 houses, determining an average heating season air change based on blower data or on decay gas data. The histogram of the air change results shows a mean of 0.63 and a median of 0.50.

Grot and Clark [54]—Measurements for 266 homes are given, which include both tracer gas (using bag samples) and pressurization tests. There is little correlation between the two types of tests.

Although the sample included 62% natural gas heating, 20% oil, 14% propane, 3% electricity, and 1% kerosene, no comparison is made between those types of systems. The data for infiltration rate do not permit a correlation with weather (it appears as if weather was not measured); however, for the entire data set, it has 19% measurements of infiltration rate to under 0.5, 40% between 0.5 and 1.0, 20% between 1.0 and 1.5, and 20% above 2.0. (A direct quote from the conclusions; there must be a typo in the last number, 1.5 instead of 2.0.)

Hartmann et al [55]—Measurement of infiltration with tracer gas techniques in apartment buildings with different window openings is reported. All apartments were nonair-conditioned. Even small window openings greatly increased the infiltration rate. All the units tested were apartments within larger buildings. The following data were the results (with windows closed):

Building	Wind, m/s	DT, °C	Infiltration, L/h
A	1.2	17	0.09
	3.5	20.5	0.17
	5.5	14.5	0.2
C	1.3	19.5	0.06
	2.0	11.5	0.07
D	2.2	12.5	0.33
	8.5	17.0	0.97
	8.5	14.0	1.12
E	2.0	3.0	0.63
	2.5	1.5	0.68
	4.5	17.5	0.67
F	1.0	16.5	0.42
	0.7	15.5	0.49
	1.5	18.0	0.72

(continued) Building	Wind, m/s	DT, °C	Infiltration, L/h
G	2.2	3.5	0.23
	0.6	14.0	0.26
H	1.1	4.0	0.13
	1.2	9.0	0.55
	3.4	12.5	0.86
I	2.4	7.0	0.42
	2.8	8.5	0.52
	4.0	8.0	0.6
K	1.2	13.0	0.35
	0.8	17.0	0.44

Jordan et al [56]—Data for two test homes, both heated with baseboard electric heating units, are presented. For the total house, infiltration rates in the order of 0.18 to 0.30 were estimated at 40°F and 10 mph wind with the stair door to the basement open in House B, and 0.10 to 0.23 with the stair door closed in Test House A.

Kronvall [36]—Data on pressure tests for 29 homes are given. From these data, (doubtful) infiltration levels ranging from 0.06 to 0.41 are obtained.

Nusgens and Guillaume [57]—Measurements in three single-family houses are given. Two were parts of a duplex; the third was a detached building. The measurements in the duplex (its heating system is not described) were primarily room by room. The global infiltration rate for one of these houses is given as 0.47 at a wind velocity of 2 m/s. The following data are given:

Wind velocity, m/s	1.0	1.6	1.7	1.9	2.5
Infiltration rate	0.32	0.50	0.36	0.46	0.68

The third house definitively had a forced air, heat-pump–driven system. The heat pump was in the basement, connected to the garage with a poorly sealed door. The following data are given for the total infiltration rates:

Wind, m/s	2.3	3.5	4.4	4.8	4.0	7.3
Infiltration	0.14[a]	0.05[a]	0.19[a]	0.17[a]	1.20	0.61

[a]Corresponds to data with the air vents covered.

Potter [58]—Data based on decay gas measurements are given for a three-story home with a gas-fired, hydronic heating system. Unfortunately, the operating temperatures are not noted. However, it appears as if for calm winds the infiltration rate would be around 0.37 ACH, whereas at 6 m/s it could be as high as 1.5 and at 4 m/s between 0.5 and 1.1 ACH.

Sherman and Grimsrud [59]—Data for 15 different homes are quoted, and the results from pressurization tests and tracer gas tests compared. Differences in the order of 40% are noted. The decay gas data do not explicitly include the operating temperatures and wind velocities, however, the data do include a description of the homes. The following results (leakage areas are in square centimetres):

Home Reference	Infiltration	Leakage Area	Comments
Ivanhoe	0.1 to 0.12	100	solar sealed wood stove
Nogal	0.22	960	solar, forced air
Telemark	0.08 to 0.13	140	radiant oil space heating and wood stove
Torey Pines	0.31 to 0.42	200	solar water greenhouse
R-10	0.45	330	baseboard electric resistance
T-1	0.16 to 0.23	330	fireplace, forced air
T-2	0.11 to 0.46	680	fireplace, forced air
Haven	0.21 to 0.37	770	fireplace, forced air
Purdue	0.50 to 0.69	855	fireplace, forced air
Neilson	0.64 to 1.36	1275	fireplace (undampered), furnace
V1	0.31 to 0.33	560	solar, wood stove
V2	0.29 to 0.64	630	solar, wood stove
Fels	0.68 to 0.76	1480	forced air
San Carlos	0.62 to 1.02	845	fireplace (undampered), furnace
Southampton	0.19 to 0.31	1640	fireplace, forced air

In order to properly interpret the just-cited values, it is necessary to go to the original references. The fact that undampered fireplaces are so noted implies that the others were dampered. The data also suggest that the heating systems were most likely not operating during the testing.

Stewart et al [60]—Data, including decay gas data, are presented for three unoccupied test houses. All houses were heated with a forced air resistance heating system and were identical except for levels of insulation (and equipment sizing). The data are summarized via a fit to the modified Reeves, McBride, and Sepsy [21] model where:

$$I = A + B \text{ (square root of } P\text{)}$$

where P is the sum of the theoretical wind and stack pressures in Pascals. The values in the table on the top of Page 93 are found. Although not indicated in the report, it appears as if the infiltration rate (as measured by the decay gas technique) is slightly higher for the noninsulated home. (Pressurization tests also confirmed this.) On the average, at a pressure of 50 Pa, the infiltration rate would be about 0.5.

	Most Insulated	Some Insulation	No Insulation
	SUMMER 1978		
A	0.282	...	0.195
B	0.037	...	0.055
	WINTER 1978–1979		
A	...	0.195	0.263
B	...	0.041	0.094
	SUMMER 1979		
A	0.129	0.151	0.157
B	0.038	0.035	0.045

Warren [4]—Preliminary results of natural ventilation in six houses are given at what is called "mean speed." Homes with flues (H and J) had these sealed. The following is found:

House Type	Year Built	Infiltration at Mean Speed
C—3-bedroom end terr	1972	1.25
D—3-bedroom semidetached	1971	0.55
F—3-bedroom end terr	1975	1.35
G—4-bedroom end terr	1975	0.80
H—3-bedroom semidetached	1957	0.30
J—3-bedroom semidetached	1957	0.50

Incidentally, direct comparison of blower test data and decay gas data is made in a few of the references. Among them: Warren and Webb [68] (not cited), Collins [6] (who suggests an uncertainty in the blower type test), Hartmann and Muhlebach [30], Lipschutz et al [5], Shaw [34], and Shaw and Tamura [3]. (For a description of the blower test itself, see Diamond et al [7].)

A few of the references in the bibliography include the same data. For instance, Bilsborrow [61] used Tamura and Wilson's [35] data, which in turn is reported in Tamura [23]. Dickinson et al [14] present essentially the same data as Grimsrud et al [62] presented earlier in Krinkel et al [63]. The base data of Sherman [64] is also in Sherman and Grimsrud [59] and Sherman and Grimsrud [65], which Sherman et al [66] and Modera et al [67] report.

Conclusions

The implications of the literature review are the following:

1. The infiltration rates are dependent on wind and temperature.
2. Seasonal average values, in the order of 0.4 to 1.0, might be descriptive and adequate for estimates of energy consumption, but these are not the same

as the design values, which should be used for sizing of heating, ventilating, and air-conditioning (HVAC) equipment.

3. There is a notable increase in the infiltration rate when combustion heating is used instead of electric resistance heating.

4. There is some increase in the infiltration rate when air distribution systems have the blowers on compared with the blowers off.

5. The pressurization data by themselves are limited; they do not readily lead to an estimate of infiltration rate, nor do they directly give a measure of the stack effects.

6. Many researchers fail to provide sufficient field data to permit generalizations. In many instances, the governing weather parameters are not well-defined.

7. There is some lack of consistency in the models proposed by the various investigators.

Of particular interest is the estimate of the expected increase in the infiltration rate attributed to the use of combustion heating instead of electric resistance heating. A few studies permit that estimate by either (a) using comparable homes with different heating systems, (b) using one home in which different systems are compared, or (c) testing with the burner off and the stack sealed in a home with combustion heating. The following can be obtained:

Reference	Increase in Infiltration Air Changes	Increase, %	Comments
Battelle [9]	0.10	. . .	. . .
Cole et al [12]	0.25	100	measured
Cole et al [11]	0.21	80	averages, ranch home
	0.09	10	averages, test home
	0.23	51	three-home averages
Dale et al [13]	0.25	60	simulated flue
Dickinson [14]	0.11	29	large sample averages, preretrofit
Dickinson [14]	0.06	18	large sample averages, postretrofit
Elkins and Wensman [17]	0.20	62	averages, two homes
Janssen et al [18]	0.09	22	same home, one data
Laschober and Healy [19]	0.19	27	same home, averages
Macriss et al [32]	0.12	22	. . .
Peterson [10]	0.10	21	. . .
Reeves et al [21]	. . .	12.5	living area only
Shaw and Brown [22]	0.10	50	same home
Tamura [23]	0.16	100	same house

The increase in infiltration rate ranges from 0.1 to 0.25 ACH. This can be explained well (in most part) by the additional requirement of combustion air. The estimates of 0.1 to 0.25 additional changes per hour generally account for the fact that the furnace will not be running continuously but will cycle on and off according to the load.

Recommendations

The data available suggest that the type of ducts and the type of heating system (and its location) will affect the infiltration rate. Any estimates at that increase are exactly that—estimates. Further field data are needed to compare the infiltration performance of different HVAC systems.

When using heating systems that are expected to cause different infiltration levels in otherwise similar homes, such differences should be accounted for. If seasonal design ACH 0.4, 0.7, and 1.0 are used for "very tight," "tight," and "average" construction homes without a combustion process, and hence without a chimney, then the representative infiltration rates for combustion heating with a chimney should be increased to no less than 0.5, 0.9, and 1.2 for "very tight," "tight," and "average-type" construction, respectively. Presently computer programs, such as DOE2, do not properly account for these changes in the infiltration load with type of heating system. These changes should be incorporated into any analysis of expected building performance.

Acknowledgments

The data and review presented were the results of a special study conducted for the Edison Electric Institute. Their cooperation is acknowledged.

References

[1] White, R. R., Goldschmidt, V. W., and Leonard, R. G., "Seasonal Performance Measurement and Modeling of a Mobile Home Gas-Fired Furnace," Report HL75-49, Herrick Laboratories, Purdue University, W. Lafayette, IN, Nov. 1975.

[2] Caffey, G. E., "Residental Air Infiltration," *ASHRAE Transactions*, Vol. 85, Pt. 1, 1979.

[3] Shaw, C. Y., and Tamura, G. T., "Mark XI Energy Research Project Air Tightness and Air Infiltration Measurements," BRNote 162, 1980, National Research Council, Ottawa, Canada.

[4] Warren, P. R., "Natural Infiltration Routes and Their Magnitude in House," Part 1, "Preliminary Studies of Domestic Ventilation," Proceedings of the Conference Controlled Ventilation—Its Contribution to Lower Energy Use and Improved Comfort, Aston University, England, 1976.

[5] Lipschutz, R. D., Girman, J. R., Dickinson, J. B., Allen, J. R., and Traynor, G. W., "Infiltration and Indoor Air Quality in Energy Efficient Houses in Eugene, Oregon," LBL-12924, Lawrence Berkeley Laboratory, Berkeley, CA, Aug. 1981.

[6] Collins, J. O., Jr., "Air Infiltration Measurement and Reduction Techniques on Electrically Heated Homes," updated report, Johns-Manville, Denver, CO, circa 1983.

[7] Diamond, R. C., Dickinson, J. B., Lipschutz, R. D., O'Regan, B., and Shohl, B., "The House Doctor's Manual," LBL Pub-3017, Lawrence Berkeley Laboratory, Berkeley, CA, Feb. 1982. (A rather entertaining description on the performance of the blower test is included.)

[8] Veenhuizen, S. D. and Lin, J. T., "A Study of Air Infiltration and Air Tightness," Report 7903, United Industries Corp., Bellevue, WA, August 1979.

[9] Battelle, Columbus Laboratories, "Analysis of Field Test Data on Residential Heating and Cooling," EA-1649, Electric Power Research Institute, Palo Alto, CA, Dec. 1980.

[10] Peterson, J. E., "Estimating Air Infiltration in Houses: An Analytical Approach," ASHRAE Journal, Vol. 21, No. 1, Jan. 1979.

[11] Cole, J. T., Zimmer, J. W., Zawacki, T. S., Kinast, J. A., Elkins, R. H., and Macriss, R. A., "Development and Field Verification of a Model of Excess Infiltration and House Air Infiltration for Single-Family Residences," final report for 1979, GRI-79/0031, Gas Research Institute, Chicago, Jan. 1980.

[12] Cole, J. T., Kinast, J. A., Zawacki, T. S., Elkins, R. H., and Macriss, R. A., "Development and Field Verification of a Model of House Air Infiltration for Single Family Residences," final report IGT, GRI-80-0082, Institute for Gas Technology, Chicago, July 1981.

[13] Dale, J. D., Wilson, D. J., and Ackerman, M., "Adaptable Modules for Air Infiltration Studies in Home Heating," International Seminar on Air Infiltration and Ventilation, 1980.

[14] Dickinson, J. B., Lipschutz, R. D., O'Regan, B. O., and Wagner, B. S., "Results of Recent Weatherization Retrofit Projects," LBL-14734, Lawrence Berkeley Laboratory, Berkeley, CA, July 1982.

[15] Dumont, R. W., Orr, H. W., and Figley, D. A., "Air Tightness Measurements of Detached Houses in the Saskatoon Area," Building Research Note No. 178, National Research Council of Canada, Ottawa, Canada, 1982.

[16] Dumont, R. W., Orr, H. W., and Hedlin, C. P., "Low Energy Houses: Some Measured Energy Consumption Figures," ASHRAE Transactions, Vol. 89, Pt. 1, 1983.

[17] Elkins, R. H. and Wensman, C. E., "Natural Ventilation of Modern Tightly Constructed Homes," America Gas Association Conference on Natural Gas Research and Technology, Chicago, 1971.

[18] Janssen, J. E., Glatzel, J. J., Torborg, R. H., and Bonne, U., "Infiltration in Residential Structures," Honeywell Corporate Research Center, Minneapolis, MN, circa 1978.

[19] Laschober, R. R. and Healy, J. H., "Statistical Analyses of Air Leakage in Split Level Residences," ASHRAE Transactions, Vol. 70, 1964.

[20] Bahnfleth, D. R., Moseley, T. D., and Harris, W. S., "Measurement of Infiltration in Two Residences," ASHRAE Transactions, Vol. 63, 1957.

[21] Reeves, G., McBride, M., and Sepsy, C. F., "Air Infiltration Model for Residences," ASHRAE Transactions, Vol. 85, Pt. 1, 1979.

[22] Shaw, C. Y. and Brown, W. C., "Effect of a Gas Furnace Chimney on the Air Leakage Characteristic of a Two-Story Detached House," NRC, Ottawa, ISSN 0701-5232, July 1982. (Also Paper No. 12, 3rd AIC Conference 20-23 Sept. 1982, London.)

[23] Tamura, G. T., "The Calculation of House Infiltration Rates," ASHRAE Transactions, Vol. 85, Pt. 1, 1979.

[24] Blomsterberg, A., "Traces Gas Measurements in Low Leakage Houses," 2nd Air Infiltration Centre Conference, Stockholm, Sweden, Sept. 1981.

[25] Dickerhoff, D. J., Grimsrud, D. T., and Lipschutz, R. D., "Component Leakage Testing in Residential Buildings," LBL 14735, Lawrence Berkeley Laboratory, Berkeley, CA, July 1982.

[26] Etheridge, D. W. and Phillips, P., "The Prediction of Ventilation Rate in Houses and the Implications for Energy Conservation," CIB Group S17 meeting, West Germany, 1977, International Council for Building Research, Studies and Documentation, Rotterdam, The Netherlands.

[27] Grimsrud, D. T., Sherman, M. H., Diamond, R. C., Cordon, P. E., and Rosenfeld, A. H., "Infiltration-Pressurization Correlations: Detailed Measurements on a California House," 1982, Lawrence Berkeley Laboratory, Berkeley, CA.

[28] Guillaume, M., Ptacek, J., Warren, P. R., and Webb, B. C., "Measurements of Ventilation Rates in Houses with Natural and Mechanical Ventilation Systems," CIB Steering Group S17, Building Research Establishment, 1978.

[29] Hartmann, P. and Muhlebach, H., "Automatic Measurements of Air Change Rates (Decay Method) in a Small Residential Building Without any Forced-Air-Heating System," EMPA, Dubendorf, Germany, circa 1980.

[30] Hartmann, P. and Muhlebach, H., "Langzeit-Untersuchungen betreffend Luftdurchkassigkeit und Luftwechsel eines Einfamilienhauses," EMPA Nr. 39 400/c, Dubendorf, Germany, April 1981.

[31] Lipschutz, R. D., Dickinson, J. B., and Diamond, R. C., "Infiltration and Leakage Measurements in New Houses Incorporating Energy Efficient Features," LBL-14733, Lawrence Berkeley Laboratory, Berkeley, CA, July 1982.

[32] Macriss, R. A., Cole, J. T., Zawacki, T. S., and Elkins, R. H., "An Air Infiltration Model for Modern Single Family Dwellings," 72nd APCA Annual Meeting, Cincinnati, Air Pollution Control Assn., Pittsburgh, PA, June 1979.

[33] Sepsy, C., McBride, M. F., Blancett, R. S., and Jones, C. D., "Fuel Utilization in Residences," EPRI EA-894, Electric Power Research Institute, Palo Alto, CA, Sept. 1978.

[34] Shaw, C. Y., "A Correlation Between Air Infiltration and Air Tightness for Houses in a Developed Residential Area," ASHRAE Transactions, Vol. 87, Pt. 2, 1981.

[35] Tamura, G. T. and Wilson, A. G., "Air Leakage and Pressure Measurements in Two Occupied Houses," ASHRAE Transactions, Vol. 85, 1979. (The infiltration data in this report is essentially that reported in Tamura [Ref 23].)

[36] Kronvall, J., "Testing of Houses for Air Leakage Using a Pressure Method," ASHRAE Transactions, Vol. 84, 1978.

[37] Treado, S. J., Burch, D. M., and Hunt, C. M., "An Investigation of Air-Infiltration Characteristics and Mechanisms for a Townhouse," NBS Technical Note 992, National Bureau of Standards, Gaithersburg, MD, 1979.

[38] Warner, C. G., "Measurement of the Ventilation of Dwellings," Journal of Hygiene, Vol. xi, No. 2, April 1940.

[39] Bassett, M., "Preliminary Survey of Air Tightness Levels in New Zealand Houses," Paper 29, Institution of Professional Engineers, New Zealand, Feb. 1983.

[40] Blomsterberg, A. K., and Harrje, D. T., "Approaches to Evaluation of Air Infiltration Energy Losses in Buildings," ASHRAE Transactions, Vol. 85, Pt. 1, 1979.

[41] Blomsterberg, A. K., Sherman, M. H., and Grimsrud, D. T., "A Model Correlating Air Tightness and Air Infiltration in Houses," LBL-9625, ASHRAE-DOE Conference on the Thermal Performance of the Exterior Envelope of Buildings, Orlando, Dec. 1979, Lawrence Berkeley Laboratory, Berkeley, CA.

[42] Coblentz, C. W. and Achenbach, P. R., "Field Measurements in Ten Electrically-Heated Houses," ASHRAE Transactions, Vol. 69, 1963.

[43] Diamond, R. C. and Grimsrud, D. T., "Guidelines for Infiltration Reductions in Light-Frame Structures," LBL-13231, Lawrence Berkeley Laboratory, Berkeley, CA, Sept. 1981.

[44] Dickinson, J. B., Grimsrud, D. T., Krinkel, D. L., and Lipschutz, R. D., "Results of the Bonneville Power Administration Weatherization and Tightening Projects at the Midway Substation Residential Community," LBL-12742, Lawrence Berkeley Laboratory, Berkeley, CA, Feb. 1982.

[45] "Indian Hills Infiltration Study," E+ Energy Consultants, final report to the Georgia Power Co., Atlanta, 30 June 1982.

[46] Goldschmidt, V. W. and Wilhelm, D. R., "Summertime Infiltration Rates in Mobile Homes," ASHRAE Transactions, Vol. 85, Pt. 1, 1979.

[47] Goldschmidt, V. W., Leonard, R. G., Ball, J. E., and Wilhelm, D. R., "Wintertime Infiltration Rates in Mobile Homes," in Building Air Change Rate and Infiltration Measurements, ASTM STP 719, American Society for Testing and Materials, Philadelphia, 1980.

[48] Mattingly, G. E., Harrje, D. T., and Heisler, G. M., "The Effectiveness of an Evergreen Windbreak for Reducing Residential Energy Consumption," ASHRAE Transactions, Vol. 85, 1979.

[49] Etheridge, D. W., Martin, L., Gale, R., and Gell, M. A., "Natural and Mechanical Ventilation Rates in a Detached House: Measurements," Applied Energy, Vol. 8, 1981.

[50] de Gids, W. F., "Natural Ventilation and Energy Consumption in Dwellings," ING-TNO Report C 482, Institute for Environmental Hygiene-TNO, Delft, Netherlands, July 1981.

[51] Goldschmidt, V. W. and Wilhelm, D. R., "Relationship of Infiltration to Weather Parameters for a Mobile Home," ASHRAE Transactions, Vol. 87, Pt. 2, 1981.

[52] Graham, R. M. and Sulatisky, M. T., "Evaluation of Electric Heating, Coranach Heating Project," Volume 1, "Main Report," Saskatchewan Power Corporation Research and Development Centre 77-40, May 1981.

[53] Grimsrud, D. T., Sherman, M. H., and Sonderegger, R. C., "Calculating Infiltration: Implications for a Construction Quality Standard," LBL-9416, Lawrence Berkeley Laboratory, Berkeley, CA, 1983.

[54] Grot, R. A. and Clark, R. E., "Air Leakage Characteristics and Weatherization Techniques for Low Income Housing," DOE/ASHRAE Conference on Thermal Performance of Exterior Envelopes of Buildings, Florida, 1979, ASHRAE, Atlanta, GA.

[55] Hartmann, P., Pfiffner, I., and Bargetzi, S., "Results of Air Change Rate Measurements in Swiss Residential Buildings," Technical Translation NRC/CNR TT-1945, Ki Klima Kalte Ingenieur, Sonderdruck, Switzerland, 1978.

[56] Jordan, R. C., Erickson, G. A., and Leonard, R. R., "Infiltration Measurements in Two Research Houses," *ASHRAE Journal*, May 1963.

[57] Nusgens, P. and Guillaume, M., "Ventilation Naturelle des Maisons Individuelles," *CSTC Revue*, No. 1, March 1980.

[58] Potter, I. N., "Effect of Fluctuating Wind Pressures on Natural Ventilation Rates," *ASHRAE Transactions*, Vol. 85, Pt. 2, 1979.

[59] Sherman, M. H. and Grimsrud, D. Y., "Infiltration-Pressurization Correlation: Simplified Physical Modeling," *ASHRAE Transactions*, Vol. 86, Pt. 2, 1980. (This paper presents no new field data not already reported in LBL-10852 and the publication by the same name by the Air Infiltration Centre.)

[60] Stewart, M. B., Jacob, T. R., and Winston, J. G., "Analysis of Infiltration by Tracer Gas Technique, Pressurization Tests, and Infrared Scans," Owens-Corning Fiberglas Corp., circa 1980.

[61] Bilsborrow, R. E., "A Comparison of Computed Infiltration Rates with Results Obtained From a Set of Full-Scale Measurements," BS2, Department of Building Sciences, University of Sheffield, Nov. 1972. (The data used is that of Tamura and Wilson [Ref 35].)

[62] Grimsrud, D. T., Sonderegger, R. C., and Sherman, M. H., "Infiltration Measurements in Audit and Retrofit Programs," LBL-12221, Lawrence Berkeley Laboratory, Berkeley, CA, April 1981 (most of the data presented is shown again in Dickinson et al [14]).

[63] Krinkel, D. L., Dickerhoff, D. J., Casey, J., and Grimsrud, D. T., "Pressurization Test Results: Bonneville Power Administration Energy Conservation Study," LBL-10996, Lawrence Berkeley Laboratory, Berkeley, CA, Dec. 1980. (Most of the data is republished in Dickinson et al [14].)

[64] Sherman, M. H., "Air Infiltration in Buildings," Ph.D. thesis issued as LBL-10712, Lawrence Berkeley Laboratory, Berkeley, CA, Oct. 1980. (Tracer gas and pressurization techniques are compared for 15 separate sites. These are the same data as in LBL-10852.)

[65] Sherman, M. H. and Grimsrud, D. T., "Measurement of Infiltration Using Fan Pressurization and Weather Data," First Symposium of the Air Infiltration Centre, Windsor, England, Oct. 1980, AIC, Bracknell, Berkshire, England. (Also LBL-10852.)

[66] Sherman, M. H., Modera, M. P., and Grimsrud, D. T., "A Predictive Air Infiltration Model—Field Validation and Sensitivity Analysis," LBL-13520, Lawrence Berkeley Laboratory, Berkeley, CA, Oct. 1981. (Reference is made to a mobile test unit located in Reno, Nevada used to obtain base data. The contents of this report are almost the same as Modera et al [Ref 67].)

[67] Modera, M. P., Sherman, M. H., and Grimsrud, D. T., "Long Term Infiltration Measurements in a Full-Scale Test Structure," LBL-13504, Lawrence Berkeley Laboratory, Berkeley, CA, Sept. 1981. (Test data obtained from a mobile test unit located in Reno, Nevada are referred to in order to test validity of a model for infiltration prediction from blower test data. The base data is not provided).

[68] Warren, P. R. and Webb, B. C., "The Relationship Between Tracer Gas and Pressurization Techniques in Dwellings," First Symposium of the Air Infiltration Centre, Windsor, England, Oct. 1980. (Some 17 houses were tested both with a pressurization and a decay gas technique. The data for the decay gas results are not explicitly shown and were limited to some twenty measurements. Although the houses are classified as to number of floors and whether detached or not, their types of HVAC systems are not described in this paper, whose major thrust appears to be the correlation of both techniques. Some of the tests appear to have been taken with open windows.)

Commercial and Industrial

Leif I. Lundin[1]

Air Leakage in Industrial Buildings—Description of Equipment

REFERENCE: Lundin, L., **"Air Leakage in Industrial Buildings—Description of Equipment,"** *Measured Air Leakage of Buildings, ASTM STP 904,* H. R. Trechsel and P. L. Lagus, Eds., American Society for Testing and Materials, Philadelphia, 1986, pp. 101–105.

ABSTRACT: Air leakage in industrial buildings—preliminary results: The National Testing Institute is currently investigating air leakage in industrial buildings. In 1980 the Institute was asked to carry out a number of pressurization/depressurization tests in industrial buildings. The buildings that were tested were constructed according to two different principles: light-concrete elements attached to a prefabricated concrete frame and sheet metal attached to a steel frame insulated with mineral wool. The measurements were asked for by a manufacturer of building materials. The results indicate that some industrial buildings are very leaky and some are very airtight. Therefore Nordtest has asked us to develop a method for pressurization tests of large buildings and for equipment to carry out those tests. The paper will describe the equipment and present preliminary results.

KEY WORDS: air leakage, tracer gas, fan, industrial buildings, equipment

The purpose of this paper is: (1) to describe an alternate method for measuring the large airflows needed to pressurize large buildings; and (2) to present pressurization results for nine buildings.

In the Swedish Building Code, there are recommendations for the maximum air leakage in dwellings—one-family houses as well as multifamily houses. Most new Swedish one-family houses meet the recommendations. There are still no recommendations for industrial buildings in Sweden. Up until now very little has been known about the airtightness of industrial buildings, and very few people have worried about it.

In mid-1980, the National Testing Institute was asked by a manufacturer

---

[1]Swedish National Testing Institute, Section of Energy Systems, Borås, Sweden.

of building materials if we were able to carry out pressurization/depressurization tests of large industrial buildings. At that time our available fan capacity was about 8000 m³/h at 60 Pa. To reach this flow we used two axial fans equipped with measuring ducts with Pitot tubes. Due to our limited measuring resources at the time, we had to tell our client that we could carry out the measurements only on industrial buildings of moderate sizes.

The test objects were selected only by our client. The design of the buildings followed two structural principles: firstly, light concrete elements attached to a prefabricated concrete frame; secondly, sheet metal attached to steel frame, with thermal insulation of mineral wool.

Some of the buildings were very leaky, and some were very tight. These results caused an animated discussion between manufacturers of building materials, contractors, and our building authorities. During that period, the National Testing Institute made the decision that equipment for measuring large industrial buildings should be developed. At the same time, Nordtest asked for a test method especially adapted to industrial buildings.

Nordtest is a joint Nordic organization with the aim of promoting technical testing. It was established in 1973 at the request of the Nordic Council and by the directive of the Nordic Council of Ministers. Nordtest's activities are carried out by the board, the secretariat, the inter-Nordic technical groups, and the supervisors of projects dealing with development of test methods. Activity is focused on the testing of building materials and constructions; fire; acoustics and noise; nondestructive testing; equipment for heating, plumbing, and sanitation; electronic apparatus and equipment; consumer goods; and mechanical and chemical testing concerning work environment.

Description of the Equipment

In order to fulfill the demands, we could expect that the capacity of the equipment had to be 75 000 m³/h at 60 Pa. This would mean a large fan and an enormous measuring duct. We had to think of another construction instead of the traditional measuring duct. Tracer gas was the solution to the problem. This way a long measuring duct is unneeded. By injecting a known constant flow of tracer gas in the airflow upstream the fan and at the same time measuring the concentration of tracer gas in the airflow downstream the fan, you can easily calculate the air flow by

$$Q = \frac{q}{c} \cdot 1\ 000\ 000$$

where

Q = airflow through the fan, m³/s,
q = injected tracer gas upstream the fan, m³/s, and
c = tracer gas concentration downstream the fan, ppm.

The tracer gas injection and mixing device is designed as two rings of tubing located in a short duct of the same diameter as the fan duct. In the walls of the tubing, holes with a very small diameter are located radially. This device will inject tracer gas into the whole duct area and give a nearly perfect mixing (Figs. 1 and 2).

The fan is an axial fan, type Axico and size 1000-mm diameter. The airflow rate is changed by changing the blade angle of the fan. This can be done continuously while the fan is running. In order to measure the tracer gas flow, there is an electronic mass flowmeter connected to the injection rings. A steady constant tracer gas flow is obtained by using a pressure equalizing container installed between the gas cylinder and the gas flowmeter. The pressure-equaling container is equipped with an automatic pressure control. The injection system is working at a pressure of 0.3 MPa.

Downstream the fan, four air sampling tubes are located in a duct of the same diameter as the fan duct.

The concentration of tracer gas in the air downstream the fan is measured by an infrared (IR) analyzer as tracer gas [nitrous oxide (N_2O)] is used. The fan unit containing the tracer gas injection system and sampling system is mounted on a special trailer. An undercarriage running on rails allows the fan unit to be moved backward and forward and also to be turned around easily on the trailer. All controls and measuring devices except for the mass flowme-

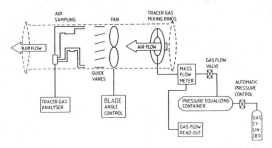

FIG. 1—*Schematic view and photo of equipment.*

ter are located in a van. To connect the fan unit to a building, there is a special connecting box which can be fitted to a normal door opening.

The tracer measurement method will give the fan the widest measuring range. Measuring static pressure and differential pressure will be very difficult at low airflows. The error in measured airflows depends on calibration of the tracer gas analyzer, calibration of the tracer gas flowmeter, and reading errors.

Description of Tested Buildings and Measuring Results

Until now we have carried out a number of measurements on large buildings using this equipment. In Table 1, you will find a short technical description of the buildings.

Building No. 1—Light concrete elements attached to a prefabricated concrete frame. On the roof are two rooms containing parts of the ventilation system. These rooms are made of sheet metal attached to a sheet frame. Inside the building is a mechanical workshop.

During the measurement, the ventilation system was shut down and sealed off on the outside of the building. All exterior doors were shut but not sealed off. Internal doors were kept open.

Building No. 2—Light concrete elements are attached to a prefabricated concrete frame. The building is new and is used as a wholesale store. During the measurements, the building was sealed off in the same manner as Building No. 1.

Building No. 3—Steel frame that has prefabricated wall elements attached. The wall elements are made of polystyrene covered on both sides with plasterboard. The facades are made of sheet metal, and the thermal insula-

TABLE 1—*Technical description of buildings.*

Building	Floor Area, m^2	Area of Building Envelope, Walls, and Roof, m^2	Volume of Building, m^3	Air Flow per m^2 of Building Envelope		
				Pressurized, 50 Pa, m^3/h	Depressurized, 50 Pa, m^3/h	Mean, 50 Pa, m^3/h
Building No. 1	4137	6796	36 373	8.0	7.7	7.9
Building No. 2	6524	9876	61 127	6.4	5.6	6.0
Building No. 3	4236	5809	31 622	3.4	2.7	3.0
Building No. 4	1840	3150	...	7.6	3.2	5.4
Building No. 5	1265	2100	8535	4.3	4.2	4.3
Building No. 6	1620	2650	10 050	3.0	3.2	3.1
Building No. 7	1025	1960	6275	4.8	5.1	5.0
Building No. 8	1846	2950	12 528	2.4	2.5	2.5
Building No. 9	4140	6804	29 975	2.1	2.0	2.1

tion on the roof is made of mineral wool. The building has a welded plastic air/vapor barrier.

The building was about two years old and was used as a tennis hall with six tennis courts and service spaces.

During the measurements, the building was sealed off in the same way as the previous buildings.

Building No. 4—Sheet metal is attached to steel frame, with thermal insulation of mineral wool. The air/vapor barrier is made of plastic. The ventilation system was closed by a tight damper.

Building No. 5—Sheet metal is attached to steel frame, with thermal insulation of mineral wool. The air/vapor barrier is made of plastic. The building has no heating and ventilation system but is heated only by the installation for light.

Building No. 6—Light concrete elements are attached to a prefabricated concrete frame. No windows are in the building envelope, but there are three large doorways with door leafs made of steel. The ventilation system was sealed during the test.

Building No. 7—Light concrete elements are attached to a prefabricated concrete frame. In the building envelope were a larger number of windows and six doorways with door leafs made of steel. The ventilation system was sealed off during the test.

Building No. 8—Light concrete elements are attached to a prefabricated concrete frame. The ventilation system was sealed off during the test.

Building No. 9—Light concrete elements are attached to a prefabricated concrete frame. The ventilation system was sealed off during the test.

Conclusions

Most industrial processes are producing "waste energy." In many cases, this energy flow has low temperature and will not be returned to the process. The most economical way of using the "waste energy" is to use it for heating the building.

In an airtight and well-thermal-insulated factory building, the waste energy can be the only energy source for its heating. This is what many building designers and manufacturers of building material are working on.

Our mission was to find out how to carry out pressurization tests in large buildings. We think that our equipment will be a useful instrument in helping building designers and contractors to find out how to make airtight buildings.

John R. Waters[1] and Martin W. Simons[1]

The Measurement of Air Infiltration in Large Single-Cell Industrial Buildings

REFERENCE: Waters, J. R. and Simons, M. W., "**The Measurement of Air Infiltration in Large Single-Cell Industrial Buildings,**" *Measured Air Leakage of Buildings, ASTM STP 904*, H. R. Trechsel and P. L. Lagus, Eds., American Society for Testing and Materials, Philadelphia, 1986, pp. 106–119.

ABSTRACT: Measurements of the air infiltration rate of three large single-cell buildings have been carried out using the tracer dilution method. The purpose of the measurements was to determine whether or not there are any special difficulties in using the tracer dilution method in this type of building prior to embarking on a more substantial measurement program. The tracers used were nitrous oxide and sulfur hexafluoride. Both were found to be satisfactory, but it was concluded that sulfur hexafluoride, in conjunction with a portable gas chromatograph, performed more reliably when used for on-site measurements and therefore was to be preferred.

KEY WORDS: air infiltration, tracer gas method, industrial buildings

A considerable body of knowledge exists on the ventilation and air infiltration of domestic buildings and domestic-size rooms in other buildings. Experimental measurements have been carried out for many years by a number of workers, several experimental techniques are well established, and a number of review papers have been published [1–4]. There is no similar body of knowledge on air infiltration in large single-cell buildings such as factories. This is partly due to lack of attention by research workers to this type of building but also may be due to doubts as to whether or not the methods used in domestic dwellings are applicable to large single-cell buildings. Nevertheless, some recent work on large enclosures has been reported. Potter et al [5] have published preliminary results of tracer decay and fan pressurization tests on two factory buildings. Lundin [6] has reported fan pressurization tests on

---

[1]Principal lecturer and senior lecturer, respectively, Department of Civil Engineering and Building, Coventry Polytechnic, Coventry CV1 5FB, United Kingdom.

three large single-cell buildings. Freeman et al [7] have compared alternative measurement techniques in rooms up to 650 m³ interval volume, but this is below the size of buildings considered in this paper.

The initial impetus for this study came from a desire to model the energy consumption of factory buildings. The natural air infiltration rate is an essential parameter in such a model, and typical values were needed for buildings of internal volume in the range 1000 to 10000 m³. It also was recognized that air movement patterns within such a building may be just as important as the infiltration rate, and that the rate itself may show significant variations throughout the space. To obtain the necessary information, a program of measurements in factory buildings was instituted. This paper reports the results of the first stage of the program, which was concerned with the evaluation and development of the measurement technique.

Objective

Most of the available measurement techniques were rejected immediately as unsuitable in this application. Fan pressurization methods do not provide infiltration rates directly and would destroy internal air movement patterns. The constant injection tracer method was rejected because the combination of a low infiltration rate with a large internal building volume would produce a long time constant, thus causing the time to reach equilibrium tracer concentration to be unacceptably long. The constant concentration tracer method was rejected partly because it assumes perfect mixing of the tracer in each cell of the building, and partly because it was anticipated that it would be difficult to maintain stability in the feed-back loop when using it in a large space. Elimination of these methods left the tracer dilution method as the best possibility among the better known techniques.

The objective, therefore, was to determine whether or not a conventional tracer dilution method could be used to measure air infiltration in large single-cell buildings. The specific questions which have been examined are:

1. Are there any special difficulties in using a tracer dilution method in a building of this type?

2. Will the tracers which are most often used in other buildings be satisfactory?

3. Is there any difficulty in obtaining satisfactory mixing of the tracer gas in a large volume space?

4. What is the extent of the spatial variation in infiltration rate throughout a large space, and can this variation be monitored by a tracer dilution method?

5. Is it possible to obtain information on internal air movement patterns?

In order to contain this part of the program within a reasonable time scale, it was restricted to unoccupied, unheated buildings.

Equipment and Experimental Technique

On-site measurements were used in order to give immediate results and hence speed up the development work. Two independent tracer gas systems were used, one based on nitrous oxide and the other on sulfur hexafluoride. These gases were chosen because they have suitable properties and are among the most popular of the tracers in current use.

Nitrous Oxide System

An infrared gas analyzer (IRGA) fitted with a Luft detector was used, with a measurement range of 0 to 100 ppm nitrous oxide in air. Although the instrument gave a continuous record of concentration with time, its response was heavily damped. For a step change in nitrous oxide concentration of 50 ppm, the instrument exhibited a time constant of several seconds.

Sulfur Hexafluoride System

This was a modified form of a small portable gas chromatograph which was originally designed for leak detection using sulfur hexafluoride. The detector was an election capture cell, and the column material was 100 to 120 mesh alumina. The instrument was capable of covering a concentration range of 10^4, but for reasons of linearity usually was operated in the range 0.1 to 0.3 ppm sulfur hexafluoride in air. It was found that in operation the retention times were short enough, and recovery from each sample sufficiently rapid, for successive readings to be taken at 1-min intervals.

Both systems could be operated via a six-point sampling unit, so that six sample points could be monitored in any experiment. Air was drawn continuously from each point at 1.4 L/min via sample lines to the sampling unit, which then diverted in turn approximately 0.7 L/min into the detector.

Injection of Tracer Gas

Several methods of injecting the tracer gas were used, ranging from the crude and simple to the complex. In order to achieve an initially uniform concentration, preliminary tests showed that bleeding the gas into the blades of a small fan was effective. Figure 1 shows the results of a typical test in a 200-m³ room in the laboratory. Similar results were obtained in factory buildings, except that the time to equilibrium was usually between 20 and 30 min. As experimental work progressed, it became clear that a starting condition with a plug of unmixed tracer at a selected point in the building was also of interest. This was achieved by bleeding the gas into a small piece of foam or fibrous material in order to randomize the exit direction.

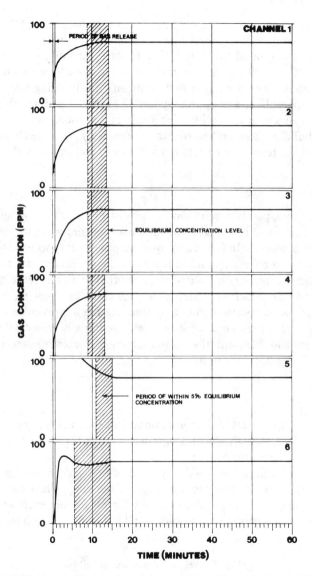

FIG. 1—*Increase in tracer concentration with mixing by means of a small fan.*

Experimental Results

Buildings Tested

Three buildings were used for infiltration measurements. All three were single story, and their principal dimensions are shown in Table 1. Figure 2 is a plan and elevation of Building B01, and the other buildings were similar. Buildings B01 and B02 were new and were situated in a light industrial urban area surrounded by buildings of similar dimensions. Building B03, which was used as a sports hall, was approximately 15 years old and was situated in a suburban residential area with open fields on one side. At the time of the tests, all buildings were unheated and unoccupied with no mechanical ventilation, and the tests were carried out with doors and windows closed.

Measurement Details

The sampling points were in most cases distributed uniformly so that they could be considered as being at the centers of imaginary "cells" of approximately equal volume. In four cases, one sampling point was used to monitor external air as a reference, and in two cases the multipoint sampler was not used. Other parameters measured were internal and external temperatures and internal air velocities. External air velocities were not measured, but wind speeds were obtained from a weather station approximately ten miles distant. Thirteen tests were carried out with an initially uniform distribution of tracer gas and three with the gas initially concentrated in one corner of the building. Table 2 gives a summary.

Typical Results

Sixteen complete sets of data were obtained. Figure 3 is a typical example of a run with an initially uniform distribution, and Fig. 4 is an example of a nonuniform initial distribution.

In most cases, the tracer gas decay curves were typical of the kind of result that would be expected from any other type of building. When starting from a uniform concentration, the decay curves for all the channels for any run tended to remain close together, with small but noticeable differences in the

TABLE 1—*Principal dimensions of buildings.*

Building	Length, m	Width, m	Height to Eaves, m	Height to Ridge, m
B01	28.000	18.000	5.500	8.000
B02	21.725	18.163	5.600	6.750
B03	33.280	17.490	6.000	7.250

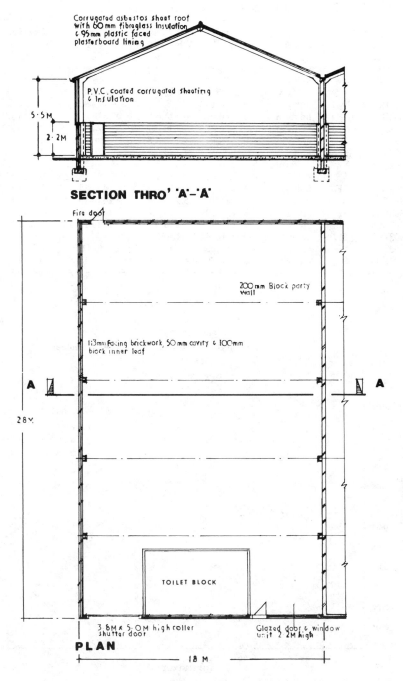

Corrugated asbestos sheet roof with 60 mm fibreglass insulation & 95 mm plastic faced plasterboard lining

P.V.C. coated corrugated sheeting & Insulation

5·5M

2·2M

SECTION THRO' 'A'-'A'

Fire door

200 mm Block party wall

1:3mm facing brickwork, 50 mm cavity & 100mm block inner leaf

A   A

28 ∨.

TOILET BLOCK

3.8M × 5.0M high roller shutter door

Glazed door & window unit 2.2M high

PLAN

18 M

FIG. 2—*Plan and elevation of Building B01.*

TABLE 2—*Conditions of experimental runs.*

Run	Tracer	Starting Condition	Internal Air Speed, m/s	External Wind Speed, m/s	Internal Temperature, °C	External Temperature, °C
B01R01	N₂O	uniform	≅0.005	zero	−1 to +3	−6.4 to −4.8
B01R02	N₂O	uniform	≅0.005	zero	−1 to +3	−3.4 to −2.9
B02R01	N₂O	uniform	0.02 to 0.10	7.2	8.1 to 9.5	7.5
B02R02	N₂O	uniform	0.01 to 0.06	4.6 to 8.8	7.5 to 8.5	6.8 to 7.9
B02R03	N₂O	uniform	0.01 to 0.08	4.1 to 6.7	7.5	6.7 to 7.2
B02R04	SF₆	uniform	0.01 to 0.06	4.6 to 8.8	7.5 to 8.5	6.8 to 7.9
B02R05	SF₆	uniform	0 to 0.08	4.1 to 6.7	7.5	6.7 to 7.2
B02R06	N₂O	uniform	0.01 to 0.06	4.6 to 7.2	7.5 to 8.5	6.8 to 7.5
B03R01	SF₆	uniform	0.02 to 0.08	0 to 2	15	12.0 to 12.3
B03R02	SF₆	uniform	0.01 to 0.10	5.7 to 7.2	14 to 15	13.4 to 14.4
B03R03	SF₆	uniform	0.01 to 0.10	5.7 to 7.7	14 to 15	14.4 to 15.4
B03R04	SF₆	plug	0.01 to 0.10	4.1 to 5.7	14 to 15	13.8 to 14.3
B03R05	SF₆	plug	0.01 to 0.10	4.1 to 7.7	14 to 15	12.9 to 13.8
B03R06	SF₆	plug	0.02 to 0.08	2.1 to 2.6	14	8.8 to 11.9
B03R07	SF₆	uniform	0.02 to 0.06	3.6 to 4.6	8.5 to 11.5	8.0 to 11.8
B03R08	SF₆	uniform	0.02 to 0.06	4.1 to 4.6	13 to 15	11.8 to 13.4

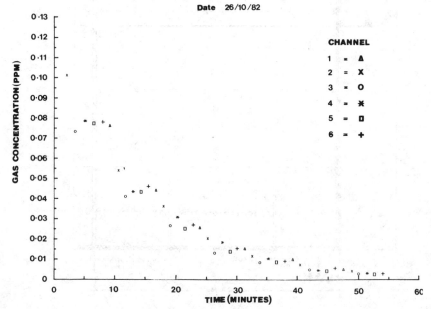

FIG. 3—*Tracer decay for Run B03R03.*

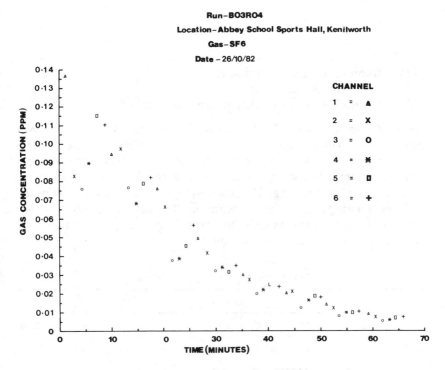

Run-B03R04

Location-Abbey School Sports Hall, Kenilworth

Gas-SF6

Date - 26/10/82

FIG. 4—*Tracer decay for Run B03R04.*

rates of decay. The readings for an individual channel in any run showed very little scatter about a smooth curve provided the decay was rapid (that is, when the infiltration rate was greater than about 2 air changes per hour). The degree of scatter was generally greater when the rate of decay was slow. In some cases, several successive readings on a channel would drift to one side of the expected decay curve before returning to it. In such cases, there was usually a drift in the opposite direction in some or all of the other channels.

In the results which started from a nonuniform distribution, the differences between the channels quickly disappeared. After approximately 20 min, the decay curves were similar in appearance to those obtained from a uniform distribution.

The results for Building B01 were unusual, but there is no evidence that they are erroneous. Unfortunately, this particular building has been unavailable for further tests.

Analysis and Discussion of Results

The single-cell model of the tracer dilution method predicts, assuming perfect mixing, a simple exponential decay of the form

$$C = C_o e^{-Nt}$$

where

C = tracer concentration at time t,
C_o = initial concentration, and
N = infiltration rate in air changes per unit time.

The results for each channel were analyzed by first converting the volumes of concentration to their natural logarithm and then performing a least squares fit to a straight line. Also, for each run the results for all channels were collected into a single data set and again fitted to a straight line to give an overall result for the whole building. The goodness of fit of each data set was examined by evaluating the correlation coefficient, R. Finally, the gradient of each best fit line was expressed as an infiltration rate in air changes per hour, and the results are collected in Tables 3 and 4.

TABLE 3—*Results for buildings B01 and B02.*[a]

| Run Number | | Channel Number | | | | | | |
---	---	1	2	3	4	5	6	All Data
B01R01	N	0.100	0.091	0.069	−0.108	−0.043	0.008	0.015
	S	5	5	5	5	5	5	30
	R	0.480	0.987	0.839	0.990	0.557	0.406	0.065
B01R02	N	0.087	0.038	0.047	0.103	0.065	0.043	0.055
	S	5	5	5	4	5	5	29
	R	0.972	0.811	0.948	0.890	0.920	0.967	0.436
B02R01	N	1.25	1.57	1.42	1.54	1.37	. . .[b]	1.42
	S	12	12	13	13	12	. . .[b]	62
	R	0.942	0.995	0.977	0.963	0.944	. . .[b]	0.933
B02R02	N	0.884	0.879	0.836	0.846	0.814	. . .[b]	0.850
	S	18	19	19	19	19	. . .[b]	94
	R	0.969	0.997	0.926	0.986	0.988	. . .[b]	0.964
B02R03	N	0.888	0.853	1.018	0.783	0.779	. . .[b]	0.864
	S	20	21	20	20	20	. . .[b]	101
	R	0.988	0.988	0.981	0.991	0.998	. . .[b]	0.961
B02R04[c]	N	0.522						0.522
	S	29						29
	R	0.928						0.928
B02R05[c]	N	0.739						0.739
	S	18						18
	R	0.985						0.985
B02R06	N	1.076	0.806	0.839	0.965	1.038	. . .[b]	0.947
	S	22	21	21	21	21	. . .[b]	106
	R	0.983	0.987	0.932	0.984	0.976	. . .[b]	0.957

[a]N = infiltration rate, ACH; S = number of points; R = correlation coefficient.
[b]Channel 6 was used to monitor external air as a zero check.
[c]Only one channel was available for these runs.

TABLE 4—*Results for building B03.*[a]

				Channel Number				
Run Number		1	2	3	4	5	6	All Data
B03R01	N	0.589	0.542	0.679	0.624	0.596	0.634	0.613
	S	19	19	19	19	19	19	114
	R	0.978	0.954	0.951	0.941	0.957	0.957	0.949
B03R02	N	4.145	4.581	4.572	4.514	4.456	4.299	4.423
	S	7	7	7	7	7	7	42
	R	0.996	0.996	0.988	0.995	0.998	0.998	0.990
B03R03	N	4.203	4.210	4.441	4.436	4.580	4.397	4.387
	S	7	7	7	7	7	7	42
	R	0.999	0.999	0.999	0.996	1.000	0.999	0.990
B03R04	N	2.837	2.695	2.917	2.752	2.887	2.909	2.817
	S	8	8	8	8	8	8	48
	R	0.996	0.977	0.989	0.995	0.995	0.997	0.978
B03R05	N	1.446	1.665	1.596	1.733	1.597	1.624	1.613
	S	11	11	11	11	11	11	66
	R	0.968	0.993	0.993	0.995	0.996	0.990	0.986
B03R06	N	1.384	1.386	1.240	1.104	1.200	1.254	1.266
	S	11	11	11	11	11	11	66
	R	0.991	0.992	0.990	0.992	0.992	0.991	0.984
B03R07	N	1.898	1.936	1.927	2.092	2.158	2.544	2.127
	S	12	11	11	11	11	11	67
	R	0.956	0.978	0.960	0.980	0.973	0.993	0.946
B03R08	N	1.548	1.462	1.877	2.002	1.934	1.783	1.793
	S	11	11	11	11	11	11	66
	R	0.925	0.959	0.945	0.973	0.987	0.987	0.946

[a]N = infiltration rate, ACH; S = number of points; R = correlation coefficient.

For Building B03, the infiltration rates obtained from the complete data sets have been plotted against wind speed in Fig. 5. The trend is consistent with expectation. The results for Building B01 show exceptionally low infiltration rates. However, this was a new building, with all doors and windows closed, and the weather was unusually calm. The anemometer at the local weather station registered zero wind velocity over the whole of the period of these runs.

The results for Buildings B02 and B03 all show a high degree of correlation with a simple exponential decay. Nevertheless, close examination of Tables 3 and 4 shows that there are at least two reasons for suspecting that more sophisticated analysis is necessary. Firstly, the differences in the infiltration rates between channels in the same run are high enough to be significant at the levels of correlation obtained. For example, referring to Run B03R07 for Channel 1, $N = 1.898$ air changes per hour (ACH) with $R = 0.956$, and for channel 6, $n = 2.544$ ACH with $R = 0.993$. Secondly, in nearly all cases, the correlation coefficient for the complete data set for a run is less than the cor-

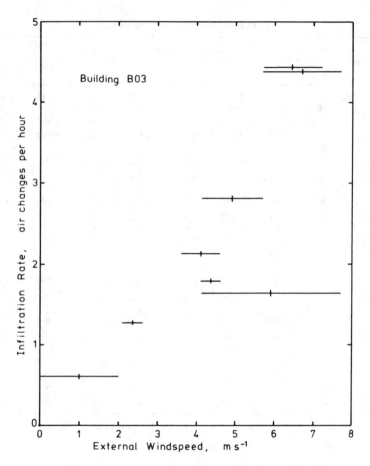

FIG. 5—*Infiltration rate versus wind speed for Building B03.*

relation coefficients for individual channels. A plausible explanation of this is that the fresh air infiltration is different in different parts of the building, and that this difference is being partially masked by a natural internal circulation process.

An improvement on single-cell theory may be achieved by treating the single large space as an assembly of smaller zones. If it is assumed that the tracer gas is always uniformly mixed in each zone and that air flow rates between zones can be defined, the problem is amenable to multizone analysis as described by, for example, Sinden [8]. To illustrate this, hypothetical tracer decay curves have been constructed for Building B03 using the following assumptions:

1. The building is divided into six imaginary zones of equal volume.
2. Wind pressure on one of the long faces of the building gives rise to a

fresh air infiltration rate equivalent to 2 ACH averaged over the whole building.

3. Interzone flow rates are chosen such that they are consistent with the measured internal air velocities.

Figure 6 shows the resulting theoretical decay curves for an initially uniform tracer gas distribution, and Fig. 7 shows the curves for the tracer gas concentrated initially in Zone 1. It is clear that in both cases the decay curves for all six zones rapidly approach an approximately parallel course. This means that, with the exception of the early part of the decay, all zones are describable by a single decay constant. This explains why a good fit to a simple exponential decay was found.

In order to perform the reverse operation and to determine the interzone flow rates from the measured decay curves, two conditions must be met. Firstly, there must be no symmetry in the initial conditions, otherwise ill-conditioning may occur and the matrix inversion will fail. Secondly, sufficient data points must be available to define the decay curves clearly during the early part of the decay when the larger decay constants still are able to exert an influence. The equipment used for this part of the project had a maximum sampling time of 1 reading per minute. When using six channels, therefore, a maximum of 1 reading every 6 min was available. This was considered to be insufficient for the results obtained here to be used for determining interzone flows.

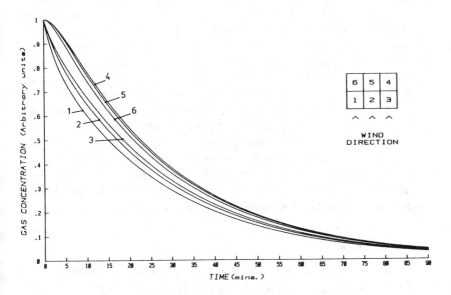

FIG. 6—*Multichamber decay, uniform initial distribution.*

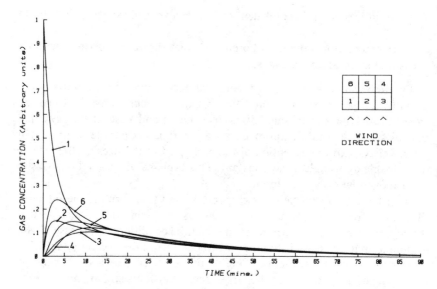

FIG. 7—*Multichamber decay, nonuniform initial distribution.*

Comments and Conclusions

The most obvious conclusion is that there is no serious difficulty in using a tracer dilution method in this type of building. The two most important on-site practical problems were the detection and elimination of leakage in the air lines and the robustness of the IRGA. The first of these problems is being cured by changes in the design of the equipment. The second has led to the abandonment of the IRGA in favor of the gas chromatograph, which was found to be much more robust and reliable. Mixing of the tracer gas did not present any difficulty, and, in any case, nonuniform initial conditions can be an advantage if internal air flows are to be examined.

It appears that the tracer dilution method is capable of yielding information on spatial variations of infiltration rate and interzone flows provided the response time is fast enough to give good definition of the decay curves over the first 10 to 15 min. On the basis of the results obtained, it is suggested that each channel should be measured at least once per minute.

Acknowledgment

The authors wish to thank the Science and Engineering Research Council of the United Kingdom, which is supporting this project under Research Grants GR/B/64604 and GR/C/38425.

References

[1] Hitchen, E. R. and Wilson, C. B., *Building Science*, Vol. 2, 1967, pp. 59–82.
[2] Hunt, C. M. in *Building Air Change Rate and Infiltration Measurements, ASTM STP 719*, C. M. Hunt, J. C. King, and H. R. Trechsel, Eds., 1980, p. 3.
[3] Sherman, M., Grimsrud, D. T., Condon, P. E., and Smith, B. V., "Air Infiltration Measurement Techniques," in *Proceedings*, 1st AIC Conference, Windsor, United Kingdom, Oct. 1980, Air Infiltration Centre, Bracknell, Berkshire, United Kingdom.
[4] Harrje, D. T., Grot, R. A., and Grimsrud, D. T., "Air Infiltration Site Measurement Techniques," in *Proceedings*, 2nd AIC Conference, Stockholm, Sweden, Sept. 1981, Air Infiltration Centre, Bracknell, Berkshire, United Kingdom.
[5] Potter, I. N., Dewsbury, J., and Jones, T. J., "The Measurement of Air Infiltration Rates in Large Enclosures and Buildings," in *Proceedings*, 4th AIC Conference, Elm, Switzerland, Sept. 1983, Air Infiltration Centre, Bracknell, Berkshire, United Kingdom.
[6] Lundin, L., "Air Leakage in Industrial Buildings—Preliminary Results," in *Proceedings*, 4th AIC Conference, Elm, Switzerland, Sept. 1983, Air Infiltration Centre, Bracknell, Berkshire, United Kingdom.
[7] Freeman, J., Gale, R., and Lilly, J. P., "Ventilation Measurements in Large Buildings," in *Proceedings*, 4th AIC Conference, Elm, Switzerland, Sept. 1983, Air Infiltration Centre, Bracknell, Berkshire, United Kingdom.
[8] Sinden, F. W., *Building and Environment*, Vol. 13, 1978, pp. 21–28.

Joseph L. Ashley[1] and Peter L. Lagus[2]

Air Infiltration Measurements in Large Military Aircraft Hangars

REFERENCE: Ashley, J. L. and Lagus, P. L., **"Air Infiltration Measurements in Large Military Aircraft Hangars,"** *Measured Air Leakage of Buildings, ASTM STP 904*, H. R. Trechsel and P. L. Lagus, Eds., American Society for Testing and Materials, Philadelphia, 1986, pp. 120–134.

ABSTRACT: Air leakage measurements by the tracer dilution technique were performed in five military aircraft hangars. The hangars were located in regions of the country having diverse weather characteristics. In several of the hangars, distinct measurements were performed to assess the degree of homogeneity of the air-tracer gas mixture in these large volume structures. Air leakage rates in the range of 0.6 to slightly above 2.0 air changes per hour (ACH) were measured. Surprisingly, these values do not differ significantly from those which might be measured in single-family residences. Since, in use, aircraft hangars often have at least one sliding door open, tracer dilution measurements were performed to show the increase in air leakage to be expected with one and two (oppositely located) doors open.

KEY WORDS: sulfur hexafluoride, tracer gas, infiltration, large buildings, aircraft hangars

Few measurements in large, open buildings have been reported. Freeman et al [1] have performed tracer dilution measurements in buildings with internal volumes ranging from 100 to 650 m^3. Their data range from a low of 0.42 air changes per hour (ACH) to a high of 13.2 ACH. The latter number was obtained in a building with all windows open. Waters and Simons [2] report measurements on three open factory buildings ranging in volume from 3000 to 4000 m^3. Their data extend from a low of 0.015 ACH to a high of 4.4 ACH. These authors explicitly discuss the problems attendant to good mixing in large, open, internal-volume buildings. Grot and Persily [3] report infiltration rates ranging from 0.20 to 0.55 in eight U.S. office buildings with internal volumes ranging from 8800 to 174000 m^3.

Potential reductions in the energy requirements of aircraft hangars have

[1]Mechanical engineer, Civil Engineering Laboratory, Port Hueneme, CA 93043.
[2]Manager, Applied Science Program, S-CUBED, La Jolla, CA 92038.

been investigated. These investigations suggest that data related to air infiltration rates are insufficient to accurately evaluate many energy conservation concepts. Accordingly, joint investigation was funded by Headquarters Air Force and its Engineering Center and the Naval Facilities Engineering Command to determine the air infiltration rates associated with military hangars.

Two Air Force hangars and three Navy hangars ranging in volume from approximately 24000 to 96000 m^3 were selected for investigation. Measurements in four of the hangars were conducted during winter 1980–1981, while measurements in the fifth hangar were undertaken in summer 1981. Air leakage (infiltration) measurements were performed as per ASTM Method for Determining Air Leakage Rate by Tracer Dilution Test (E 741-80), using sulfur hexafluoride (SF_6) and a portable electron-capture gas chromatograph manufactured by S-CUBED.[3]

The objective of the investigation was to obtain data using existing measurement technology, from which guidelines could be developed for use by engineering personnel when evaluating hangar energy conservation concepts that may be influenced by air infiltration.

Sampling Technique and Data Analysis

Conventional tracer gas dilution techniques achieve initial homogenous gas mixtures by using central ventilation systems, multiple gas injections throughout a building, portable blowers, or all three. Disposable plastic syringes often are used to obtain gas samples. These samples are analyzed to establish that an initial homogeneous mixture of tracer gas and air exists inside a building, as well as to provide samples of time-dependent tracer gas concentration decay. This sampling method is satisfactory [4–6] for dwellings and office buildings where ceiling heights seldom exceed 3 to 4 m, where portable blowers or ventilation systems can rapidly mix the tracer gas and interior air, and where gas concentration samples can be obtained with hand-held sampling devices.

Building air infiltration rates can be calculated from data obtained using a tracer gas dilution method by measuring the logarithmic decay rate of tracer gas concentration with respect to time, according to Eq 1 [4].

$$V \dot{C}(t) + q \cdot C(t) = F(t) \tag{1}$$

and

$$I = q/V = \left(\frac{1}{t}\right) \log_e (C_o/C) \tag{2}$$

where we assume $C_{initial}$ is negligible, and

---

[3]Citing the trade name of the product is not an endorsement by the U.S. Navy but is provided to assist in the traceability of the equipment specifications and performance.

where

V = volume,
t = time,
C = tracer gas concentration at time t,
C_o = tracer gas concentration at time 0,
q = average air leakage rate into the structure, and
I = air change rate (infiltration rate).

A problem commonly associated with the tracer gas dilution measurement method was magnified by the physical characteristics of aircraft hangars. The establishment of a homogeneous mixture of tracer gas and air inside a hangar, with subsequent acquisition of representative samples, is critical if accurate air infiltration rates are to be measured. Hangars are large-volume, high-ceiling, open-bay structures. These characteristics complicate the attainment of an initially homogeneous gas mixture and the subsequent acquisition of tracer-laden air samples. Accordingly, tracer gas samplers were developed that could inject a tracer gas at, or obtain samples from, any height up to 15 m above floor level. They consisted of a pulse pump connected to an approximately 15-m length of 0.635-cm polypropylene tubing. The output from the pump was fed into a Mylar sampling bag. Suspension for the sample lines was provided by overhead cranes, aircraft service scaffolding, overhead aircraft grounding cables, overhead personnel safety cables, or helium-filled weather balloons.

When used in the tracer gas injection mode, the sampler pumps 90 L/h through the tubing. Tracer gas is injected into the tubing on the sampler pump's discharge side. Approximately 20 s is required for the tracer gas to be transported from the pump to the array's discharge point. The pump is operated for 10 min after the tracer gas injection in order to purge the tracer gas from the tubing. Initial testing disclosed that this technique resulted in no contamination of samples due to potential SF_6 retention of the tubing.

Conversion of the array from tracer gas injection to the sampling mode is accomplished by switching the 0.635-cm tubing from the pump's discharge port to its intake port. After a 5-min purge period, the pump's output is reduced to a rate of 4 L/h. During testing, mixing is allowed to occur for roughly 30 min after tracer injection. After this, a 1-L sample bag is attached to the pump's discharge port. The maximum sampling time for a 1-L bag is 15 min. During an air infiltration test measurement period, all gas sample bags are replaced at equal time intervals.

For most of the hangar testing, five samplers were used to inject tracer gas and to obtain samples. The height of the sampling point varied from 40 to 60% of the maximum hangar height and was dependent upon the method used for array suspension. In addition, circulating fans within the hangar were turned on for the duration of the test. No tests were done with the circulating fans turned off. A 1-L sample bag was obtained from each sample point during each time interval. To expedite analysis, in some cases a 2-cm³ sample was removed by syringe from each bag filled during a common time interval. This effectively mixed each sample and provided an averaged sample for that particular time interval. The overall hangar air infiltration rate was then inferred using the averaged samples from each time interval.

Unlike syringe samples, which are essentially instantaneous, the samplers gathered gas samples over a period of time. To utilize Eq 2 in calculating infiltration rates, the instantaneous value of time used in Eq 2 was replaced by the time at which the sample bag is half full.

For this approach to be valid, the following conditions must be met:

1. Constant sample bag fill rate.
2. Constant sample bag filling intervals.
3. Steady-state condition in the pressure distribution inside and outside.
4. Small change in concentration during sample line transit time.

Hangar Data Acquisition

Naval Air Rework Facility (NARF), Norfolk

Hangar V-147 was selected for evaluation. The hangar possesses approximate dimensions of 120 m long, 48 m wide, and 17 m high with aircraft access doors located across the entire northern and southern ends. The hangar shares its western wall with another hangar that is a mirror image of V-147. Six movable overhead cranes are located on ceiling tracks that provide service to all working areas of the hangar's floor. Closure doors are of the staggered-section variety commonly found in military aircraft hangars. Some air leakage protection is afforded by rubber-boot seals along the base of each door section.

Ambient weather conditions during the test period, 10–11 Feb. 1981, were winds gusting from 8 to 12 m/s from the northwest, with the outside air temperatures decreasing from 1.6 to 0.6°C. The weather station at Naval Air Station Norfolk was used as the source for weather data.

Overhead cranes were used to suspend the five samplers 11.6 m above the floor level. Ten cubic centimeters of tracer gas was injected into each sampler and another 10 cm³ was injected at floor level in the general area of each of the five samplers. The tracer gas was mixed with the air inside the hangar by using the hangar's unit air circulating heaters.

These heaters, which were located in the ceiling near each sampler, circulated large quantities of warm air that easily could be felt at floor level. Gas samples were taken from the bags and from floor level syringes. A summary of the data obtained from Hangar V-147 is presented in Table 1. All times shown are elapsed times at a particular sample location. Samples were taken contemporaneously. Blanks in the table indicate that a sample from a particular location was not individually analyzed, generally due to time pressures

TABLE 1—*Air infiltration data for Hangar V-147, NARF Norfolk, VA.*

Elapsed Time, min	Sample Bags[a]						Syringe Samples[b]					
	1	2	3	4	5	Average[c]	1	2	3	4	5	Average[c]
0	820	748	757	848	739	802	857	730	793	802	767	790
15	...	...	...	...	...	580	...	...	...	...	...	...
30	...	...	...	...	...	405	...	...	...	...	...	...
45	325	263	271	317	217	279	317	249	302	310	256	287
60	...	...	...	...	...	176	...	...	...	...	...	...
ACH[d]	1.23	1.39	1.37	1.31	1.34	1.41[e]	1.32	1.44	1.29	1.27	1.46	1.35

SF$_6$ Concentration, ppt

[a]11.6 m above floor.
[b]Floor level.
[c]This is a physically averaged sample as described in section entitled, "Sampling Technique and Data Analysis."
[d]Air infiltration rate.
[e]Calculated over same interval as syringe samples.

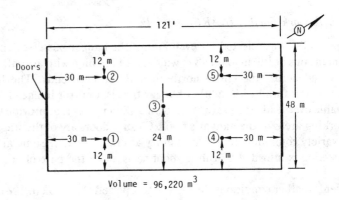

Volume = 96,220 m^3

on the experimenters. Raw concentrations are shown so as to provide a more complete description of the spatial and temporal evaluation of tracer concentration within large open structures. A comparison of the results from the floor level syringe samples (instantaneous) and the ceiling level bag samples (time-dependent) showed that both sampling methods produced similar results; the maximum variance at any one point was 9%. The difference in the air infiltration rate measured by syringe at floor level and sample bags at 11.6 m was 0.06 ACH, or slightly less than 5%.

Minot Air Force Base (AFB), North Dakota

Hangar 867, a B-52 maintenance facility, was selected for evaluation. The hangar is approximately 61 m wide by 40 m long with a maximum height at the roof peak of 15.8 m. All exterior surfaces were insulated. There are no seals installed on the hangar aircraft access doors. Cracks as wide as 3.75 cm exist between the door panels. A large hole, which allows the tail of a B-52 to protrude from the hangar, is located at the center of the hangar doors. A canvass drawstring seal is used to seal the space between the B-52's tail and the hole. Hot-air unit heaters are suspended from the ceiling at a height of 8.5 m. Canvass ducts are attached to the heaters to direct the heated air to floor level. Aircraft access doors are located only on the northern side of the hangar, with smaller vehicle access doors located on the southern side.

Weather conditions were measured by the base facility at the Minot Air Force Base (AFB). Tests were conducted on 19 Feb. 1981, during which the wind speed decreased from 8 to 5.8 m/s from the northwest. The outside air temperature increased from 4.4 to 7.8°C.

Overhead cranes were used to suspend two samplers, and movable aircraft service scaffolds were used to suspend the remaining three samplers. The sample point height was roughly 6 m above floor level.

Five cubic centimeters of tracer gas was injected into each sampler and dispersed at the 6-m level within the hangar. Another 5 cm^3 was injected at floor level in the vicinity of each sample point and at each corner of the hangar.

Strong drafts were noticeable throughout the hangar. These drafts arose from wind blowing through the numerous cracks between the hangar door panels and around the protruding B-52 tail assembly. Twenty minutes after the initial injection of SF_6 only minute traces of the gas were detectable in the floor level syringe samples and from the samplers. During this time, the wind was gusting from 10 to 12 m/s from the northwest. Apparently, the combination of the cracks and the wind was sufficient to displace most of the tracer gas from the hangar. The hangar was surveyed to determine if any temporary repairs could be made. The canvass seal between the hangar doors and the protruding B-52 tail assembly had gaps of up to 0.6 m. This seal was temporarily repaired with duct tape. No other repairs were made to the hangar.

When the wind subsided to a steady 8.2 m/s, an additional 70 cm^3 of SF_6 was injected into the hangar. This time the gas was released at a constant rate at floor level across the north side of the hangar where the aircraft access doors were located. Mixing of the gas with the air inside the hangar was aided by the drafts of air blown through the cracks in the door. Within 30 min, a semihomogeneous, measurable mixture existed and data acquisition commenced.

A summary of data obtained from Hangar 867 is presented in Table 2. For these measurements, the syringe-measured air infiltration rate was 20% lower than the bag-measured rate. However, instrument problems precluded analysis of most of the syringe samples, and it is possible that those presented are in error.

TABLE 2—*Air infiltration data for Hangar 867, Minot AFB, ND.*

	SF$_6$ Concentration, ppt											
	Sample Bags[a]						Syringe Samples[b]					
Elapsed Time, min	1	2	3	4	5	Average[c]	1	2	3	4	5	Average[c]
0	...	...	...	...	74.3	54.9	...	...	...	...	64.0	49.0
10	...	...	29.4	36.6	...	30.3	...	...	28.9	31.2	...	...
30	23.7	21.9	19.4	24.5	24.5	22.8	...	...	...	...	...	25.4
40	...	...	...	17.4	...	13.4	...	...	...	16.1	...	...
50	7.0	11.0	8.8	1.4	14.5	10.3	...	...	...	...	...	...
60	...	...	...	...	...	...	...	...	...	...	...	...
ACH[d]	3.66	2.06	1.81	1.75	1.96	1.62[e]	...	...	...	1.32	...	1.31

[a]6 m above floor.
[b]Floor level.
[c]This is a physically averaged sample as described in section entitled, "Sampling Technique and Data Analysis."
[d]Air infiltration rate.
[e]Calculated over same interval as syringe samples.

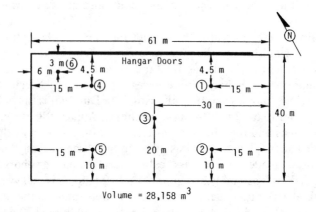

Volume = 28,158 m³

Mc Clellan Air Force Base, California

Hangar 365 was selected by the Air Force for evaluation at McClellan AFB. The hangar is approximately 37 m wide by 61 m long, with a maximum height of 10.7 m. Large amounts of glass were used in the hangar doors and walls. Spring-tensioned, overhead-mounted aircraft grounding cables were located throughout the hangar. The grounding cables provided suspension for four of the samplers, and a movable aircraft service scaffold provided suspension for the fifth sampler. The height of the sample point was 4.6 m above floor level.

Ambient weather conditions during the test period, 25 Feb. 1981, were variable winds from 0 to 2 m/s from the east with an outside air temperature of approximately 7°C. The base's weather facilities were used for weather data measurements.

SF_6 was injected into the hangar using the samplers and floor level syringes. Mixing was attempted using ceiling-mounted unit heaters. Floor-level syringe samples were obtained at three points along the hangar's centerline (denoted 6, 7, and 8 on the plot contained in Table 3).

A summary of data obtained from Hangar 365 is presented in Table 3. The bag-measured and syringe-measured air infiltration rates differ by 3%.

TABLE 3—*Air infiltration data for Hangar 365, McClellan AFB, CA.*

	SF_6 Concentration, ppt									
	Sample Bags[a]						Syringe Samples[b]			
Elapsed Time, min	1	2	3	4	5	Average[c]	6	7	8	Average[c]
0	14.9	21.5	26.3	20.7	19.8	21.9	20.3	24.5	...	22.4
10	...	...	...	...	...	19.0	16.9	17.8	17.8	17.5
20	...	...	...	...	...	16.9	...	...	...	...
30	10.7	14.5	14.1	14.5	17.4	14.9	...	...	...	...
40	...	...	...	...	...	12.6	14.1	11.4	12.6	12.7
50	...	...	...	...	...	12.6	...	...	...	...
60	9.9	10.7	11.4	11.8	13.4	11.4	10.3	11.2	12.6	11.4
ACH[d]	0.41	0.70	0.84	0.56	0.39	0.66	0.68	0.78	0.41	0.67

[a]4.5 m above floor.
[b]Floor level.
[c]This is a physically averaged sample as described in section entitled, "Sampling Technique and Data Analysis."
[d]Air infiltration rate.

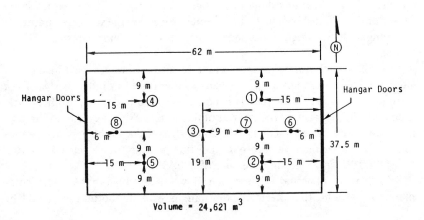

Naval Air Station (NAS), Brunswick, Maine

Hangar 250 was selected for evaluation at NAS Brunswick. The hangar measures roughly 73 m long by 43 m wide, with a maximum height of 18.3 m. The hangar door seals were in excellent condition. The hangar is used to service and wash patrol aircraft. A system of movable personnel safety cables is located throughout the hangar. These cables are attached to maintenance personnel while washing the aircraft to prevent them from slipping and falling.

Ambient weather conditions during the test period (10–11 March 1981) were mild for the area. The wind was very light, ranging from 0 to 0.5 m/s from the northwest. The outside air temperature was almost constant and varied little from 0°C. The air station's weather facilities were used for weather data measurements.

The personnel safety cables were used to support three samplers, and movable aircraft service scaffolds were used for the remaining two samplers. One hundred twenty cubic centimeters of SF_6 was injected into the hangar; 10 cm^3 was discharged at 7.6 m above the floor by each sampler, and 10 cm^3 was injected at floor level in the vicinity of each sampler. The remaining 20 cm^3 was injected at floor level at points remote from the samplers' locations. Floor-level syringe samples were taken along the hangar's centerline at a point 6.1 m from each end of the hangar and at the center of the hangar.

A summary of data obtained from Hangar 250 is presented in Table 4. The bag-measured and syringe-measured air infiltration rates differ by less than 6%.

Naval Air Rework Facility (NARF), Norfolk, Virginia

Hangar V-88 at NARF Norfolk was selected for evaluation. Measurements were performed on 22 July 1981 in the central bay of a three-bay hangar. The central bay is separated from the outlying bays by double brick walls, between which are located various shops and offices. A plan view of the central section of Building V-88 is shown in Table 5. Note, especially, the staggered nature of the hangar doors. Such doors may be expected to exhibit considerable air leakage.

For this test, the sampler and syringe release techniques used in the previous four tests were not used. Instead, a compressed cylinder of 1% SF_6 in nitrogen was used as a source. This bottle was mounted on a portable bottle rack and wheeled around the interior of the hangar. SF_6 was released through a critical orifice valve attached to the down-stream side of the pressure regulator. In this experiment, a Nupro Type-S fine metering valve was used with a C_V of 0.00125 and a driving pressure of 200 kPa.

Prior to onset of actual SF_6 injection, it was determined that a single, complete pass around the interior of the hangar with the bottle rack could be

TABLE 4—*Air infiltration data for Hangar 250, NAS, Brunswick, ME.*

	\multicolumn{11}{c}{SF_6 Concentration, ppt}										
Elapsed Time, min	\multicolumn{5}{c}{Sample Bags[a]}					Average[c]	\multicolumn{5}{c}{Syringe Samples[b]}
	1	2	3	4	5	Average[c]	1	2	3	4	5	Average[c]
0	...	3173	2981	2779	2580	2711	...	...	2686	...	...	...
10	...	2574	2653	2156	2379	2507	...	...	...	...	...	...
20	...	2200	...	1906	...	2022	...	...	...	...	...	...
30	...	1874	1820	1526	1510	1720	...	...	...	...	...	...
40	...	1641	...	...	...	1526	...	...	...	...	...	...
50	...	...	...	...	...	1352	...	...	...	...	...	...
60	...	1310	1246	1236	1151	1201	...	...	1092	...	...	...
ACH[d]	...	0.88	0.87	0.81	0.81	0.85	...	...	0.90	...	...	...

[a]7.6 m above floor.
[b]Floor level.
[c]This is a physically averaged sample as described in section entitled, "Sampling Technique and Data Analysis."
[d]Air infiltration rate.

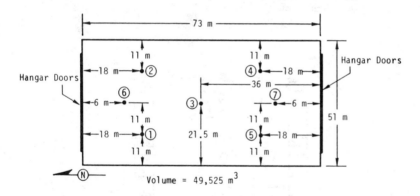

Volume = 49,525 m^3

accomplished in 5 min. Accordingly, actual SF_6 injection occurred for three passes around the hangar, or approximately 15 min. Initial calculations showed that an initial concentration on the order of 100 ppt could be expected.

SF_6 mixing in the hangar was effected by the use of eight overhead ceiling circulatory fans and eleven 0.6-m-diameter floor-stand fans. These fans were adjusted to provide peripheral circulation of air within the hangar.

Samples were drawn at three locations, which are marked on the figure in Table 5. Samples were drawn at 5 intervals for 1 h. Measured data are provided in Table 5. After this, one section of the downwind hangar door (in this case, the north door) was opened. Note that one section of door is roughly 3.8 m wide by 12.1 m high. Tracer concentration samples were drawn at the

TABLE 5—*Air infiltration data for Hangar V-88, NARF Norfolk, VA.*

Elapsed Time, min	SF₆ Concentration, ppt			
	Syringe Samples[a]			
	A	B	C	Average[b]
0	969	1350	1550	1287
10	920	1350	1300	1191
20	880	1100	1150	1043
30	770	1050	1050	957
40	750	960	950	887
50	660	820	710	730
60	540	720	700	653
ACH[c]	0.55	0.65	0.81	0.68

[a]Floor level.
[b]This is a physically averaged sample as described in section entitled, "Sampling Technique and Data Analysis."
[c]Air infiltration rate.

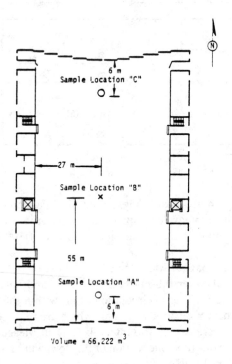

three locations every 5 min for a period of 20 min. After this, one section of the south-facing door (which, for these tests, was the windward side) was opened, and samples were drawn every 2 min for 10 min. Thus, a measure of air leakage within the hangar for the case of the hangar bay completely closed, with one section of downwind door open, and with one section of downwind door and one section of upwind door open was obtained. Data are presented in Table 6.

Discussion

The concentration data presented in Table 1, and to a lesser extent the data presented in Tables 3 and 5, illustrate the degree of homogeneity which can be obtained within these large-volume structures. In particular, for Hangar V-147 (data contained in Table 1) the standard deviations of the various concentrations determined by sample bag and syringes range from 6 to 16% of the mean. The standard deviation of the mean air change rates at the various sample locations, however, was less than 6%. The agreement between the measured mean rate from the sample bag and the measured mean rate from the syringe samples was within 5%. Similar agreement exists for the data contained in Table 3 for Hangar 365. This agreement suggests that it is possible to obtain representative air infiltration rates in large-volume structures using the tracer dilution technique without the necessity for large numbers of sample positions at various spatial locations throughout the volume.

To further illustrate the degree of homogeneity obtained, with its attendant effect on the inferred air infiltration rates, mean values of the various concentrations measured are presented in Table 7 along with the attendant standard deviations of the measurement expressed as a percentage of the mean value. Note that, with few exceptions, the standard deviations (and, hence, the presumed homogeneity) were within roughly 15% of the mean value measured. The mean air infiltration rates determined from the bag samples and syringe samples generally are very close; however, the standard deviations of these measurements are such that differences of up to 25% could occur. Thus, the reasonable agreement between the measurements drawn from sample bags and from syringes, while gratifying, may not be as good as first appears. How-

TABLE 6—*Measured air leakage rates for door opening with average meterological conditions in Hangar V-88, NARF, Norfolk, VA.*

Condition	Air Change Rate	Wind Speed	Indoor/Outdoor Temperature Difference
Downwind door— open one section	0.75 ACH	3 m/s	2.5°C
Upwind and downwind door— open one section	6.25 ACH	3 m/s	2.5°C

ever, the data do suggest that limited measurements in large-volume structures may be representative of the actual air infiltration rate to within uncertainties given in Table 7.

Conclusions

The measurement of air infiltration rates associated with the five hangars encountered no major problems. The heating systems of the various hangars created enough turbulence to obtain relatively homogeneous tracer gas/air mixtures. Air infiltration rates calculated from bag samples suspended roughly midway between floor and ceiling were comparable with rates calculated from floor-level syringe samples. As indicated in Tables 1 through 5, tracer gas concentration decay is not the same everywhere inside a hangar. It is dependent upon location; thus, slightly different air infiltration rates can be measured at different locations within a hangar. The air change rate measured near an outer wall will reflect the effects of local air leakage before one measured in the center of a hangar.

In order to determine an air change rate which reflects the entire hangar, several readings should be obtained over a crosssection of the hangar floor and averaged together. Data obtained from the various hangars suggest that floor-level syringe samples provide a reasonably accurate measurement of hangar air infiltration, thereby eliminating the requirement for elevated samplers to measure tracer gas concentrations.

TABLE 7—*Comparison of Calculated and Prepared Averaged Concentrations and Inferred Air Infiltration Rates.*

Hangar	Volume, m^3	Sample Bag Concentration, ppt			Syringe Concentration, ppt		
		Mean	Standard Deviation, % of Mean	I_{mean}, ACH	Mean	Standard Deviation, % of Mean	I_{mean}, ACH
V-147	96220	782	6	1.33	740	6	1.36
		274	16		287	11	
867	28158	22.8	10	2.25	...	...	...
		10.5	27		...	...	
365	24621	20.6	20		17.5	3	
		14.2	17	0.58	12.7	11	0.62
		11.4	11		11.4	11	
250	49525	2878	9		...	...	
		2410	7	0.84	...	...	...
		1682	11		...	...	
V-88	66222	...	...		1286	23	
		...	...	...	956	17	0.67
		...	...		653	15	

Air infiltration rates in the range of 0.62 to 2.10 were measured. These rates lie midway between the extremes reported by Waters and Simons [2] and are somewhat higher than typical values presented by Grot and Persily [3]. These values are comparable to those which have been measured in rowhousing at Norfolk [7] as well as those obtained in single-family residences [8].

Acknowledgments

Performance of this work was undertaken under Contract MIPR N-81-6 and Contract N-68-305-80-C-0066, both through the Civil Engineering Laboratory, Naval Construction Battalion Center, Port Hueneme, California 93043.

References

[1] Freeman, J., Gale, R., and Lily, J. P., "Ventilation Measurements in Large Buildings," in *Proceedings*, Fourth AIC Conference, Air Infiltration Centre, Bracknell, England, 1983.
[2] Waters, J. R. and Simons, M. W., "The Measurement of Air Infiltration in Large Single-Cell Industrial Buildings," this publication.
[3] Grot, R. A. and Persily, A. K., "Air Infiltration and Air Tightness Tests in Eight U.S. Office Buildings," in *Proceedings*, Fourth AIC Conference, Air Infiltration Centre, Bracknell, England, 1983.
[4] *Building Air Change Rate and Infiltration Measurements, ASTM STP 719*, C. M. Hunt, J. C. King, and H. R. Trechsel, Eds., American Society for Testing and Materials, Philadelphia, 1978.
[5] Ashley, S. K., "Calculation of Natural Infiltration Reduction from Fan Pressurization Results with Cost Effective Projections," Technical Memorandum M63-81-06, Civil Engineering Laboratory, Port Hueneme, CA, June 1981.
[6] King, J. C., "Instrumentation Package for Field Energy Surveys," TechData Sheet 79-02, Civil Engineering Laboratory, Port Hueneme, CA, March 1979.
[7] Lagus, P. L., Ellefson, L. D., Broce, R. D., and Talkington, H. A., "Air Leakage Measurements and Energy Consumption in Navy Housing at Norfolk, Virginia," Report SSS-R-80-4233, S-CUBED, La Jolla, CA, 1980.
[8] Grot, R. A. and Clark, R. E., "Air Leakage Characteristics and Weatherization Techniques for Low Income Housing," in *Proceedings*, ASHRAE/DOE-ORNL Conference on the Thermal Performance of the Exterior Envelopes of Buildings, Kissimmee, Florida, 1979, ASHRAE, Atlanta, GA.

DISCUSSION

M. Sherman[1] (written discussion)—In your talk you mentioned that you used the same tubing and pump for sampling and injection. We find that most tubing adsorbs SF_6 and can interfer with subsequent sampling at concentrations in the range of a 100 ppt. Could you comment on the materials

---

[1]Lawrence Berkeley Laboratory, Berkeley, CA.

and concentration ranges you used and on how you deal with the adsorption problem.

J. L. Ashley and P. L. Lagus (authors' closure)—One of us (P. Lagus) has used a brand of polypropylene tubing denoted "Impolene" to draw tracer samples up to 650 m with no tracer retention after flushing with air.

A. Birenzwige[2] (written discussion)—Were the mixing fans operating throughout the sampling period?

J. L. Ashley and P. L. Lagus (authors' closure)—Yes.

[2]U.S. Army, CRDC Edgewood Area, APG, MD 12010.

Charles M. Hunt[1]

Some Induced-Pressure Measurements in a High-Rise Office Building

REFERENCE: Hunt, C. M., "Some Induced-Pressure Measurements in a High-Rise Office Building," *Measured Air Leakage of Buildings, ASTM STP 904*, H. R. Trechsel and P. L. Lagus, Eds., American Society for Testing and Materials, Philadelphia, 1986, pp. 135–150.

ABSTRACT: Induced-pressure measurements were made in the tower of an eleven-story office building using a fan of 7.55-m³/s capacity. The fan was used to depressurize the entire tower as well as a single floor. Sulfur hexafluoride (SF_6) tracer gas was used to trace air movements from floor to floor during single-floor depressurization.

Average flow coefficients of approximately 5×10^{-4} m³/m² · s · Pa$^{0.65}$ for the tower and 7×10^{-4} m³/m² · s · Pa$^{0.65}$ for the single floor were estimated from single point measurements. The effect of opening and closing office doors also was determined.

By simultaneous solution of flow equations for the whole tower and a single floor, it was estimated that about 80 to 90% of the airflow during depressurization of a single floor came from floors above and below. From SF_6 tracer gas measurements, it was estimated that about 50% of the flow could be traced to the floor below.

The pressure difference measurements upon which the previous estimates are based were in the 3- to 10-Pa range. Uncertainties in the estimates of flow coefficients and airflow from above and below are discussed in the text. The results essentially are descriptive, but they suggest an experimental approach to the determination of flow coefficients for modeling through the wall and for floor-to-floor components of airflow in building ventilation.

KEY WORDS: ventilation—large buildings, induced-pressure tests in buildings, air movements in buildings, sulfur hexafluoride tracer measurements, infiltration

Fan-induced pressure tests have become a common method of assessing the tightness of homes. Air is blown in or drawn out of a building at several measured rates, and induced indoor-outdoor pressure differences are measured. There are published descriptions of the method [1,2], and there is also an

---

[1]Chemical engineer, retired, Center for Building Technology, National Bureau of Standards, Washington, D.C.

ASTM standard, Method for Determining Air Leakage Rate by Fan Pressurization Test (E 779-81).

Induced-pressure measurements have been scaled up for use in large buildings, although the logistical problems become much greater than with single-family residences and increase with the increasing size of the building. If a building has a central, forced ventilation system, it may be possible to use the building's own ventilating fans [3]. However, it is sometimes difficult to obtain an accurate measure of flow rate, particularly when there are a number of fans, each supplying a different zone, or when a building may not have a central, forced ventilation system. An alternate procedure, where possible, is to use a high-capacity fan which may be moved from building to building. Shaw describes such a fan, with a maximum capacity of 24 m^3/s, which is used to depressurize supermarkets [4] and schools [5]. It operates from its own trailer and draws air from the building through a long 0.9-m-diameter duct.

The present report describes exploratory tests in which a fan with 7.55-m^3/s capacity was used to depressurize the tower of an eleven-story office building. This fan had about one third the capacity of the one used by Shaw but was much larger than those normally used for single-family residences. The building, having an envelope area of nearly 7000 m^3, was larger than the schools with envelope areas from about 1100 to 2100 m^2 [5] or the supermarkets with areas from about 700 to 3500 m^2 [4]. Thus the present measurements were a test of equipment as well as of the building. The fan was of a size to enable it to be moved through doors inside the building. Use was made of this fact to depressurize a single floor and to compare floor-to-floor flow resistance with that of the exterior envelope. Sulfur hexafluoride (SF_6) tracer-gas measurements were used to trace air movement from floor to floor during single-floor fan operation.

Air exchange rate measurements of the building were previously reported [6]. The present report is a preliminary work to measure the flow resistance of internal and external elements of the building structure and to aid in analysis of air movement through the building envelope and within the building.

Apparatus

The 7.55-m^3/s axial fan and the accessories that were used to depressurize the whole tower of the building and a single floor are shown in Fig. 1. The fan motor was 3740 W (5 hp) and was driven by a 7000-w, 230-v single-phase, gasoline generator (also shown in Fig. 1). The starting winding connections of the fan motor were modified to permit manual operation in order to accommodate the starting load. Flow rates were measured with a Pitot-static flow monitoring assembly with a built-in flow straightener that was mounted approximately one fan diameter, or 0.77 m, upstream from the fan (also shown in Fig. 1).

FIG. 1—*The 7.55-m³/s axial fan, flow measuring assembly, and 7000-w generator used in induced-pressure tests.*

A gas chromatograph with an electron capture detector was used for the SF_6 tracer gas measurements. It was incorporated in a semiautomated air-sampling system that was a compact modification of the apparatus described previously [7].

Building Description

Measurements were made in the tower of the Administration Building of the National Bureau of Standards. The tower, comprising Floors 2 through 11, is separated from the rest of the building by a mezzanine that contains most of the mechanical equipment for the building. The tower has its own ventilation system. A diagrammatic representation of the building is shown in Fig. 2. Dimensions of some of the important structural elements of the tower are given in Table 1.

Whole-Building Depressurization

The fan was placed at the first-floor level, where it drew air from the tower through a closed stairwell and vented it into a courtyard. This position is designated in Fig. 3 as Fan Location 1. Pathways of air egress were opened to facilitate depressurization, while air intake pathways were sealed or re-

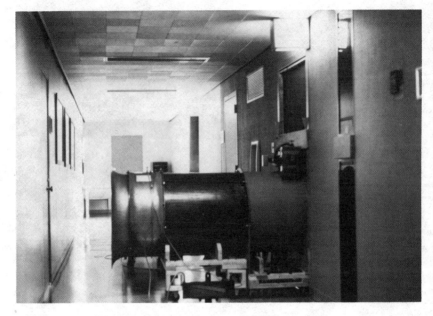

FIG. 2—*Fan and flow-measuring apparatus in position for drawing air from the sixth floor and ejecting it into the stairwell.*

TABLE 1— *Dimensions of the tower of the National Bureau of Standards Administration Building.*

Number of floors	10
Floor-to-floor distance	3.1 m
Floor area per floor	890 m²
Outside wall area per floor	500 m²
Total envelope area including top and bottom surfaces	6 780 m²
Total volume	28 000 m³

stricted. For example, doors in the west stairwell where the fan was located were opened, while doors in the east stairwell and on the first floor and in the basement of the west stairwell were closed and covered around the edges with thin plastic films. Plastic sheets were sealed over the stairwell, toilet, and elevator vents, as well as over ventilation grilles in the stairwells.

Unsealed plastic sheets were placed in the air handling units to restrict inflow of outdoor air. These sheets did not provide complete seals but covered the open areas. Smoke tests during fan operation showed no airflow around the borders of contact, which indicates that the main leakages were elsewhere in the building.

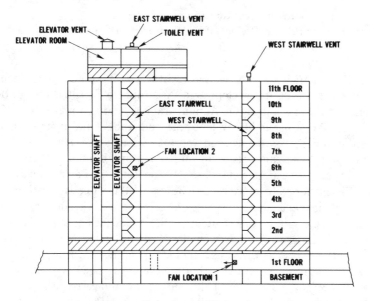

FIG. 3—*Vertical section through building along an east-west axis.*

The fan was then turned on, and indoor-outdoor pressure differences were measured between the north side of the building and the hall at the second and eleventh floor levels with a Magnehelic[2] gage. Measurements also were made with a capacitance gage as a calibration check. The fan was turned off, and the cycle was repeated. The average pressure difference due to the fan was 3 Pa. This difference is smaller than commonly observed fluctuations due to wind. Thus, a single fan of this size did not deliver enough air to develop a curve of flow rate versus inside-outside pressure difference for this building. Nevertheless, measurements were performed when wind activity was low enough to permit stable and repeatable measurements and, for descriptive purposes, to permit some rounded estimates of the tightness and flow characteristics of the building to be made.

An empirical equation commonly used to represent flow as a function of pressure difference is

$$Q = kA(\Delta p)^n \tag{1}$$

where

Q = airflow rate, m^3/s,
A = area over which flow is distributed, m^2,

---

[2]Proprietory names are used to more accurately describe experiments. This does not comprise an endorsement of the product by the National Bureau of Standards.

Δp = indoor-outdoor pressure difference, Pa,
k = average flow coefficient of the flow area, $m^3/m^2 \cdot s \cdot Pa^n$, and
n = flow exponent.

Average flow coefficient treats the flow resistance as if it were homogeneously distributed over the entire envelope area. According to Eq 1, the average flow coefficient of the envelope of the Administration Building tower is 5×10^{-4} $m^3/m^2 \cdot s \cdot Pa^{0.65}$, using the envelope area from Table 1 and assuming a flow exponent of 0.65, a commonly used approximation [3-6,8-10].

In a computational analysis of air infiltration in tall buildings, Shaw and Tamura [8] used an estimate of 0.93×10^{-4} $m^3/m^2 \cdot s \cdot Pa^{0.65}$ as an average flow coefficient for walls of average tightness. If this value is substituted in Eq 1, it predicts that a fan delivery rate of 7.55 m^3/s would produce a pressure difference of nearly 46 Pa in a structure with the dimensions of the Administration Building tower. A modern single-family residence of good construction, but with no special provisions for building tightness such as plastic films in the walls, was observed by the author to have an average flow coefficient of 1.33×10^{-4} $m^3/m^2 \cdot s \cdot Pa^{0.65}$. This coefficient would correspond to a pressure drop in the Administration Building tower of 26 Pa. Finally, a value of 1.5×10^{-4} $m^3/m^2 \cdot s \cdot Pa^{0.65}$ has been calculated using data obtained by Shaw [9] for a five-story apartment building. This would correspond to a pressure drop across the tower envelope of about 21 Pa. Thus, the envelope of the Administration Building tower was loose compared to these other structures, but the previous examples are cited to point out that a fan capacity of 7.55 m^3/s might be sufficient to develop flow-pressure relationships for some buildings of the size of the Administration Building tower.

On the other hand, in measurements of schools, Shaw and Jones [5] estimated average flow coefficients to be 3.0×10^{-4}, 5.0×10^{-4}, and 7.0×10^{-4} $m^3/m^2 \cdot s \cdot Pa^{0.65}$ for buildings of tight, average, and loose construction, respectively. Corresponding estimates for supermarkets [4] were 2.7×10^{-4}, 9.6×10^{-4}, and 16.5×10^{-4} $m^3/m^2 \cdot s \cdot Pa^{0.65}$. These latter values are more in line with the estimated coefficient of the Administration Building tower.

Shaw's supermarket study also presented data in which Eq 1 was applicable to pressures as low as 3.5 Pa. Tamura [10] developed an air infiltration model in which the average flow coefficient in Eq 1 serves as the measure of tightness. He applied it to houses and obtained satisfactory agreement with infiltration rates obtained by the tracer-gas dilution method.

However, the laws governing flow through building surfaces are an area of active research. Work by Sherman, Grimsrud, and Sonderegger [11] present evidence that Eq 1 is not applicable over the entire pressure range of interest in air infiltration. At high and very low pressures, for example, flow rates are reported proportional to the square root of the pressure as in orifice flow. Modera, Sherman, and Grimsrud [12] developed an infiltration model which uses effective leakage area instead of the average flow coefficient as the tightness parameter. They define flow at low pressures by

$$Q = L \sqrt{\frac{2}{\rho} \Delta p} \qquad (2)$$

where

Q = air flow rate, m^3/s,
L = effective leakage area, m^2,
ρ = density of air, kg/m^3, and
Δp = indoor-outdoor pressure difference.

At pressures in the range of 10 to 60 Pa, flow is defined by

$$Q = K\Delta p^n \qquad (3)$$

where

Q = air flow rate, m^3/s,
Δp = indoor-outdoor pressure difference,
n = flow exponent, and
K = a graphically determined constant.

Equation 3 has a form similar to Eq 1, where K has the same dimensions as kA. Since, according to the model, the relationship between Q and p changes between 0 and 60 Pa, a more generalized definition of L is

$$L = K \sqrt{\frac{\rho}{2}} (\Delta p_r)^{n-1/2} \qquad (4)$$

where

L = effective leakage area, m^2,
K = graphically determined constant,
ρ = density of air, kg/m^3,
n = flow exponent appropriate to the pressure, and
Δp_r = pressure difference at an arbitrarily selected reference pressure, selected by the authors at 4 Pa.

Since the present data are based on a single point, the flow exponent, n, in Eq 1, is an assumed value which is considered representative of a number of buildings at intermediate pressures. If Eq 2 is taken as the governing equation, a pressure difference of 3 Pa at a flow rate of 7.55 m^3/s corresponds to an effective leakage area of approximately 3.4 m^2. The data are unsuitable to permit full application of Eqs 2, 3, and 4.

Single-Floor Depressurization

The fan was moved to the sixth floor (Fan Location 2 in Fig. 3), and air was drawn from the hallway and ejected into the stairwell. All doors to the outdoors at the top and bottom of the stairwell were opened to minimize back pressure. Figure 2 is a picture of the fan in position, and Fig. 4 is a diagram of the floor plan showing the location of the fan. The pressure drop on the sixth floor produced by the fan was measured between the hall and the west, or nonfan, stairwell.

It was noted that 15 office doors which opened into the hall could be opened at this floor level. When they were open, the fan-induced pressure change was 5 Pa. This is only slightly greater than the value obtained during whole-building depressurization, which suggests very low resistance to airflow between floors. When all doors were closed, an induced pressure of 10 Pa was observed.

The area of the envelope of a single floor is 2280 m^2 (Table 1). If flow is averaged over this area, it is equivalent to a flow coefficient of 12×10^{-4} m^3/m$^2 \cdot$ s $\cdot$ Pa$^{0.65}$ with doors open and 7×10^{-4} m^3/m$^2 \cdot$ s $\cdot$ Pa$^{0.65}$ with doors closed.

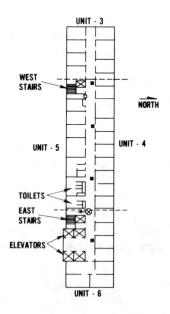

FIG. 4—*Typical floor plan showing location of the fan on the sixth floor and the location-sampling points:* $\otimes$ = *fan location (sixth floor);* $\square$ = *location differential pressure gage;* $\blacksquare$ = *network sampling points (fifth, sixth, and seventh floors).*

Fan-Tracer Measurements

To trace air movement between floors during fan operation, SF_6 tracer gas concentration was monitored as a function of time on the fifth, sixth, and seventh floors. Sampling networks were used to sample on each floor, with sampling points distributed at floor level at locations indicated in Fig. 4. Each network integrated the flow from the four sampling locations on each floor.

The fifth floor was seeded by distributing 100 mL of SF_6 over several locations, and the fan was turned on. The concentration of tracer gas on the fifth and sixth floors is plotted as a function of time in Fig. 5. No tracer gas was detected on the seventh floor. After an elapsed time of 75 to 80 min, 100 mL of SF_6 was released near the window grilles on the fourth floor. The amount of tracer gas reaching the fifth and sixth floors from the fourth floor caused only a small transient increase in the concentration. This small effect suggests that most of the upward movement of air to the fan came from the floor immediately below.

Analysis of Air Movement Between Floors

To analyze air movement between floors, consider the concentration of tracer gas on the fan floor to be expressed by the relationship

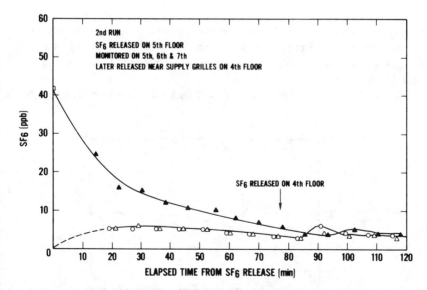

FIG. 5—SF_6 concentration on fifth and sixth floors after release on the fifth floor: $\blacktriangle$ = fifth floor hall network (SF_6 release floor); $\bigcirc$ = sixth floor hall (single point near fan); $\triangle$ = sixth floor hall network; $\square$ = Initial concentration of fifth floor (based on volume of SF_6 released and volume of space).

$$c_j = \frac{g}{\dot{v}_j}(1 - e^{-I_j t}) \tag{5}$$

where

c_j = concentration of tracer gas at the jth (fan) floor,
g = rate at which tracer gas enters the jth floor,
I_j = air exchange rate of the jth floor, h^{-1},
$\dot{v}_j$ = volume rate at which air enters and leaves the jth floor, and
t = elapsed time.

However

$$g = c_i \dot{v}_{ij} \tag{6}$$

where

c_i = concentration of tracer gas on the ith floor where it was released, and
$\dot{v}_{ij}$ = volume rate at which air passes from ith floor to jth floor.

Substituting Eq 6 in Eq 5

$$\frac{c_j}{c_i} = \frac{\dot{v}_{ij}}{\dot{v}_j}(1 - e^{-I_j t}) \tag{7}$$

Thus the fraction of total air flow entering and leaving the jth floor which comes from the ith floor, $\dot{v}_{ij}/\dot{v}_j$ approaches c_j/c_i with increasing time. The foregoing analysis is idealized and assumes perfect mixing of tracer gas on both floors.

In Fig. 6, c_j/c_i is plotted against time and levels off somewhere near 0.5.

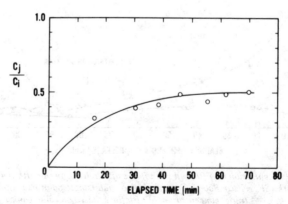

FIG. 6—*Ratio of tracer gas concentrations on the fan floor to that on the source floor, c_j/c_i plotted as a function of time.*

According to this analysis, about half of the air reaching the fan floor came from the floor below. Because of structural similarities from floor to floor, a comparable volume of air also should come from the floor immediately above.

It is also possible to make an independent analysis of floor-to-floor air movement from the fan depressurization data. The outside wall represents about 23% of the exterior surface of a single floor (Table 1). The total airflow is the sum of floor-to-floor and outside wall flows. If it is hypothesized that k, the average flow coefficient of a single floor, is a weighted average of coefficients for floor-to-floor and outside wall flow, then

$$k \approx 0.23\,k_w + 0.77\,k_f \qquad (8a)$$

where k_w and k_f are the flow coefficients averaged over the outside wall area and the areas between floors, respectively. When office doors are closed, this corresponds to

$$7 \times 10^{-4} \approx 0.23\,k_w + 0.77\,k_f \qquad (8b)$$

Similarly, the area between the tower and the lower floors represents about 12% of the tower envelope area. Thus, for the tower

$$5 \times 10^{-4} \approx 0.88\,k_w + 0.12\,k_f \qquad (9)$$

Solving Eqs 8b and 9 simultaneously leads to the empirical values

$$k_w \approx 5 \times 10^{-4} \ \frac{m^3}{m^2 \cdot s \cdot Pa^{0.65}}$$

$$k_f \approx 8 \times 10^{-4} \ \frac{m^3}{m^2 \cdot s \cdot Pa^{0.65}}$$

Taking into consideration the relative floor area together with these flow constants and wall areas leads to the estimate that, during depressurization of a single floor, 84% of the air comes from floors above and below and 16% through the outside wall.

If, for purposes of approximation, it is assumed that opening 15 office doors on each floor produced an increase in flow coefficient proportional to that obtained for a single floor, an analysis with doors open leads to the equations

$$12 \times 10^{-4} \approx 0.23 k_w + 0.77 k_f \qquad (10)$$

$$12/7 \times 5 \times 10^{-4} \approx 0.88 k_w + 0.12 k_f \qquad (11)$$

and

$$k_w \approx 8 \times 10^{-4} \ \frac{m^3}{m^2 \cdot s \cdot Pa^{0.65}}$$

$$k_f \approx 13 \times 10^{-4} \ \frac{m^3}{m^2 \cdot s \cdot Pa^{0.65}}$$

and 84% of the air is calculated to come from the floors above and below.

In this analysis, airflow from above and below are treated as equal. This assumes no structural dissimilarities between the two floor interfaces. Thus, 42% of the total flow is calculated to come from each direction with office doors closed or open.

The assumption of equal flow from above and below disregards any possible stack effect. The stack pressure at 31 m, the height of the tower, would be about 1.2 Pa for an inside-outside temperature difference of 1 K at an average temperature of 299 K (26°C). The average pressure difference across a single floor would be one tenth of this or 0.12 Pa. If the average flow coefficient between floors is 13×10^{-4} m^3/m^2 · s · Pa$^{0.65}$ and the floor area 890 m^2, according to Eq 1, the flow rate at 0.12 Pa would be 0.3 m^3/s per degree inside-outside temperature difference. This is 4% of the total flow of 7.55 m^3/s. If flow due to fan and stack effect are additive, equal flow from above and below would not exist. On the other hand, if flow is fan-dominated, analogous to the loss of stack effect in building infiltration at moderate-to-high wind speeds [13], there would be no stack effect. At the time these measurements were made, the temperature in the west (nonfan) stairwell was 0.5°C lower than the outside temperature of 26°C. Thus the stack effect, if any, would have been small and negative.

Measurement Uncertainties

The foregoing analyses, based on single point measurements, do not permit experimental determination of the flow exponent, n, nor do they provide an estimate of the repeatability of k, the flow coefficient, or F, the combined fraction of air coming from above and below. However, it is possible to determine the sensitivity of k and F to differences in n by repeating the calculation at more than one assigned value of n. The values $n = 0.55$ and $n = 0.65$ have been selected for the purpose.

It also is possible to estimate a range of k and F values corresponding to a given uncertainty in the pressure measurement. For Magnehelic gage measurements, a value of ± 2.7 Pa is selected. This number is based upon several separate measurements of Q as a function of Δp in a room in the same building. The data were fitted to Eq 1, and 2.7 Pa was the pooled standard deviation [14] between the measured Δp and the values from the equation. A pooled standard deviation is used instead of a simple standard deviation because five sets of measurements were made, each with different leakage pathways sealed. The whole-tower measurements, on the other hand, were simultaneously made with a Magnehelic gage and a variable capacitance gage, and both gave the same result. For computational purposes an uncertainty of ±1 Pa is selected.

Table 2 summarizes the values of k calculated with $n = 0.55$ and $n = 0.65$ and also the range of values corresponding to the specified pressure uncertainties. The ranges of k values are rather broad, particularly in the doors-open condition. It also should be noted that the effect pressure uncertainty is unsymmetrical. A negative differential pressure displacement has a larger effect than an equal positive displacement.

The calculation of F involves the simultaneous solution of two equations such as Eqs 8b and 9, each with a large range in the value of k. The corresponding ranges of F have been calculated and are given in Table 3. This calculation represents a "worst case." That is, if the k value for the whole tower is at the upper end of the range in Table 2, the value for the single floor is at the lower end, and vice versa.

The results in Table 3 indicate that there is no magnification of errors in

TABLE 2—*Effect of specified uncertainties in* p *and* n *on the calculated average flow coefficients (average flow coefficients 10^{-4} $m^3/m^2 \cdot s \cdot Pa^n$).*

		$n = 0.55$		$n = 0.65$	
	p	k	Range	k	Range
Whole tower	Pa	...	...	...	...
Doors closed	3 ± 1	6	5 to 8	5	5 to 7
Doors open	...[a]	10	7 to 15	9	7 to 15
Single floor	...	...	...	...	...
Doors closed	10 ± 2.7	9	8 to 11	7	6 to 9
Doors open	5 ± 2.7	14	11 to 21	12	9 to 19

[a]Whole tower range of k with doors closed multiplied by $(10 \pm 2.7/5 \pm 2.7)^n$ to estimate range with doors open; $k_{doors\ open} = k_{doors\ closed} \times 12/7$.

TABLE 3—*Effect of specified uncertainties in* p *and* n *on* F*, the fraction of air flowing from above and below during fan operation.*

	$n = 0.55$		$n = 0.65$	
	F	Range	F	Range
Doors closed	0.87	0.77 to 0.92	0.84	0.74 to 0.89
Doors open	0.85	0.68 to 0.96	0.84	0.59 to 0.94

the calculation of F. In fact, there is partial cancellation. Also, the range of F is unsymmetrical with respect to the values calculated from measured data. The best estimate is probably between 0.8 and 0.9, which corresponds to about 40 to 45% flow from above or below. This estimate compares with about 50% from below by SF_6 tracer gas measurements. These results are essentially descriptive, but they suggest an experimental approach to the determination of flow coefficients for modeling horizontal and vertical components of airflow in building ventilation.

Summary and Conclusions

Exploratory depressurization measurements were made in the tower of an eleven-story office building using a 7.55-m^3/s fan. Some of the salient observations and conclusions from these measurements are:

1. The fan developed pressures in the 3- to 10-Pa range. It is estimated that about 60 to 70 m^3/s would be required to develop a pressure difference of 50 Pa in the whole tower.

2. Under wind conditions sufficiently calm to permit stable pressure readings, a fan-induced pressure difference of 3 Pa was obtained. Assuming a flow equation of the form

$$Q = kA(\Delta p)^{0.65}$$

an average flow coefficient of 5×10^{-4} $m^3/m^2 \cdot s \cdot Pa^{0.65}$ was calculated.

3. A single floor of the building also was depressurized, and the opening and closing of office doors was found to influence the induced pressure. A value of 10 Pa was obtained with all office doors closed and 5 Pa with 15 doors open. These values correspond to flow coefficients of 7×10^{-4} $m^3/m^2 \cdot s \cdot Pa^{0.65}$ and 12×10^{-4} $m^3/m^2 \cdot s \cdot Pa^{0.65}$, respectively, when averaged over the envelope area of a single floor.

4. Flow to the fan was treated as the sum of the fraction of air passing through the wall, $f_w k_w$, and the fraction coming from floors above and below, $f_f k_f$, and is expressed by the equation

$$k \approx f_w k_w + f_f k_f$$

Simultaneous solution of flow equations for the whole tower and single floor lead to estimates of k_w and k_f, which permit calculation of F, the fraction of air coming from the floors above and below, by the relationship

$$F \approx \frac{f_f k_f}{f_f k_f + f_w k_w}$$

F was estimated to be about 80 to 90% of the total flow, or about 40 to 45% from above or below.

5. It was estimated from SF_6 tracer measurements that about half of the air reaching the fan during depressurization of a single floor could be traced to the floor below.

6. Ranges of uncertainty in flow coefficients and the combined fraction of air from above and below are given in the text. The results of the foregoing analyses are essentially descriptive, but they suggest an experimental approach to the determination of flow coefficients for lateral and vertical air movements in modeling building ventilation.

Conversion of SI to English units

1. $Pa \times 0.004015 = $ in water (H_2O).
2. $m^3/s \times 2118.9 = ft^3/min$.
3. $m/s \times 196.85 = ft/min$.
4. $m^3/m^2 \cdot s \cdot Pa^n \times 196.85(0.004015)^n = ft^3/ft^2 \cdot min. (in H_2O)^n$, where n is the flow exponent.

Acknowledgments

The author is indebted to Julius Cohen for diagnosing and making the wiring changes necessary to start a 3740-w (5 hp) motor with a 7000-w generator. He also is indebted to Samuel Price, Michael McCall, Seth Weinberg, and Theodore Ray for assistance in conducting the measurements. He wishes to thank John Brewer, chief of the Plant Division, and Daniel Tucker for cooperation in scheduling measurements in the building.

This report was part of a study of air exchange rates in large buildings under the sponsorship of the Office of the Assistant Secretary for Conservation and Solar Applications, Department of Energy.

References

[1] Tamura, G. T., *ASHRAE Transactions*, Vol. 81, Part 1, 1975, pp. 202–211.
[2] Blomsterberg, A. K. and Harrje, D. T., *ASHRAE Transactions*, Vol. 85, Part II, 1979, pp. 797–815.
[3] Shaw, C. Y., Sander, D. M., and Tamura, G. T., *ASHRAE Transactions*, Vol. 79, Part II, 1973, pp. 40–48.
[4] Shaw, C. Y., *ASHRAE Journal*, Vol. 23, No. 3, March 1981, pp. 44–46.
[5] Shaw, C. Y. and Jones, L., *ASHRAE Transactions*, Vol. 85, Part 1, 1979, pp. 85–95.
[6] Hunt, C. M. and Treado, S. J., in *Proceedings*, ASHRAE SP-28, DOE-ASHRAE Symposium on Thermal Performance of Exterior Envelope of Buildings, Dec. 1979, Kissimmee, Florida, ASHRAE, Atlanta, GA, 1981, pp. 160–177.
[7] Hunt, C. M. and Treado, S. A., "A Prototype Semi-Automated System for Measuring Air Infiltration in Buildings Using Sulfur Hexafluoride as a Tracer," Technical Note 898, National Bureau of Standards, Washington, DC, March 1976.

[8] Shaw, C. Y. and Tamura, G. T., *ASHRAE Transactions*, Vol. 83, Part II, 1977, pp. 145-158.

[9] Shaw, C. Y., *ASHRAE Transactions*, Vol. 86, Part I, 1980, pp. 241-257.

[10] Tamura, G. T., *ASHRAE Transactions*, Vol. 85, Part I, 1979, pp. 58-71.

[11] Sherman, M. H., Grimsrud, D. T. and Sonderegger, R. C., "The Low Pressure Leakage Function of a Building," Report LBL-9162, Lawrence Berkeley Laboratory, Berkeley, CA, Nov. 1979. Also, ASHRAE/DOE-ORNL Conference on Thermal Performance of Exterior Envelopes of Buildings, Kissimmee, Florida, 3-5 Dec. 1979, ASHRAE, Atlanta, 1981.

[12] Modera, M. P., Sherman, M. H., and Grimsrud, D. T., "A Predictive Air Infiltration Model, Long-Term Field-Test Validation," Report LBL-13509, Lawrence Berkeley Laboratory, Berkeley, CA, Nov. 1981.

[13] Malik, N., "Air Infiltration in Homes," M.S. thesis in Engineering, Report PU/CES 58, Princeton University Center for Environmental Studies, 1977.

[14] Youden, W. S., "Statistical Methods for Chemists," Wiley, New York, 1951, pp. 12,16.

Richard A. Grot[1] and Andrew K. Persily[1]

Measured Air Infiltration and Ventilation Rates in Eight Large Office Buildings

REFERENCE: Grot, R. A. and Persily, A. K., **"Measured Air Infiltration and Ventilation Rates in Eight Large Office Buildings,"** *Measured Air Leakage of Buildings, ASTM STP 904*, H. R. Trechsel and P. L. Lagus, Eds., American Society for Testing and Materials, Philadelphia, 1986, pp. 151–183.

ABSTRACT: Air infiltration and ventilation rate measurements were made during all seasons of the year in eight federal office buildings using an automatic air infiltration system designed at the National Bureau of Standards. The eight federal office buildings were located in Anchorage, Alaska; Ann Arbor, Michigan; Columbia, South Carolina; Fayetteville, Arkansas; Huron, South Dakota; Norfolk, Virginia; Pittsfield, Massachusetts; and Springfield, Massachusetts. These buildings ranged in size from 1730 m² (18 600 ft²) for the building in Pittsfield to 45 500 m² (490 000 ft²) for the Anchorage federal building. All were constructed within the last 10 years. Air infiltration rates were found to vary from 0.2 to 0.7 air changes per hour and constituted from 23% to 61% of the building design load. Minimum ventilation rates in the tighter buildings were found to be less than what would be recommended for occupied offices.

KEY WORDS: air infiltration, office buildings, tracer gas, ventilation

The air infiltration and ventilation rates of the eight federal office buildings were tested using tracer gas techniques [1]. The measurement employed the tracer gas decay method using sulfur hexafluoride (SF_6) as the tracer. This test was designed to produce a measure of the total air infiltration rate of each building and the rates of the major zones of the building. Sample and injection tubing was installed in each zone along with wiring for measuring interior temperatures, the status of the building's heating, ventilating, and air conditioning (HVAC) fans, and exterior weather conditions (wind speed, wind direction, and exterior temperature). The automatic air infiltration system previously designed by the National Bureau of Standards (NBS) for large

[1]Group leader and mechanical engineer, respectively, Center for Building Technology, National Bureau of Standards, Gaithersburg, MD 20899.

buildings was installed in each building for a period of about a week during the fall, winter, and spring (three automated air infiltration systems were used on this project). Tests were performed both during periods of occupancy and nonoccupancy, with the outside air intake dampers operated normally and closed, respectively. Tracer gas measurements were made for a total of about 200 h in each building.

Building Descriptions

The eight federal office buildings are located in the cities shown in the map in Fig. 1, and their floor areas and volumes are given in Table 1. In general

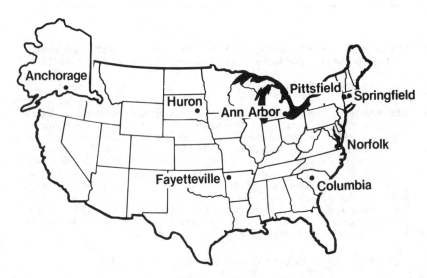

FIG. 1—*Location of the eight federal office buildings.*

TABLE 1—*Building dimensions.*

Location	Occupiable Floor Area, m^2	Volume, m^3
Anchorage	45 500	174 000
Ann Arbor	4 900	31 700
Columbia	24 700	159 000
Fayetteville	3 400	21 300
Huron	6 420	27 500
Norfolk	17 300	60 300
Pittsfield	1 730	8 520
Springfield	13 500	57 700

these are new buildings[2] (less than 3 years old) constructed to the U.S. federal energy guidelines of less than 630 MJ/m^2 per year of on-site energy and less than 1200 MJ/m^2 per year of off-site energy. The building in Fayetteville, Arkansas is 7 years old and was built before the energy guidelines for new federal office buildings were in effect. Though these buildings tend to perform better than most existing federal office buildings, none has met the energy guidelines during its first few years of occupancy.

The office buildings in Anchorage, Alaska; Springfield, Massachusetts; Norfolk, Virginia; and Columbia, South Carolina had occupiable floor areas over 10 000 m^2 with varying heights. The Columbia building is 15 stories high, the Norfolk building 8 stories, the Anchorage building between 2 and 6 depending on the module, and the Springfield building 5 stories. The buildings in Pittsfield, Massachusetts; Huron, South Dakota; Ann Arbor, Michigan; and Fayetteville, Arkansas had less then 10 000 m^2 occupiable floor area. These small office buildings range in height from two to five stories. Schematic diagrams and a photograph of all buildings are given in Figs. 2 through 9.

The mechanisms for controlling outside air intake vary among the eight buildings. In most buildings, outside air intake is kept to a minimum when the building is being heated or cooled in order to reduce the space conditioning load. During mild weather, outside air often is used to cool the building. The amount of outside air intake, and the times when outside air intake is increased, are controlled by a variety of schemes. An economizer control uses the outside temperature to determine when outside air should be used for cooling. Enthalpy control uses indoor and outdoor humidity levels in addition to temperature. The amount of outside air intake for cooling generally is determined by a control system which compares the discharge or return air temperature to some temperature setting. The control strategies used in each building are outlined in following paragraphs, along with other information on mechanical systems and the zoning of the buildings.

All but two of the buildings have variable volume air handlers in the major zones of the buildings. They are heated by perimeter heating systems which are generally hydronic. In the Norfolk building, heaters and air conditioners have been added to the air system on floors which proved difficult to heat and cool. They all have central chiller systems for cooling and for the core spaces of the buildings. The buildings in Anchorage and Springfield have underground garages.

The Anchorage building is divided into six modules (each with its own ventilation system) which are connected by an open lobby/atrium and communicate freely. Anchorage is the only building without return fans. The mechanical systems are computer-controlled and use a minimum of outside air during the heating season. During warmer weather, outside air is used to cool the

[2]A more complete description of these buildings can be found in Ref 2.

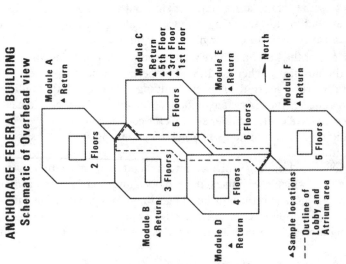

FIG. 2—*Schematic diagram and photograph of Federal building in Anchorage, AK.*

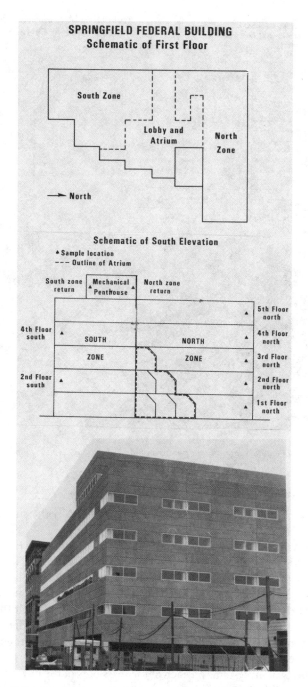

FIG. 3—*Schematic diagram and photograph of Federal building in Springfield, MA.*

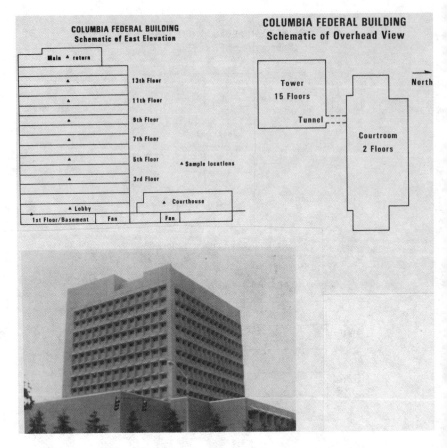

FIG. 4—*Schematic diagram and photograph of Federal building in Columbia, SC.*

building, with the outside air intake level determined by the supply air temperature.

In Ann Arbor, the building's main mechanical system serves most of the building with separate systems for the lobby and post office. The outside air intake is based on the outside air temperature (an economizer), and the amount of outside air intake is controlled by the return air temperature.

Columbia has a single mechanical system for Floors 2 through 16 and separate systems for the lobby and the first floor/basement zones. The mechanical system is controlled by a computer and uses an enthalpy controller to determine outside air intake levels.

There are two fan systems on each of the five floors of the Fayetteville building with an additional system for the courtroom on the fifth floor. The outside air intake is controlled manually by the building operator.

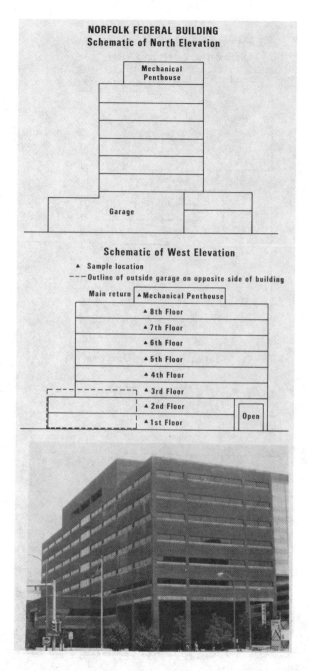

FIG. 5—*Schematic diagram and photograph of Federal building in Norfolk, VA.*

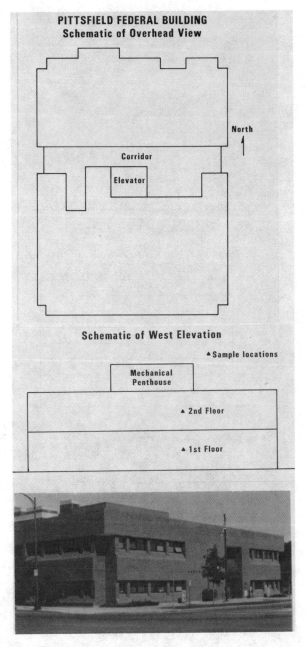

FIG. 6—*Schematic diagram and photograph of Federal building in Pittsfield, MA.*

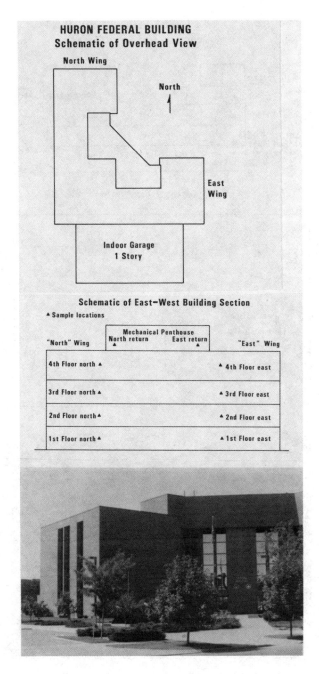

FIG. 7—*Schematic diagram and photograph of Federal building in Huron, SD.*

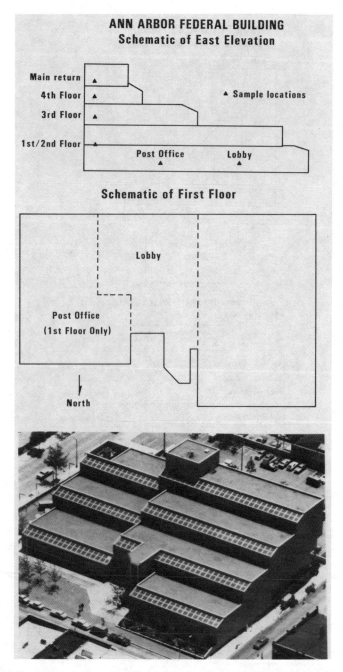

FIG. 8—*Schematic diagram and photograph of Federal building in Ann Arbor, MI.*

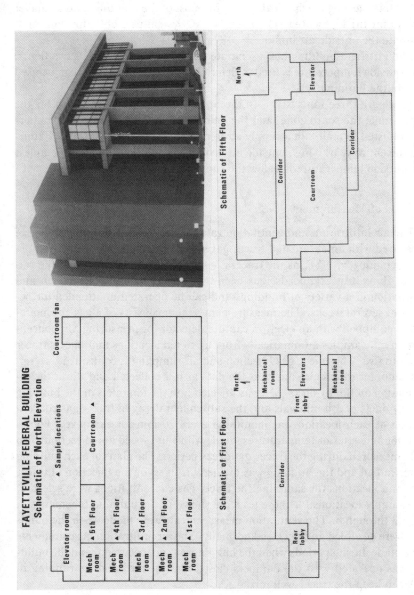

FIG. 9—*Schematic diagram and photograph of Federal building in Fayetteville, AR.*

The Huron building has two mechanical systems, one for the north zone and another for the south zone. On each floor, the north and south zones are open to each other. The outside air intake is based on enthalpy control.

Norfolk has one mechanical system for most of the building, and a smaller system for the lobby area. The main HVAC system uses enthalpy control to regulate the outside air intake.

The Pittsfield building has a separate fan system for each of its two floors. The outside temperature is used to determine whether outside air can be used to cool the building.

There are three fan systems in the Springfield building, one each for the north zone, the south zone, and the lobby/atrium. The outside air dampers are adjusted to maintain a supply air temperature of about 13°C (55°F) during the entire year. Thus, outside air is used to condition the building unless the outside temperature is below the supply air temperature setting.

Method of Measurement

The air infiltration and ventilation rates of the eight office buildings were measured with an automated tracer-gas system employing the tracer-gas decay technique with SF_6 as the tracer [2-4]. This system, designed at the National Bureau of Standards, has been used to measure air infiltration and ventilation in a variety of buildings and can be operated unattended for periods of several weeks. The measurement system consists of a gas chromatograph equipped with an electron capture detector for measuring SF_6 concentrations. It samples automatically from up to ten locations and injects tracer gas into five. The tracer-gas injection and air sampling is controlled by a microcomputer which also analyzes the data as it is collected and stores the information on floppy disks. SF_6 was injected into the fan inlets of the building supply ducts at 3-h intervals and the subsequent decay in tracer-gas concentration at each location was monitored every 10 min for the next 3 hours. Interior and exterior temperatures, along with wind speed and direction, also were measured during the tracer-gas decay period. The plans of each building were studied and the building was divided in zones for the injection of tracer gas, and locations for sampling the tracer-gas concentrations were selected. The sample locations for these tests are shown in the building schematics in Figs. 2 through 8. The ventilation measurements were made when the buildings were occupied and operated normally. The air infiltration measurements were made during periods when the building was not occupied, and the building was operated with the dampers closed and the air handlers running in order to keep the tracer well mixed.

Results of the Air Infiltration Tests

The summary of the tracer gas test results in Table 2 show average infiltration rates under winter conditions, neglecting extremely high wind speeds.

TABLE 2—*Average^a air infiltration rates on each federal building.*

Location	Changes per Hour	Percent of Design Heat Load
Anchorage	0.28	55
Ann Arbor	0.70	48
Columbia	0.40	52
Fayetteville	0.33	23
Huron	0.20	30
Norfolk	0.52	52
Pittsfield	0.32	30
Springfield	0.52	61

^{a}Average excluding extreme wind speeds.

These results[3] indicate that the buildings in Huron and Anchorage are experiencing relatively low natural leakage rates. The buildings with the highest natural rates are Ann Arbor, Norfolk, and Springfield. By using the results of these tests, it is possible to estimate the contribution of air infiltration to the design load of the buildings. These estimates also are included in Table 2. As can be seen, air infiltration contributes from 23 to 61% of the building heat load.

As mentioned earlier, tracer gas concentrations were measured in several locations in each building, and, in general, good mixing was achieved in all the buildings. There are, however, some specific zones which exhibit high air exchange rates compared to the rest of the building—the lobby in Springfield, the first floor in Norfolk, and the lobby in Columbia. Similarly high rates also are seen in the first floor in Fayetteville and the lobby and post office in Ann Arbor. The lobbies generally exhibit larger exchange rates due to the exterior doors in these zones. The post office in Ann Arbor has large leaky doors for loading and unloading mail.

The air infiltration rates for each building are plotted against the inside-outside temperature difference ΔT in Fig. 10. Among the eight buildings there are varying degrees of dependence of infiltration on temperature difference. The most noticeable dependence occurs in the cases of Ann Arbor, Huron, Norfolk, and Springfield. These buildings, with the exception of Huron, are also the leakiest. The lines shown in Fig. 10 are based on linear regressions of infiltration against temperature difference for positive values of ΔT. The equations of these lines are given by:

Anchorage: $I = 0.16 + 0.003 \Delta T$ $R^2 = 0.18$; standard error = 0.07
Ann Arbor: $I = 0.44 + 0.011 \Delta T$ $R^2 = 0.35$; standard error = 0.11
Columbia: $I = 0.33 + 0.005 \Delta T$ $R^2 = 0.05$; standard error = 0.12

[3]Preliminary results of these tests are given in Ref 5.

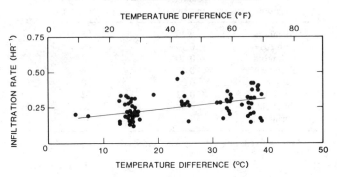

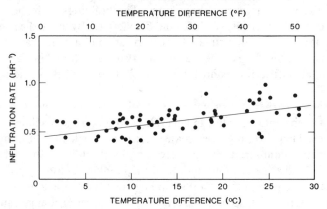

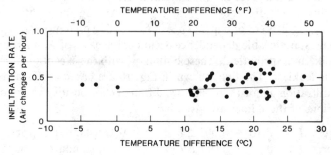

FIG. 10—*Infiltration rates versus indoor-outdoor temperature difference.*

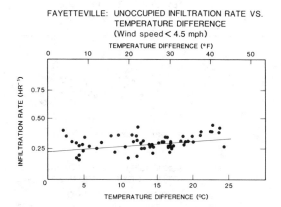

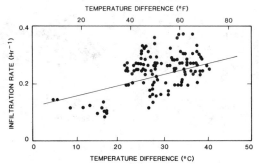

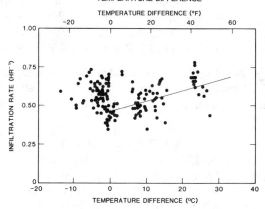

FIG. 10—*Continued.*

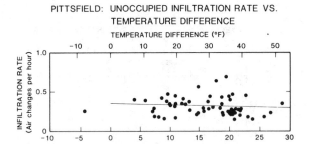

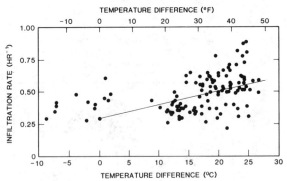

FIG. 10—*Continued.*

Fayetteville:	$I = 0.24 + 0.004 \, \Delta T$	$R^2 = 0.15$; standard error $= 0.06$
Huron:	$I = 0.11 + 0.005 \, \Delta T$	$R^2 = 0.26$; standard error $= 0.06$
Norfolk:	$I = 0.46 + 0.006 \, \Delta T$	$R^2 = 0.29$; standard error $= 0.08$
Pittsfield:	$I = 0.35 - 0.003 \, \Delta T$	$R^2 = 0.02$; standard error $= 0.11$
Springfield:	$I = 0.17 + 0.017 \, \Delta T$	$R^2 = 0.28$; standard error $= 0.12$

Some of the buildings' infiltration rates also exhibited a dependence on wind speed u. Figure 11 shows several plots of infiltration against u, with regression lines drawn in. The equations of these lines are given by the following:

Ann Arbor ΔT from 20 to 25°C: $R^2 = 0.41$;
   $I = 0.40 + 0.113 \, u$ standard error $= 0.15$
Fayetteville ΔT from 0 to 5°C: $R^2 = 0.67$;
   $I = -0.17 + 0.228 \, u$ standard error $= 0.21$
Huron ΔT from 20 to 25°C: $R^2 = 0.22$;
   $I = 0.23 + 0.010 \, u$ standard error $= 0.02$
Huron ΔT from 25 to 30°C: $R^2 = 0.48$;
   $I = 0.21 + 0.018 \, u$ standard error $= 0.08$

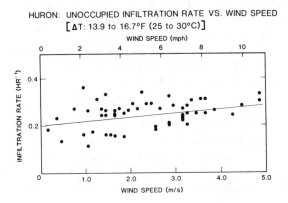

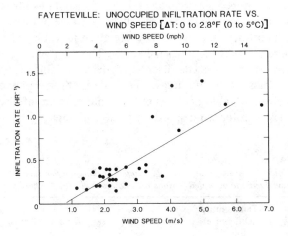

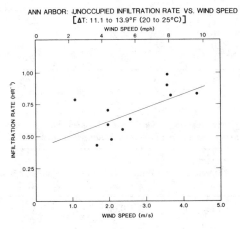

FIG. 11—*Infiltration rates versus wind speed for various buildings.*

Tables 3 through 10 give mean measured infiltration rates for each building within various ranges of temperature difference. Means are given for wind speeds less than and greater than 2.0 m/s.

In order to assess the accuracy of more complicated models for explaining the dependence of the measured air infiltration rates on the weather, the following six models were fitted to the data:

Model 1: $I = Q(a\,u + b\,\Delta T + c\,u\,\Delta T)$
Model 2: $I = Q(a\,u^2 + B\,\Delta T + c\,u^2\,\Delta T)$
Model 3: $I = Q(a\,u + b\,\Delta T)^{0.5}$
Model 4: $I = Q(a\,u^2 + b\,\Delta T)^{0.5}$
Model 5: $I = Q(a\,u + b\,\Delta T)^{0.65}$
Model 6: $I = Q(a\,u^2 + \Delta T)^{0.65}$

where Q is the induced air exchange rate at 25 Pa obtained from the pressurization test on the buildings [5] (see following article in these proceedings).

The results of these fits to the data are given in Tables 11 to 16. The R^2 given in these tables is the uncorrected R^2. The numbers in parentheses are the standard errors of the coefficients. Model 1 explains the variance in the data best for most of the buildings. The analysis of the explained variance of Model 1 is given in Table 17. Most of the variance in air infiltration is attributed to variance in the wind speed for these buildings.

TABLE 3—*Average air exchange rates in various temperature difference bins during unoccupied periods with dampers closed, Anchorage, AK.*

Temperature Difference Bin, °C	Wind < 2.0 m/s, X/h	Wind > 2.0 m/s, X/h
0,10	0.19	...
10,20	0.20	0.23
20,30	0.38	0.24
30,40	0.25	0.31

TABLE 4—*Average air exchange rates in various temperature difference bins during unoccupied period with dampers closed, Columbia, SC.*

Temperature Difference Bin, °C	Wind < 2.0 m/s, X/h	Wind > 2.0 m/s, X/h
−10 < 0	0.40	0.40
0 < 10	0.37	0.33
10 < 20	0.41	0.38
20 < 30	0.34	0.51

TABLE 5—*Average air exchange rates in various temperature difference bins during unoccupied periods with dampers closed, Norfolk, VA.*

Temperature Difference Bin, °C	Wind < 2.0 m/s, X/h	Wind > 2.0 m/s, X/h
−20 < −10	0.56	. . .
−10 < 0	0.56	0.55
0 < 10	0.50	0.50
10 < 20	0.49	0.54

TABLE 6—*Average air exchange rates in various temperature difference bins during unoccupied periods with dampers closed, Springfield, MA.*

Temperature Difference Bin, °C	Wind < 2.0 m/s, X/h	Wind > 2.0 m/s, X/h
−10 < 0	0.38	0.35
0 < 10	0.44	. . .
10 < 20	0.43	0.56
20 < 30	0.55	0.53

TABLE 7—*Average air exchange rates in various temperature difference bins during unoccupied periods with dampers closed, Pittsfield, MA.*

Temperature Difference Bin, °C	Wind < 2.0 m/s, X/h	Wind > 2.0 m/s, X/h
−10 < 0	0.25	. . .
0 < 10	0.29	0.37
10 < 20	0.36	0.31
20 < 30	0.26	. . .

TABLE 8—*Average air exchange rates in various temperature difference bins during unoccupied periods with dampers closed, Huron, SD.*

Temperature Difference Bin, °C	Wind < 2.0 m/s, X/h	Wind > 2.0 m/s, X/h
0 < 10	0.13	0.14
10 < 20	0.10	0.11
20 < 30	0.23	0.26
30 < 40	0.26	0.26
40 < 50	0.26	. . .

TABLE 9—*Average air exchange rates in various temperature difference bins during unoccupied periods with dampers closed, Fayetteville, AR.*

Temperature Difference Bin, °C	Wind < 2.0 m/s, X/h	Wind > 2.0 m/s, X/h
−10 < 0		0.37
0 < 10	0.28	0.50
10 < 20	0.29	0.35
20 < 30	0.39	0.35

TABLE 10—*Average air exchange rates in various temperature difference bins during unoccupied periods with dampers closed, Ann Arbor, MI.*

Temperature Difference Bin, °C	Wind < 2.0 m/s, X/h	Wind > 2.0 m/s, X/h
0 < 10	0.53	0.52
10 < 20	0.59	0.64
20 < 30	0.61	0.73

TABLE 11—*Results of fitting model 1 to the measured air infiltration data.*

Model 1

$$I = Q(a u + b \Delta T + c u \Delta T)$$

Location	No. of Points	Q	a	b	c	Standard Error	R^2
Anchorage	97	0.80	0.129[a] (0.019)	0.0123 (0.0009)	−0.00476 (0.0007)	0.10	0.91
Ann Arbor	62	0.86	0.211 (0.023)	0.0408 (0.0033)	−0.0102 (0.0012)	0.16	0.95
Columbia	46	0.67	0.345 (0.055)	0.0271 (0.0034)	−0.0140 (0.0031)	0.18	0.93
Fayetteville[b]	122	...	0.0903 (0.0071)	0.0183 (0.0011)	−0.00445 (0.00078)	0.11	0.90
Huron	153	0.45	0.130 (0.018)	0.0173 (0.0006)	−0.00384	0.12	0.96
Norfolk	171	1.45	0.182 (0.007)	0.0371 (0.0032)	−0.0167 (0.0015)	0.12	0.90
Pittsfield	67	0.95	0.193 (0.051)	0.0172 (0.0015)	−0.0113 (0.0039)	0.15	0.81
Springfield	127	1.43	0.149 (0.017)	0.0174 (0.0008)	−0.0069 (0.0010)	0.09	0.93
Combined[c]	723	...	0.182 (0.007)	0.0159 (0.0006)	−0.0053 (0.0003)	0.18	0.86

[a]Values in parentheses are the standard errors of the coefficients.
[b]Since there was no measurement of Q in this building, it was assumed to be equal to 1.0.
[c]Excluding Fayetteville.

TABLE 12—*The results of fitting Model 2 to the measured air infiltration data.*

Model 2

$$I = Q(a u^2 + b u \Delta T + c u^2 \Delta T)$$

Location	No. of Points	Q	a	b	c	Standard Error	R^2
Anchorage	97	0.80	0.0499[a] (0.0098)	0.0124 (0.0006)	−0.00182	0.10	0.89
Ann Arbor	62	0.86	0.0798 (0.0108)	0.0393 (0.0026)	−0.00339 (0.00041)	0.18	0.94
Columbia	46	0.67	0.147 (0.034)	0.0303 (0.0025)	−0.00647 (0.00165)	0.21	0.90
Fayetteville	122	. . .	0.0156 (0.0022)	0.0195 (0.0012)	−0.00073 (0.00030)	0.13	0.83
Huron	153	0.45	0.0411 (0.0054)	0.0176 (0.0005)	−0.00123 (0.00017)	0.12	0.96
Norfolk	171	1.45	0.0623 (0.0045)	0.0343 (0.0025)	−0.00556 (0.00054)	0.18	0.77
Pittsfield	67	0.95	0.0479 (0.0246)	0.0170 (0.0013)	−0.00320 (0.00223)	0.16	0.78
Springfield	127	1.43	0.0568 (0.0099)	0.0178 (0.0007)	−0.00273 (0.00055)	0.10	0.92
Combined	723	. . .	0.0531 (0.0030)	0.0175 (0.0005)	−0.00163 (0.00011)	0.20	0.81

[a]Values in parentheses are the standard error of the estimated coefficient.

TABLE 13—*The results of fitting Model 3 to the measured air infiltration data.*

Model 3

$$I = Q(a u + b \Delta T)^{0.5}$$

Location	No. of Points	Q	a	b	Standard Error	R^2
Anchorage	97	0.80	0.00653[a] (0.00785)	0.00367 (0.00051)	0.062	0.74
Ann Arbor	62	0.86	0.07107 (0.02543)	0.02317 (0.00367)	0.209	0.87
Columbia	46	0.67	0.1137 (0.0414)	0.01323 (0.00384)	0.224	0.79
Fayetteville	122	. . .	0.0258 (0.0038)	0.00455 (0.00061)	0.0074	0.69
Huron	153	0.45	0.0140 (0.0076)	0.00945 (0.00068)	0.125	0.86
Norfolk	171	1.45	0.0551 (0.0039)	0.00260 (0.00080)	0.073	0.78
Pittsfield	67	0.95	0.0243 (0.0135)	0.00517 (0.00853)	0.100	0.55
Springfield	127	1.43	0.0183 (0.0071)	0.00576 (0.00050)	0.063	0.80
Combined	723	. . .	0.0622 (0.0051)	0.00557 (0.00049)	0.171	0.63

[a]Values in parentheses are the standard error of the estimated coefficient.

TABLE 14— *The results of fitting model 4 to the measured air infiltration data.*

Model 4

$$I = Q(a\,u^2 + b\,\Delta T)^{0.5}$$

Location	No. of Points	Q	a	b	Standard Error	R^2
Anchorage	97	0.80	0.00107[a] (0.00202)	0.00392 (0.00035)	0.062	0.74
Ann Arbor	62	0.86	0.01053 (0.00669)	0.02831 (0.00309)	0.218	0.86
Columbia	46	0.67	0.02399 (0.01273)	0.0187 (0.0028)	0.233	0.77
Fayetteville	122	...	0.00528 (0.00095)	0.00584 (0.00056)	0.078	0.65
Huron	153	0.45	0.00231 (0.00153)	0.00996 (0.00050)	0.126	0.86
Norfolk	171	1.45	0.0105 (0.0016)	0.00696 (0.00093)	0.095	0.62
Pittsfield	67	0.95	0.00518 (0.00404)	0.00577 (0.00074)	0.101	0.54
Springfield	127	1.43	0.00466 (0.00275)	0.00636 (0.00039)	0.064	0.80
Combined	723	...	0.0125 (0.0014)	0.00780 (0.00042)	0.178	0.60

[a]Values in parentheses are the standard error of the estimated coefficient.

TABLE 15— *The results of fitting Model 5 to the measured air infiltration data.*

Model 5

$$I = Q(a\,u + b\,u\,\Delta T)^{0.65}$$

Location	No. of Points	Q	a	b	Standard Error	R^2
Anchorage	97	0.80	0.0131[a] (0.0103)	0.00574 (0.00068)	0.081	0.81
Ann Arbor	62	0.86	0.0848 (0.0259)	0.0249 (0.0037)	0.213	0.89
Columbia	46	0.67	0.128 (0.041)	0.0161 (0.0038)	0.220	0.84
Fayetteville	122	...	0.0382 (0.0078)	0.00778 (0.00074)	0.089	0.80
Huron	153	0.45	0.0172 (0.0080)	0.0122 (0.0007)	0.131	0.90
Norfolk	171	1.45	0.00876 (0.0057)	0.00331 (0.00116)	0.104	0.80
Pittsfield	67	0.95	0.0362 (0.0168)	0.00825 (0.00106)	0.124	0.66
Springfield	127	1.43	0.0300 (0.0088)	0.00881 (0.00062)	0.079	0.86
Combined	723	...	0.0791 (0.0054)	0.00755 (0.00052)	0.181	0.73

[a]Values in parentheses are the standard error of the coefficient.

TABLE 16—*The results of fitting Model 6 to the measured air infiltration data.*

Model 6

$$I = Q(a\,u^2 + b\,\Delta T)^{0.65}$$

Location	No. of Points	Q	a	b	Standard Error	R^2
Anchorage	97	0.80	0.00132[a] (0.00268)	0.00634 (0.00046)	0.082	0.81
Ann Arbor	62	0.86	0.00799 (0.00702)	0.0328 (0.0032)	0.229	0.88
Columbia	46	0.67	0.0239 (0.0128)	0.0227 (0.0028)	0.234	0.82
Fayetteville	122	...	0.00749 (0.00120)	0.00977 (0.00070)	0.097	0.76
Huron	153	0.45	0.00248 (0.00160)	0.0129 (0.0005)	0.131	0.90
Norfolk	171	1.45	0.0168 (0.0024)	0.0102 (0.0014)	0.143	0.63
Pittsfield	67	0.95	0.00824 (0.00503)	0.00910 (0.00092)	0.126	0.65
Springfield	127	1.43	0.00737 (0.00348)	0.00983 (0.00050)	0.081	0.85
Combined	723	...	0.0144 (0.0015)	0.0107 (0.0005)	0.194	0.68

[a]Values in parentheses are the standard error of the coefficient.

TABLE 17—*Analysis of explained variance for Model 1.*

Model 1

$$I = Q(a\,u + b\,u\,\Delta T + c\,u\,\Delta T)$$

Location	Regression Variance	Fraction Attributed to		
		U	DT	$U * DT$
Anchorage	8.8	0.79	0.16	0.05
Ann Arbor	31.2	0.86	0.08	0.06
Columbia	17.7	0.88	0.08	0.04
Fayetteville	11.9	0.72	0.25	0.03
Huron	43.9	0.77	0.21	0.01
Norfolk	22.3	0.91	0.01	0.09
Pittsfield	6.2	0.48	0.48	0.03
Springfield	14.4	0.73	0.24	0.03
Combined	133.4	0.83	0.11	0.06

NOTE: U = wind speed (m/s); DT = temperature difference.

Measured Ventilation Rates

In most of the buildings the measured ventilation rates exhibit a seasonal dependence such that the lowest ventilation rates occur during maximum heating and cooling loads.[4] This can be seen in the plots of ventilation rate versus inside-outside temperature difference for each federal building shown in Figs. 12 through 19. Table 18 shows mean ventilation rates, along with the standard deviations of these means, for 5 K intervals of temperature difference for all eight buildings. The mean ventilation rates can be somewhat misleading for mild temperature conditions. Buildings with enthalpy control are operated at low or high ventilation rates at the same outside temperature because of differences in outside humidity. This variable rate at the same outside temperature also occurs in buildings with other types of control systems.

Also, as discussed in following paragraphs, the ventilation rate at a given temperature can be affected by weather conditions in buildings for which weather-induced infiltration is a significant portion of the total ventilation rate.

Figure 12 shows the ventilation rate in the Anchorage federal building as a function of temperature difference. There are low ventilation rates, about 0.25 to 0.50 exchanges per hour, during cold outside conditions and higher ventilation rates for temperature differences below 20 K. None of the measurements in Anchorage were made under conditions which were warm enough for the building's air conditioning system to be used for cooling and for the ventilation rate to again be minimized.

Figure 13 shows the ventilation rate of the Ann Arbor federal building plotted against temperature difference. These data exhibit a large amount of scatter due in part to some very high ventilation rates induced by high wind speeds. This implies that the infiltration rate of the Ann Arbor building was strongly dependent on wind speed and that infiltration became a significant portion of the net ventilation rate under windy conditions. Figure 20 is a plot of these ventilation rates versus wind speed for a limited range of temperature difference, and indeed a strong dependence on wind is evident. A similar dependence of infiltration on wind speed was noted earlier in Fig. 11. These large, wind-induced rates were not considered in calculating the Ann Arbor mean ventilation rates in Table 18. Under cold outside conditions, $\Delta T > 20$ K, this building was operated at about 0.5 exchanges per hour. For milder temperatures, outside air was used to cool the building with ventilation rates as large as 3.0 exchanges per hour. When the temperature difference was close to zero, the ventilation rates did return to 0.5 exchanges per hour.

The Columbia building's ventilation rates are shown in Fig. 14. The measurements cover a wide range of warm temperature conditions (ΔT from -10 to 5 K), but there is no clear dependence of ventilation rate on temperature difference for the summer. If the weather-dependent natural ventilation, or

---

[4]A more detailed analysis of the performance of the ventilation systems is given in Ref 6.

infiltration, is a large fraction of the net ventilation rate which was measured, then the data may show a dependence on temperature difference. Such a dependence would tend to imply that infiltration is similar in magnitude to the intentional ventilation.

Figure 15 shows the ventilation rate versus temperature difference plot for the Fayetteville building. When the building is being heated or cooled, the ventilation rate is about 0.34 exchanges per hour. Under mild temperature conditions, ΔT from 0 to 5 K, the ventilation rate varies between 0.35 and 1.5 exchanges per hour. The ten high ventilation rates between 1.0 and 1.5 exchanges per hour were measured under very windy conditions and probably were due to a dominance of natural ventilation or infiltration, as in the Ann Arbor building. Attempts to pressure test this building using its own supply fans, while successful in the other seven federal buildings, were unsuccessful in Fayetteville because the ventilation system could not bring in enough outside air to raise the internal pressure significantly. Thus, the ventilation rates of 1.0 exchanges per hour and higher are probably not due to mechanical ventilation alone and contain a large component of natural ventilation induced by the high wind speeds during these measurements. The wind speed dependence of infiltration for this building is evident in Fig. 11.

The Huron building, whose ventilation rates are plotted in Fig. 16, has the lowest ventilation rates of all the buildings examined. Under hot and cold outside temperature conditions, ventilation rates of 0.2 exchanges per hour and less were measured. The cold weather ventilation measurements exhibit a dependence on both wind speed and temperature difference. This is the only building which showed a significant dependence of measured ventilation rate on temperature difference.

Figure 10 shows the dependence of infiltration on ΔT for this building, which also appears in the ventilation data in Fig. 16. Additional scatter in Fig. 11 is due to wind-induced infiltration. This dependence of ventilation on wind is shown in Fig. 21. Plots of infiltration versus wind speed, shown in Fig. 11, also show some dependence, though not as strong as for ventilation. It is possible that the wind effects are enhanced when the outside air intake dampers are open.

The ventilation rates of the federal building in Norfolk are plotted in Fig. 17. In this building the winter and summer ventilation rates are comparable, both around 0.6 to 0.7 exchanges per hour. Figure 18 is a plot of the Pittsfield ventilation rates. It appears that the minimum ventilation rates during cold weather are lower than the warm weather ventilation rates.

The Springfield building ventilation rates, shown in Fig. 19, exhibit an unusual pattern. The ventilation rates under warm conditions, $\Delta T < 10$ K, are relatively constant at about 0.6 exchanges per hour. For temperature differences greater than about 15 K, the ventilation rate varies from a minimum of 0.6 to a maximum of about 1.25 exchanges per hour. It is not clear if the high ventilation rates are due to intentional outside air intake or to a strong depen-

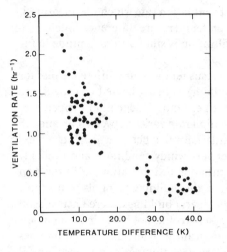

FIG. 12— *Ventilation rate versus inside-outside temperature difference for the Anchorage building.*

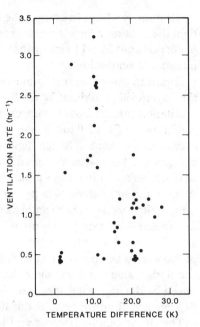

FIG. 13— *Ventilation rate versus inside-outside temperature difference for the Ann Arbor building.*

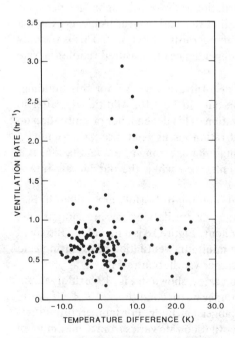

FIG. 14— *Ventilation rate versus inside-outside temperature difference for the Columbia building.*

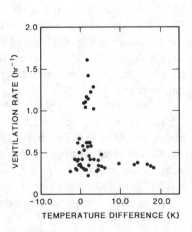

FIG. 15— *Ventilation rate versus inside-outside temperature difference for the Fayetteville building.*

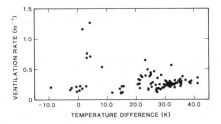

FIG. 16— *Ventilation rate versus inside-outside temperature difference for the Huron building.*

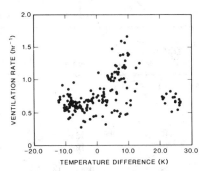

FIG. 17— *Ventilation rate versus inside-outside temperature difference for the Norfolk building.*

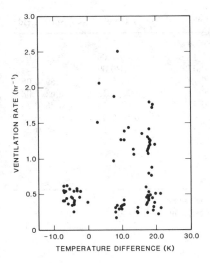

FIG. 18— *Ventilation rate versus inside-outside temperature difference for the Pittsfield building.*

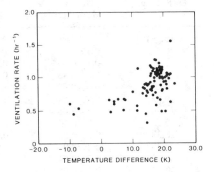

FIG. 19— *Ventilation rate versus inside-outside temperature difference for the Springfield building.*

dence of infiltration on temperature difference. The outside air intake is controlled to maintain the supply air temperature at about 13°C. This is, indeed, the temperature difference at which the ventilation rate is seen to increase. Measurements of infiltration made with the outside air dampers closed show a similar, but less extreme, dependence on temperature difference (see Fig. 10). Thus, the dependence of the net measured ventilation on ΔT appears to be a combination of the outside air intake control strategy and a significant portion of temperature-dependent infiltration.

TABLE 18—*Average ventilation rates in the buildings.*[a]

Temperature Difference, K	Anchorage	Ann Arbor[b]	Columbia	Fayetteville
−10,−5	...	...	0.68/0.18	...
−5,0	...	...	0.68/0.21	0.36/9.12
0,5	...	0.94/0.95	0.69/0.32	0.65/0.39
5,10	1.34/0.36	1.94/0.42	1.10/0.90	0.35/0.07
10,15	1.22/0.25	1.96/0.97	1.09/0.56	0.35/0.01
15,20	1.10/0.23	0.86/0.20	0.64/0.26	0.32/0.02
20,25	...	0.47/0.07	0.62/0.24	...
25,30	0.46/0.14	...	...	...
30,35	0.24/0.04	...	...	...
35,40	0.36/0.10	...	...	...
40,45	0.26/0.02	...	...	...

Temperature Difference, K	Huron, Mean/SD[c]	Norfolk	Pittsfield	Springfield
−15,−10	...	0.73/0.09	...	...
−10,−5	0.19/0.00	0.62/0.11	0.49/0.09	0.55/0.09
−5,0	0.16/0.04	0.58/0.07	0.43/0.09	...
0,5	0.53/0.43	0.75/0.19	1.19/0.73	0.59/0.08
5,10	0.52/0.00	1.00/0.32	1.25/1.15	0.62/0.08
10,15	0.13/0.04	1.05/0.37	0.67/0.48	0.76/0.20
15,20	0.14/0.06	...	0.84/0.47	0.96/0.20
20,25	0.32/0.14	0.70/0.09	0.38/0.14	0.95/0.22
25,30	0.25/0.05	0.66/0.06	...	...
30,35	0.26/0.07	...	...	...
35,40	0.29/0.04	...	...	...
40,45	0.31/0.06	...	...	...

[a]All the ventilation rates are in units of exchanges per hour.
[b]Calculations neglect some very high, wind-induced ventilation rates.
[c]Standard deviation of the mean ventilation rate.

Minimum Ventilation Requirements

The measurements of actual ventilation rates in occupied office buildings are compared to ventilation standards and design specifications of minimum fresh air intake. A certain minimum ventilation rate must be maintained to remove pollutants generated inside a building. These minimum ventilation rates are determined by the building occupancy level (number of people per 100 m^2 of floor area) and the extent and nature of the activities within the building (smoking, painting, and other pollutant-generating activities). In some of the buildings, the mechanical equipment specifications give a minimum outside air intake level in units of volumetric air flow. Another commonly accepted minimum ventilation rate is equal to 10% of the HVAC system's total air flow rate. The American Society of Heating, Refrigerating, and

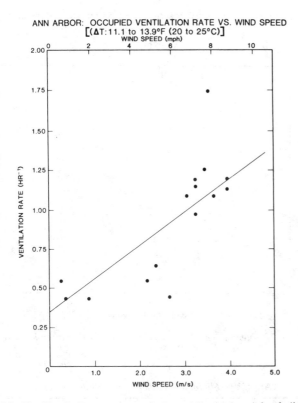

ANN ARBOR: OCCUPIED VENTILATION RATE VS. WIND SPEED
[(ΔT:11.1 to 13.9°F (20 to 25°C)]

FIG. 20— *Ventilation rate versus wind speed for the Ann Arbor building.*

Air-Conditioning Engineers (ASHRAE) has established minimum recommended building ventilation rates which are a function of occupancy levels, building type (for example, office, store, hotel), and room type (for example, kitchen, office, conference room) [7]. The measured minimum ventilation rates are compared to the ASHRAE recommendation and the 10% rule in Table 19. In all the buildings, except the Fayetteville building, the 10% total air rate is less than the ASHRAE recommendation for smoking conditions. The ASHRAE nonsmoking value is less than all the 10% rates. Since smoking is permitted in all the buildings, the nonsmoking recommendation is not relevant to the operation of these buildings.

Rather than compare the different ventilation standards to each other, it is more important to compare them to the ventilation rates measured in the buildings. The ASHRAE smoking recommendation is used for these comparisons. In Anchorage and Huron, the minimum ventilation rates when the buildings are heated or cooled are about one third of the smoking rate. In fact, these measured ventilation rates are close to the ASHRAE nonsmoking

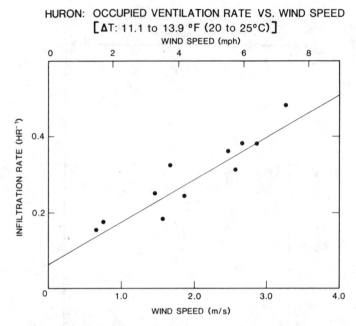

FIG. 21—*Ventilation rate versus wind speed for the Huron building.*

TABLE 19—*Minimum ventilation rates in the buildings.*[a]

Building	10% of Total Air	Measured Building Minimum	Measured Minimum as Percent of ASHRAE Recommendation[b]
Anchorage	0.28	0.26	39
Ann Arbor	0.36	0.47	70
Columbia	0.28	0.62	92
Fayetteville	0.57	0.32	48
Huron	0.31	0.13	19
Norfolk	0.25	0.62	92
Pittsfield	0.32	0.38	57
Springfield	0.44	0.55	83

[a]ASHRAE 62-81 Recommended Ventilation Rate: Smoking 0.67; Nonsmoking 0.17. All the ventilation rates are in units of exchanges per hour.
[b]Based on ASHRAE 62-81 smoking requirement.

rates. In all the other buildings, the lowest measured ventilation rates are very close to, and at times lower than, the smoking ventilation rates. Thus, all of the buildings are at times being operated at ventilation rates which are lower than may be desirable for the maintenance of indoor air quality. As will be discussed in following paragraphs, local variations in air distribution may lead to ventilation rates in specific zones which are very low.

The question of the adequacy of outside air intake is primarily an issue during hot and cold weather when outside air intake is at a minimum. This minimum outside air intake is often assured by having a minimum outside air damper position or by keeping a certain portion of the outside air dampers open at all times. In other cases the outside air dampers are closed completely, and it is assumed that leakage through the building envelope will fulfill the minimum outside air requirements.

It is interesting to compare the measured ventilation rates under conditions of minimum outside air intake to measurements of building infiltration made with the dampers totally closed and the HVAC fans running. This comparison provides an indication of how much additional air is really brought in through the outside air intake to meet ventilation requirements and how much of the outside air intake results from uncontrolled air leakage. In Ann Arbor, Columbia, Pittsfield, and Springfield, the ventilation rates are about 0.2 exchanges per hour higher during occupied periods than the exchange rates when the building outside air dampers are closed tightly. In Anchorage and Fayetteville, the difference is only 0.1 exchanges per hour, and in Huron and Norfolk the difference is insignificant. Thus, during times of minimum outside air intake, little of the outside air enters the Huron and Norfolk buildings through the outside air intake vents. In the rest of the buildings, the amount of air brought in through the vents is comparable to the ASHRAE nonsmoking ventilation recommendation. Thus, either the minimum outside air damper settings are much too low or the building designers are relying on residual air leakage or infiltration to meet outside air ventilation requirements.

Table 20 shows the monthly average ventilation rates for all nine buildings based on monthly average outside temperatures for the cities or nearby cities and an assumed inside temperature of 23°C. The ventilation rate for each month is based on the averages in Table 18 or visual inspection of the plots of ventilation versus temperature difference (Figs. 12 through 19) when the mean ventilation rate is not representative of the data. Again, there are some very low monthly average ventilation rates in some of the buildings. In many cases, the monthly average ventilation rate is lower than the ASHRAE recommendation. Even when the monthly average is not below the recommendation, there will be periods during the month when the ventilation rate is lower.

In measuring the ventilation rates in the eight office buildings, it has been found that there are times when the mechanical systems are bringing in minimum amounts of outside air which are close to or below suggested ventilation levels. The measured rates are averages over an entire building, and there are local variations in ventilation and uniformity of air distribution among zones, floors, rooms, and parts of rooms. Some of these variations are evident during the ventilation measurements after the injection of the SF_6 tracer. The SF_6 concentration on some of the floors does not attain the same initial concentration or decrease at the same rate as the rest of the building. There are many ways to define ventilation efficiency, but they generally quantify the departure

TABLE 20—*Monthly Average Ventilation Rates.*[a]

Month	Anchorage[b]	Ann Arbor[c]	Columbia	Fayetteville[d]
January	0.46	0.47	0.64	0.32
February	0.46	0.47	1.09	0.32
March	0.46	0.47	1.09	0.35
April	0.75	1.96	1.10	0.35
May	1.10	1.94	0.69	0.65
June	1.22	0.94	0.68	0.36
July	1.22	0.50	0.68	0.36
August	1.22	0.50	0.68	0.36
September	1.22	1.94	0.68	0.36
October	0.75	1.96	1.10	0.35
November	0.46	0.86	1.09	0.35
December	0.46	0.47	0.64	0.32

Month	Huron	Norfolk	Pittsfield[e]	Springfield[c]
January	0.26	0.70	0.40	1.00
February	0.26	0.70	0.40	1.00
March	0.32	1.05	0.38	0.95
April	0.14	1.00	0.67	0.76
May	0.52	0.75	1.25	0.62
June	0.53	0.58	0.50	0.59
July	0.16	0.58	0.50	0.59
August	0.53	0.58	1.19	0.59
September	0.52	0.75	1.25	0.62
October	0.13	1.00	0.67	0.76
November	0.32	1.05	0.84	0.96
December	0.26	0.70	0.40	1.00

[a]All the ventilation rates are in units of exchanges per hour.
[b]Based on outside temperatures from Homer, AK.
[c]Based on an average of outside temperatures from Flint and Detroit, MI.
[d]Based on outside temperatures from Ft. Smith, AR.
[e]Based on outside temperatures from Hartford, CT.

from uniform mixing of the supply air flowing into a space with the air in that space. In addition to a floor not receiving its proper portion of supply airflow, there also can be distribution problems on a floor. Individual rooms may not receive the appropriate amount of supply air even though the floor or zone is properly ventilated. This can happen when partitions are installed in a room and obstruct the intended airflow through the space. Finally, even within a well-ventilated room the supply air may be removed through exhaust or return ducts before it mixes with the rest of the interior air. Occurrences of such "short-circuiting" further reduce the effective ventilation rate in the occupied spaces of a building. Thus, low ventilation efficiency can reduce an already low ventilation rate to a lower effective ventilation rate for the occupants of a building. The extent of such air distribution problems in buildings is not known and needs to be investigated. Tracer gas techniques can be used to study air distribution and measure ventilation efficiency on a large scale (floors and zones) and on a small scale (within a room).

Conclusions

The average natural air infiltration rates measured in these buildings varied from 0.20 air changes per hour for the Huron federal building to 0.70 air changes per hour for the Ann Arbor federal building. The component of the design heating load from these buildings ranged from 23% for the uninsulated Fayetteville federal building to 61% for the new Springfield federal building. For four of the buildings, air infiltration contributed to over 50% of the heating loads. Two of the federal buildings, Anchorage and Huron, have low air infiltration rates (0.28 and 0.20 air changes per hour). However, even for these buildings, air infiltration was a very important part of the heating load.

Ventilation rates under occupied conditions also were measured in the eight buildings. It was found that for hot and cold outside temperatures, the buildings are operated at minimum ventilation levels to reduce space conditioning loads. At mild temperatures, outside air is used to cool the buildings, and the ventilation rates increase significantly. The minimum ventilation rates show little temperature-dependence in most of the buildings, but some of the buildings exhibit a dependence on wind speed. In most of the buildings, the summer and winter minimum ventilation rates are similar, but in some buildings there is a notable difference between the two minimum ventilation rates. The minimum ventilation rates were compared to minimum outside air intake levels suggested by ASHRAE, and it was found that most of the buildings were operated very close to or below the ASHRAE recommendation. Two of the buildings were operated well below this recommended ventilation rate. Local variations in air distribution and problems of ventilation efficiency can lead to effective ventilation rates in the specific area of the building which are significantly lower than the average rate for the building.

References

[1] Grot, R. A., Burch, D. M., Silberstein, S., and Galowin, L., "Measurement Methods for Evaluation of Thermal Integrity of Building Envelopes," NBSIR 82-2605, National Bureau of Standards, Washington, DC, 1982.

[2] Grot, R. A., Persily, A. K., Chang, Y. M., Fang, J. B., Weber, S., and Galowin, L. S., "Evaluation of the Thermal Integrity of the Building Envelopes of Eight Federal Office Buildings," NBSIR 85-3147, National Bureau of Standards, Washington, DC, 1985.

[3] Grot, R. A., Hunt, C. M., and Harrje, D. T., "Automated Air Infiltration Measurements in Large Buildings," *Proceedings*, First Air Infiltration Centre Conference, Bracknell, England, 1980.

[4] Grot, R. A., "Air Infiltration and Ventilation Rates in Two Large Office Buildings," *Proceedings*, Second ASHRAE/DoE Conference on the Thermal Performance of the Exterior Envelopes of Buildings, ASHRAE SP 38, Atlanta, GA, 1983.

[5] Grot, R. A. and Persily, A. K., "Air Infiltration and Air Tightness Tests in Eight U.S. Office Buildings," *Proceedings*, Fourth Air Infiltration Centre Conference, Bracknell, England, 1983.

[6] Persily, A. K. and Grot, R. A., "Ventilation in Large Office Buildings," *ASHRAE Transactions*, Vol. 91, Pt. 2, Atlanta, GA, 1985.

Andrew K. Persily[1] and Richard A. Grot[1]

Pressurization Testing of Federal Buildings

REFERENCE: Persily, A. K. and Grot, R. A., **"Pressurization Testing of Federal Buildings,"** *Measured Air Leakage of Buildings, ASTM STP 904*, H. R. Trechsel and P. L. Lagus, Eds., American Society for Testing and Materials, Philadelphia, 1986, pp. 184–200.

ABSTRACT: Seven federal buildings ranging in size from 1900 to 48 000 m² of floor area were pressure tested to determine the airtightness of the building envelopes. These tests are part of a larger project to evaluate the thermal integrity of the envelopes of federal buildings. The buildings were pressurized using the air-handling equipment in the buildings and a constant-injection, tracer gas technique to measure the airflow through the fans. In addition, selected windows in some of these buildings were pressure tested separately to determine the airtightness of individual components.

The results of the whole building and component pressurization tests are presented and discussed. In addition, the component pressurization test results are used to estimate the contribution of the windows to the total building air leakage. The results of the building pressurization tests are compared empirically to measured infiltration rates on the same buildings. The large building infiltration model developed by Shaw and Tamura of the National Research Council of Canada is applied to the buildings to predict air infiltration rates induced by weather.

KEY WORDS: air infiltration, air leakage, airtightness, component pressurization, large building infiltration, pressurization testing

Whole building pressurization testing has been used for many years to evaluate the airtightness of single-family homes [1,2]. In this test method, a fan induces a large and uniform pressure difference across the building envelope, and the airflow rate required to induce this pressure difference is measured. The rate of airflow required to induce a specific pressure difference between inside and outside serves as a measure of the airtightness of the building shell. Although the test conditions differ considerably from those which normally induce air exchange, pressurization testing provides a quick and quantitative

[1]Mechanical engineer and group leader, respectively, Center for Building Technology, National Bureau of Standards, Gaithersburg, MD 20899.

measurement of building tightness. The technique has been used to evaluate the airtightness of a small number of large buildings [3,4].

As part of a project to evaluate the thermal integrity of eight federal buildings located throughout the country [5,6], a whole building pressurization test method was developed that employs the air handlers in the building. Most previous pressurization measurements on large buildings involved bringing a high capacity fan to the building as is done on a smaller scale for homes. In addition to using the existing air-handling equipment to pressure test the buildings, these tests employed a constant-injection, tracer gas measurement technique to measure the airflow rate required to induce each inside-outside pressure difference.

The federal buildings discussed in this paper were all constructed in the last ten years, most within the last five, and the occupiable floor areas range from about 1900 to 48 000 m². Seven of the eight federal buildings were subjected to whole building pressurization tests. As part of the evaluation of their thermal envelopes of these buildings, pressurization testing also was applied to individual windows to evaluate the airtightness of these components [7].

Test Methods

The buildings were pressure tested in a manner similar to that used in houses [1]. A large airflow into the building induced a large and constant pressure difference across the building envelope. Several different pressure differences were induced, and the flow required to induce each pressure difference was measured.

During the whole building pressurization tests, the building ventilation system was arranged as shown in Fig. 1. The supply fans were operating while all

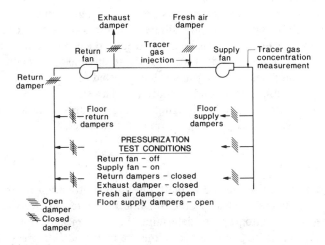

FIG. 1—*Building pressurization testing set-up.*

return and exhaust fans were turned off. All return dampers were closed so that the supply air flowing into the building only could leave the interior through outside doors, windows, and other leakage sites. The airflow through the supply fans was measured using a constant-flow, tracer gas injection scheme [8].

Tracer gas [sulfur hexafluoride (SF_6)] was injected at a constant and known rate into the airstream being brought into the building at a location close to the outside air intake vent. The tracer gas concentration was measured in the supply duct downstream from the injection point. Under conditions of good mixing of the tracer with the airflow, the airflow rate can be determined from the SF_6 injection rate and the measured concentration according to

$$Q = i/c \tag{1}$$

where

Q = airflow rate,
i = tracer gas injection rate, and
c = tracer gas concentration.

The air flow rate Q into the building was modulated either by adjusting the outside air intake dampers or the intake vanes on the centrifugal supply fans. In buildings with more than one large supply fan, individual fans could be turned on or off to further adjust the flow. For each induced flow rate Q, the inside-outside pressure differences was measured at several locations as discussed in following paragraphs. All of the pressurization tests were conducted under relatively mild wind speed conditions (less than 2 m/s) and at outside temperatures between 10 and 20°C in order to avoid weather-induced pressure differences during the tests.

The component pressurization tests were conducted by measuring the airflow necessary to induce pressure differences across individual components [7]. A temporary enclosure was installed around the component being tested from inside the building, and air was blown into this enclosure so that it could leave only through leaks in the window being tested. The airflow was induced with a large vacuum cleaner and measured with an electronic flowmeter. The airflow rate was modulated by diverting varying amounts of the airflow out of the vacuum cleaner at a point upstream of the flowmeter.

Test Equipment

The equipment used in the whole building pressurization measurements includes flowmeters to measure the SF_6 injection rate, an electron capture detector gas chromatograph to determine the SF_6 concentration, and magnetic linkage pressure gages to determine the inside-outside pressure difference. The SF_6 flowmeters were variable-area, float-type rotameters equipped with a control valve to adjust the SF_6 injection rate. Each flowmeter was individually calibrated for SF_6 by the manufacturer within an accuracy of $\pm 1\%$ of full scale. The SF_6 concentration downstream of the injection was measured with the same system used in the tracer gas measurements of air infiltration rates of these buildings [6].

The gas chromatograph/electron capture detector was calibrated within $\pm 3\%$ in the range of 10 to 250 ppb. The inside-outside pressure differences induced during the pressurization tests were measured with magnetic linkage pressure gages that were individually calibrated against an inclined manometer. The pressure gages were accurate within roughly ± 0.6 Pa. The induced pressure differences across the building shell were measured at several locations in each building. The same pressure gages were used in the pressure tests of individual components. The flowmeters used in these tests were electronic devices utilizing hot-wire anemometer principles and had an accuracy of $\pm 2\%$.

Details of Whole Building Pressurization

The following section briefly describes the test buildings and outlines the details of the whole building pressurization measurement in each building, including location and number of pressure difference measurements, fan operation, and pressure differences achieved.

Anchorage

The federal building in Anchorage is a 48 470-m^2 building divided into six connected modules. The modules vary in height from two to six stories. The building has six supply fans of varying capacities, one for each module. All of the modules are open to each other, and the airflow from any of the six fans pressurizes the entire building. All six fans were used in the pressurization tests, and, therefore, SF_6 was injected in and sampled from six locations in the building.

Four different inside-outside pressure differences were induced in this building, ranging from 14 to 38 Pa. For the lowest pressure difference, only four of the six fans were operated. The next highest pressure difference employed five of the fans, and the other pressure differences were obtained using all six fans. The pressure differences were measured at two ends of the building on the ground floor and at the fifth floor of one of the modules. The variation in pressure difference among these three locations was only ± 1 Pa.

Ann Arbor

The federal building in Ann Arbor is a 5270-m^2, four-story building with a terraced roof construction; that is, each story has less floor area than the story below. There is a post office in part of the lower two floors which has its own air-handling system. The lobby also has a separate air handler. The rest of the building is served by a main air handler located on the third floor. This building was pressurized using only the main supply fan. Four inside-outside pressure differences were induced, ranging from about 10 to 60 Pa. The pressure differences were measured at two locations on the ground floor and on the third floor.

The post office on the first floor, which occupies about 16% of the total building volume, is not served by the fan used in the pressurization test. Although there is not a great deal of communication between the main volume and the post office, a significant pressure difference did develop between the post office and the outside during these tests. The post office-outside pressure difference was about one half of the main volume-outside pressure difference. In analyzing the test data, the total building volume (including the post office) was assumed to be involved in the test.

Columbia

The federal building in Columbia is a 21 600-m², 15-story building. It also has a two-story courthouse attached through an underground passageway, but only the 15-story tower was pressure tested. The building has two large air-handling systems located in a mechanical room on the 15th floor. The first floor, basement, and lobby are served by two air handlers located in the basement. Although two large fans are in this building, only one fan running at partial capacity was needed to induce inside-outside pressures from 26 to 60 Pa. The pressure difference was measured at the odd-numbered floors from 3 to 13.

Huron

The federal building in Huron is a 6910-m² building with four stories. Two main supply fans in a mechanical penthouse serve two zones which communicate freely. Both fans were used to pressurize the building for some of the data points, and only one for the others. The induced pressure differences ranged from 17 to 50 Pa and were measured at the two locations on each of the four floors.

Norfolk

The Norfolk federal building is an eight-story building with a floor area of 18 570 m². The building has one large supply fan in the mechanical penthouse, which was sufficient to induce inside-outside pressure differences from 8 to 30 Pa. These pressure differences were measured on each floor of the building.

Pittsfield

This two-story building has a floor area of 1860 m² and a separate fan for each story. The locations for communication between the floors include two stairwells, an elevator shaft, and other smaller leakage sites. It was not obvious that we would be able to develop the same pressure difference on the two floors since each floor is served by a separate fan; however, we were able to develop essentially identical pressure differences on each floor. These pressure differences were measured at two locations on each floor and ranged from 25 to almost 100 Pa.

Springfield

The Springfield federal building is a 14 560-m², five-story building. Two large supply fans located in a penthouse serve the north and south zones, respectively. On the upper floors, the two zones are connected through passageways. On the first two floors, both zones open onto an atrium. During the pressurization test, all doors between the zones and into the atrium were open. The north zone fan was used to obtain pressure differences of 10 and 14 Pa, while both fans were used to induce a 23-Pa pressure difference. The inside-outside pressure differences were measured on all five floors of the north zone and on the second and fourth floors of the south zone.

Whole Building Pressurization Results

The following section presents the results of the pressurization tests on the seven federal buildings and some analysis of these data. In addition, the airtightness values of these buildings are compared to measurements made in several Canadian office buildings.

The test data for each building is in the form of several combinations of airflow Q and inside-outside pressure difference Δp. For each building, the Q and Δp values are fit to a curve of the form

$$Q = C\Delta p^n \qquad (2)$$

Table 1 presents equations for the curve fits for each of the seven buildings and the ranges of pressure differences that were achieved. Five of the seven exponents n are, as expected, in the approximate range of ½ to 1. The exponent for Springfield is quite large due to difficulties in maintaining the low flow rates at a constant level, however the flow at 23 Pa was repeatable and is believed to be accurate. There are many ways to quantify the results of pressurization tests. The test results for homes are often presented in terms of the induced flow rate at an inside-outside pressure difference of 50 Pa. The ranges of measured pressure differences in Table 1 are variable over the seven

TABLE 1—*Curve fits to pressurization data for the federal buildings and the pressure measurement range.*

Building	Curve Fit[a]	Range of Measured Pressure Difference, Pa
Anchorage	$Q = (2.14 \times 10^4)\Delta p^{0.61}$	14 to 38
Ann Arbor	$Q = (3.17 \times 10^3)\Delta p^{0.67}$	11 to 61
Columbia	$Q = (1.83 \times 10^4)\Delta p^{0.47}$	26 to 60
Huron	$Q = (1.58 \times 10^3)\Delta p^{0.64}$	17 to 50
Norfolk	$Q = (8.08 \times 10^3)\Delta p^{0.74}$	8 to 30
Pittsfield	$Q = (2.55 \times 10^3)\Delta p^{0.36}$	25 to 97
Springfield	$Q = (9.90 \times 10^1)\Delta p^{2.09}$	10 to 23

[a]Q is in units of m³/h, and Δp is in Pa.

buildings, but they all have measurements at roughly 25 Pa. In addition, the measurements close to 25 Pa were repeatable in the buildings that had flow exponents out of the range from ½ to 1. Therefore, the flow at 25 Pa as determined with Eq 2 is used to compare the airtightness of these buildings. By using the 25-Pa flow rates as a measure of airtightness, we need not compare values extrapolated out of the range of measurements.

The 25-Pa flow rates in units of building volumes or air changes per hour (ACH) and m³/h/m² of building envelope (wall and roof) area are presented in Table 2. The flows are normalized by envelope area to provide a measure of the construction quality of the building shells in terms of airtightness. Note that these flow rates in ACH are significantly larger than the infiltration rates induced by weather. The 50-Pa exchange rates of the buildings are about 1.5 times the 25-Pa flows shown in the table (assuming $n = 0.65$ in Eq 2) and are low compared to those measured in homes. U.S. homes generally range from about 5 to greater than 20 ACH at 50 Pa [9]. Swedish and Canadian homes are being built with 50-Pa flow rates of less than 2 ACH [10,11]. Thus, the 50-Pa flow rates of these federal buildings correspond to very tight houses.

TABLE 2—*Pressurization test results in terms of 25-Pa flow rates.*

Building	Flow at 25 Pa, Volumes/h	Flow at 25 Pa, m³/h/m² of Envelope Area
Anchorage	0.80	6.7
Ann Arbor	0.86	4.1
Columbia	0.67	6.0
Huron	0.45	1.9
Norfolk	1.45	7.2
Pittsfield	0.95	3.5
Springfield	1.43	9.2

In comparing the pressurization test results of the federal buildings to each other and to residential buildings, the important factor of surface to volume ratio arises. Figure 2 shows the surface to volume ratios S/V in m^2/m^3 for the federal buildings and two sample houses. The one-story house is assumed to have a 110-m^2 square floor area and 2.5-m ceilings. The two-story home also has a square floor plan with roughly 100 m^2 on each floor and a 5-m building height. We see in the figure that the large sizes of the federal buildings lead to values of S/V that are about one third of those associated with homes.

Figure 3 shows the 25-Pa flows listed in Table 2. The vertical scale on the left shows the 25-Pa flows in ACH for the seven federal buildings and the two sample houses shown in Fig. 2 (2.0 ACH at 50 Pa—very tight). The vertical scale on the right shows the 25-Pa flows in $m^3/h/m^2$ of envelope area. We see that in moving from ACH to $m^3/h/m^2$ the ranking of the buildings' tightness changes significantly. Also, the spread in the leakage values using the second measure is larger than the spread in ACH. The most significant change occurs for the sample houses which are almost the leakiest in terms of ACH but almost the tightest in terms of $m^3/h/m^2$ of envelope area. Thus, while the federal buildings appear to be quite tight in terms of ACH compared to houses, the airtightness per unit of envelope area is not as impressive.

The airtightness of the federal buildings in units of $m^3/h/m^2$ is worse if one considers the fact that the roofs are of low-slope, built-up design, constructed to be impervious to both water and air. Therefore, it might be more appropri-

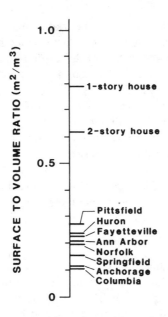

FIG. 2—*Surface to volume ratios of federal buildings and houses.*

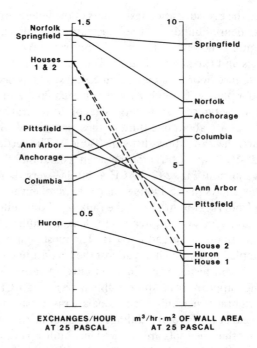

FIG. 3—*Results of pressurization test results.*

ate to normalize the 25-Pa flows by the wall area alone instead of using the total envelope area, including the roof. Normalizing the leakage rate with the wall area will lead to higher values of the 25-Pa flows in $m^3/h/m^2$.

These values of induced flow per unit envelope area may be compared to values obtained previously in Canada [3,12]. In the Canadian work, building leakage coefficients were determined for eight office buildings with construction dates ranging from 1964 to 1974 and heights from 9 to 25 stories. Seven of the eight Canadian buildings ranged from 2.4 to 6.2 $m^3/h/m^2$ at 25 Pa, and one had a value of 11.0 $m^3/h/m^2$. These Canadian values are flows per square metre of wall area as opposed to envelope area as used in Table 2. Comparing these values to those listed in Table 2, we see that the federal buildings are comparable in tightness to these Canadian buildings.

Results of Component Pressurization

Windows were individually pressure tested in six of the eight buildings. Because of the large variation in component size and frame arrangements, it was difficult to seal the test apparatus. For these reasons, only a small number of components were tested and the results should be considered preliminary. The results are expressed in units of L/s of induced air flow at 75 Pa/m of crack length for windows and include both frame and sash leakage. The American Society of Heating, Refrigerating, and Air-Conditioning Engineers' "Handbook of Fundamentals" [13] lists a window leakage standard of 0.77 L/s/m (sash leakage only), varying somewhat with window type. Table 3 shows the results of the window pressurization tests for the six buildings tested. In addition, this table lists samples of window leakage measurements from the literature [4,14,15].

In Table 3 we see a wide variation in the measured window leakage rates, even for the relatively small number of windows tested. The operable windows in the Columbia building are very leaky, along with some cracks around windows in the Fayetteville buildings through which daylight is visible. Most of the other windows tested are somewhat leakier than the standard of 0.77 L/s/ m. As mentioned earlier, the standard applies to sash leakage only, while our measurements include both sash and frame leakage. The field tests of many new residential windows (sash and frame leakage) yielded an average value very close to this standard [14]. The office building from Ref. 15, built in the mid-1960s, has very leaky windows. Several windows from Canadian supermarkets and shopping centers [4] had leakage values comparable to those in the office buildings discussed in this report. Most of the windows tested in the federal buildings and those in the literature are leakier than the 0.77 L/s/m standard.

Window leakage rates can be combined with the total window crack length to estimate the net window leakage in the buildings. These window leakage values are compared with the total building leakage from the whole building pressurization tests to determine the fraction of total building leakage associ-

TABLE 3—*Results of window pressurization tests.*

Building	Window	Air Flow Rates at 75 Pa, L/s/m
Anchorage	inoperable	3.22, 0.67, 1.09, 0.89, 0.98
Ann Arbor	inoperable	0.91, 1.04
Columbia	operable	4.41, 5.56, 3.61, 3.22
Fayetteville	inoperable	0.44, 0.32
	window cracks[a]	7.40, 5.96
Norfolk	inoperable	1.23, 1.56, 1.47
Pittsfield	operable	1.30, 0.41

Past Measurements	Air Flow Rates at 75 Pa, L/s/m
Window leakage standard (Ref 11)	0.77
Residential windows (Ref 12)	mean value of 0.81
Office building (Ref 13)	1.36, 3.54, 3.55, 3.56, 4.13, 4.97, 5.08, 10.81, 11.94, 16.04
Supermarkets and shopping malls (Ref 14)	0.20, 0.20, 0.55, 0.60, 1.10, 1.10, 1.20, 2.40

[a]These are cracks around particularly leaky windows.

ated with windows. This fraction is generally around 20% for houses [9]. Since only a small number of windows were tested in the buildings, the measured leakage values may not be representative of the building average. Therefore, in calculating the fraction of building leakage associated with windows, the standard of 0.77 L/s/m is used along with two and three times this value.

In addition, the average of the measured values is used when available. Table 4 presents the results of these calculations of the fraction of total building leakage attributable to windows at 25 Pa. The total building leakage is based on the equations in Table 1. Although it is not entirely clear as to which window leakage value is appropriate for each building, the windows account for about 10 to 20% of the total building leakage at 25 Pa. This percentage is similar to the fraction of leakage associated with windows in homes.

TABLE 4—*Fraction of total building leakage associated with windows.*

Building	Window Leakage at 25 Pa[a], L/s/m		Fraction of Building Associated with Windows, %
Anchorage		0.36	8.8
		0.72	17.6
		1.08	26.4
	Measured[b]	0.55	13.4
Ann Arbor		0.36	6.2
		0.72	12.4
		1.08	18.6
	Measured[b]	0.53	9.1
Columbia		0.36	6.4
		0.72	12.8
		1.08	19.2
	Measured[b]	1.74	30.9
Huron		0.36	13.3
		0.72	26.6
		1.08	39.9
Norfolk		0.36	6.4
		0.72	12.8
		1.08	19.2
	Measured[b]	0.68	12.1
Pittsfield		0.36	8.3
		0.72	16.6
		1.08	24.9
	Measured[b]	0.43	10.0
Springfield		0.36	7.1
		0.72	14.2
		1.08	21.3

[a]0.36, 0.72, and 1.08 L/s/m correspond to 1, 2, and 3 times the standard of 0.77 L/s/m at 75 Pa.
[b]This value is the average for all the windows tested in this building.

The Relation of Pressurization Test Results to Air Infiltration Rates

While the pressurization tests are useful for comparing buildings to each other and to airtightness standards, the question remains of how the pressurization test results are related to air infiltration rates induced by weather. This question has been studied extensively in houses [9] and less so in large buildings [16-20]. The existence of both whole building pressurization test results and air infiltration measurements for the seven federal buildings allows a comparison of the two measurements. Figure 4 is a plot which compares tracer gas measurements of infiltration rates in the buildings to the 25-Pa flow rates in ACH from the pressurization tests. The infiltration rates are measurements of the leakage induced by weather, and the rates for each building correspond to approximately the same weather conditions. The correlation between these two variables is as strong as it is for homes, but the slope of infiltration rate versus pressurization flow is steeper for these large buildings than it is for houses. Such a simple relation between pressurization and infiltration neglects the dependence of infiltration on weather conditions. A more complex model of the pressurization/infiltration relation in large buildings which accounts for weather effects is discussed in paragraphs that follow.

Shaw and Tamura, of the National Research Council of Canada, have developed a model which predicts infiltration in large buildings [16]. This model consists of predictive equations for infiltration based on a computer model building and wind tunnel tests of a model of a 40-story building. The buildings considered in the work of Shaw and Tamura are generally taller than the federal buildings discussed in this report. Other large building infiltration models exist but were not applied to this data [21].

This large building model has separate predictive equations for wind- and

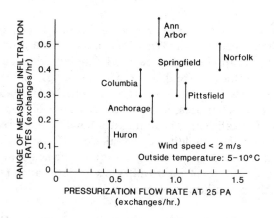

FIG. 4—*Weather-induced infiltration rates versus pressurization test results.*

temperature-induced infiltration. The wind-induced infiltration Q_w is expressed as

$$Q_w = \alpha C' \text{LH}(\rho u^2 C_p/2)^n \tag{3}$$

where

α = a factor to account for wind directions other than normal to the longest building wall, which is of length L,

H = the building height,

C' and n = the building flow coefficient and exponent from Eq 2,

C' = the leakage coefficient of the walls, determined by dividing the value of C in Eq 2 by the building wall area,

ρ = the air density,

u = the wind speed, and

C_p = the wind pressure coefficient for the windward wall.

The stack-induced infiltration is expressed as

$$Q_s = C'S[3464\gamma(\Delta T/T_{\text{in}} T_{\text{out}})]^n [(\beta H)^{n+1}/n + 1] \tag{4}$$

where

S = the building perimeter,

ΔT = the inside-outside temperature difference,

β = the height of the neutral pressure level divided by the building height, and

γ = a thermal draft coefficient that accounts for the extent of vertical communication in the building.

A value of $\gamma = 0.0$ corresponds to no openings between floors, and 1.0 corresponds to a totally open interior. While there is no straightforward technique for determining the appropriate value of γ for an individual building, Shaw and Tamura suggest a value of 0.80 for office buildings, and this value was used for all the federal buildings with two exceptions. In Anchorage, all floors open onto a central lobby area, and, therefore, a value of 0.95 was used for the thermal draft coefficient. The Springfield building has a vertically open atrium on the front of the building, and a value of 0.87 was used. The neutral pressure level is assumed to equal one half the building height in all the buildings. The wind Q_w and temperature difference Q_s infiltration rates are combined to yield the net infiltration rate according to

$$Q_{ws} = \max(Q_w, Q_s) \{1 + 0.24[(\min Q_w, Q_s)/\max(Q_w, Q_s)]^{3.3}\} \tag{5}$$

The max and min functions correspond to the maximum or minimum value in the brackets.

Table 5 compares the measurements of infiltration in the seven buildings to predicted rates from the Shaw-Tamura model. The predictions are made for the same weather conditions as the measurements, a wind speed of 2 m/s and an outside temperature of 7°C. In all buildings, the predictions are much lower than the measurements, especially in Ann Arbor and Springfield. The Springfield predictions are low because the curve fit to the building's pressurization data (Eq 2) has a large value for the flow exponent ($n = 2.09$) and a correspondingly low value for the flow coefficient. This low flow coefficient value leads to low predicted infiltration rates. If, instead, we assume the exponent is equal to 0.65 and use the 25-Pa flow rate to get a new flow coefficient, these predictions are more accurate. These second Springfield predictions correspond to the Springfield-Adjusted values in Table 5.

This result of generally low predictions compared to measurements also was found by Hunt and Treado [17] in an eleven-story office building. They attributed the larger measured infiltration rates to toilet exhausts and other forced ventilation. However, in the seven federal buildings discussed here, the toilet, elevator, and all other exhausts were off during the infiltration measurements.

It is not clear why the predicted infiltration rates are generally so much lower than the measurements. One potential explanation for the disagreement is the existence of open elevator shafts in the buildings, which are quite susceptible to stack-induced infiltration. Another reason may have to do with the fact that during the infiltration measurement the HVAC system was running to keep the interior air well mixed. Even though the outside air supply and exhaust dampers were closed, they could have leaked. However, in Anchorage and Pittsfield, infiltration measurements were made with these

TABLE 5—*Predictions of the Shaw-Tamura large building model.*

Building	Measured Infiltration[a] Exchanges/h (Wind Speed < 2 m/s; $T_{out} \sim 7°C$)	Predicted Infiltration, Exchanges/h ($u = 2$ m/s; $T_{out} = 7°C$)
Anchorage	0.25	0.07
Ann Arbor	0.55	0.02
Columbia	0.35	0.13
Huron	0.15	0.03
Norfolk	0.50	0.15
Pittsfield	0.35	0.14
Springfield	0.40	0.01
Springfield-Adjusted	. . .	0.25

[a]Representative infiltration rate for specified weather conditions.

dampers sealed with plastic, and the measured rates were no different from the rates when the dampers were closed but not sealed. Another factor to consider is leakage due to local pressurization when the fans are running. All the buildings use ceiling plenums as return ducts, and leakage in the outside walls surrounding this plenum space will lead to the intake of outside air through these leaks and increased air exchange rates. Such plenum leaks were seen in Fayetteville, and their existence is suspected in other buildings. However, it is difficult to estimate the contribution of such leakage to the net air exchange of the building.

Another reason for the disagreement between the model predictions and the measurements may be that the model was developed for taller buildings (about 40 stories) than the federal buildings (from 2 to 15 stories). Another factor could be that the wind speed measurements at the federal buildings were made roughly 5 m above the roof, while the model calls for free stream wind speed at the building height. However, predicted infiltration rates for higher wind speeds do not exhibit significantly larger errors than the 2 m/s predictions shown in Table 5, and, therefore, wind speed measurement errors do not appear a likely source of measurement error.

Conclusions

As part of a project designed to evaluate the thermal integrity of the building envelopes of eight federal buildings, the airtightness of the envelopes were evaluated using pressurization techniques. Seven of the buildings were subjected to whole building pressurization tests, and the 25-Pa flow rates were found to vary between 0.45 and 1.45 ACH. The airtightness levels of these large buildings correspond to tight houses in terms of ACH. The airtightness of the buildings in units of flow per envelope area range from 1.9 to 9.2 m³/h/ m² and is higher than for tight houses due to the low surface to volume ratios of the federal buildings. Therefore, the airtightness in ACH from the pressurization tests provides a misleading indication of the federal buildings' airtightness.

A small number of windows in six of the buildings were pressure tested individually, and, while a wide range of leakiness levels was evident, they were generally leakier than a common window tightness standard. The fraction of total building leakage associated with windows was calculated to be about 10 to 20%, a percentage similar to that found in houses. The large building infiltration model of Shaw and Tamura was applied to the seven buildings which were pressure tested, and the predictions were lower than the infiltration rates measured with tracer gas.

Acknowledgments

The research in these federal office buildings was sponsored by the Public Building Service of the General Services Administration. The authors acknowledge the technical assistance of Douglas Pruitt in conducting the tests and the data analysis efforts of Charlene Frith.

References

[1] "Method for Determining Air Leakage Rate by Fan Pressurization Test," ASTM E 779-81, The American Society for Testing and Materials, Philadelphia, 1981.

[2] Kronvall, J., "Testing of Homes for Air Leakage Using a Pressure Method," *ASHRAE Transactions*, Vol. 84(I), 1978.

[3] Shaw, C. Y., Sander, D. M., and Tamura, G. T., "Air Leakage Measurements of the Exterior Walls of Tall Buildings," *ASHRAE Transactions*, Vol. 79(II), 1973.

[4] Shaw, C. Y., "Air Tightness: Supermarkets and Shopping Malls," *ASHRAE Journal*, March 1981.

[5] Grot, R. A., Burch, D. M., Silberstein, S., and Galowin, L., "Measurement Methods for Evaluation of Thermal Integrity of Building Envelopes," NBSIR 82-2605, National Bureau of Standards, Washington, DC, 1982.

[6] Grot, R. A., Chang, Y. L., Persily, A. K., and Fang, J. B., "Interim Report on NBS Thermal Integrity Diagnostic Tests on Eight GSA Federal Office Buildings," NBSIR 83-2768, National Bureau of Standards, Washington, DC, 1983.

[7] "Test Method for Rate of Air Leakage Through Exterior Windows, Curtain Walls, and Doors," ASTM E 283-73, The American Society for Testing and Materials, Philadelphia, 1973.

[8] Svensson, A., "Methods for Measurement of Airflow Rates in Ventilation Systems," Bulletin M83:11, The National Swedish Institute for Building Research, Stockholm, 1983.

[9] Persily, A., "Understanding Air Infiltration in Homes," Report No. 129, Center for Energy and Environmental Studies, Princeton University, Princeton, NJ. 1982.

[10] Dumont, R. S., Orr, H. W., and Figley, D. A., "Air Tightness Measurements of Detached Houses in the Saskatoon Area," Building Research Note No. 178, Division of Building Research, National Research Council of Canada, Ottawa, 1981.

[11] Kronvall, J., "Airtightness—Measurements and Measurement Methods," Report D8, Swedish Council of Building Research, 1980.

[12] Tamura, G. T. and Shaw, C. Y., "Studies of Exterior Wall Air Tightness and Air Infiltration of Tall Buildings," *ASHRAE Transactions*, Vol. 82(I), 1976.

[13] "ASHRAE Handbook of Fundamentals," The American Society of Heating, Refrigerating and Air Conditioning Engineers, Atlanta, 1985.

[14] Weidt, J. L., Weidt, J., and Selkowitz, S., "Field Air Leakage of Newly Installed Residential Windows," DOE/ASHRAE Conference on the Thermal Performance of Exterior Envelopes of Buildings, Orlando, Florida, Dec. 1979.

[15] Ward, I. C. and Sharples, S., "An Investigation of the Infiltration Characteristics of Windows and Doors in a Tall Building Using Pressurization Techniques," Report BS 68, Department of Building Science, University of Sheffield, Sheffield, England, 1982.

[16] Shaw, C. Y. and Tamura, G. T., "The Calculation of Air Infiltration Rates Caused by Wind and Stack Action for Tall Buildings," *ASHRAE Transactions*, Vol. 83(II), 1977.

[17] Hunt, C. M. and Treado, S. J., "Air Exchange Measurements in a High-Rise Office Building," DOE/ASHRAE Conference on the Thermal Performance of Exterior Envelopes of Buildings, Orlando, Florida, Dec. 1979.

[18] Freeman, J., Gale, R., and Lilly, J. P., "Ventilation Measurements in Large Buildings," in *Air Infiltration Reduction in Existing Buildings*, Proceedings of the 4th Air Infiltration Centre Conference, Elm, Switzerland, Sept. 1983, AIC, Bracknell, England.

[19] de Gids, W. F., Phaff, J. C., Knoll, B., "An Overview of Ventilation Research in Large Nonresidential Buildings," in *Air Infiltration Reduction in Existing Buildings*, Proceedings of the 4th Air Infiltration Centre Conference, Elm, Switzerland, Sept. 1983, AIC, Bracknell, England.

[20] Zuercher, C. H. and Feustel, H., "Air Infiltration in High-Rise Buildings," in *Air Infiltration Reduction in Existing Buildings*, Proceedings of the 4th Air Infiltration Centre Conference, Elm, Switzerland, Sept. 1983, AIC, Bracknell, England.

[21] Liddament, M. and Allen, C., "The Validation and Comparison of Mathematical Models of Air Infiltration," Technical Note 11, Air Infiltration Centre, Sept. 1983, AIC, Bracknell, England.

DISCUSSION

Helmut Feustel [1] *(written discussion)*—(1) What were your upper limits for wind speeds and temperature differences between inside and outside for your pressurization tests? (2) Where does one measure pressure differences in high-rise buildings? (3) Could you explain the high number for the pressure exponent (over 2.0) for one of your pressurization tests?

A. K. Persily and R. A. Grot (authors' closure)—(1) As mentioned in the report, during all the tests the wind speed was less than 2 m/s and the outside temperature was between 10 and 20°C. Obviously, large wind speeds and temperature differences will interfere with the test pressures during the test, and pressure tests under these conditions should be avoided. It is difficult to state precise limits for any given building. (2) The locations of the pressure difference measurement points in each building are given in the report. It is necessary to measure the pressure at several points in order to ensure that a uniform pressure difference is being induced across the entire building shell. The exact number at measurement locations depends on the building shape and size. They should cover a range in height and more than one side of the building. (3) In testing the building (Springfield) with a large value of n, it was difficult to obtain the low pressure readings. These points were therefore less accurate than the higher pressure points, and this is probably the reason for the unexpected curve fit.

[1]Lawrence Berkeley Laboratory, Berkeley, CA 94720.

Technique for Measurements and Infiltration Reduction

Russell N. Dietz,[1] *Robert W. Goodrich,*[2] *Edgar A. Cote,*[2] *and Robert F. Wieser*[2]

Detailed Description and Performance of a Passive Perfluorocarbon Tracer System for Building Ventilation and Air Exchange Measurements

REFERENCE: Dietz, R. N., Goodrich, R. W., Cote, E. A., and Wieser, R. F., "**Detailed Description and Performance of a Passive Perfluorocarbon Tracer System for Building Ventilation and Air Exchange Measurements,**" *Measured Air Leakage of Buildings, ASTM STP 904*, H. R. Trechsel and P. L. Lagus, Eds., American Society for Testing and Materials, Philadelphia, 1986, pp. 203–264.

ABSTRACT: The manufacturing procedures for and the performance of a building air infiltration kit consisting of miniature passive perfluorocarbon tracer (PFT) permeation sources and passive adsorption tube samplers are described. With four PFT types available, homes and buildings with up to four separate zones can be evaluated fully under steady state conditions for the air infiltration and exfiltration rates from each zone as well as for the air exchange rates between zones using this inexpensive and nonobtrusive field kit. Complete details on deployment in homes and on gas chromatographic analysis of the passive samplers are presented. Examples of total air changes per hour (ACH) results in several studies showed average values between 0.25 to 0.64 h^{-1}. A generalized correlation was used to characterize the leakiness of eleven homes in the United States and Canada, showing ACH dependency only on inside-outside temperature difference, on wind speed to the 1.5 power, and on a subjective terrain factor; the approach has application in evaluating weatherization performance. Details of multizone measurements in four homes provided insight into the role of attics, crawl spaces, and basements on the indoor air quality and weatherization needs for the living zone.

KEY WORDS: air infiltration, perfluorocarbon tracers, passive sampler, multizone modeling, gas chromatograph, air leakage, weatherization, indoor air quality

[1]Head, Tracer Technology Center, Department of Applied Science, Brookhaven National Laboratory, Upton, NY 11973.
[2]Chemical associate, technical associate, and technical specialist, respectively, Department of Applied Science, Brookhaven National Laboratory, Upton, NY 11973.

During the last decade, concern for the quality of indoor air has increased, mainly motivated by the energy conservation and alternative fuel practices now employed in many homes [1], but also from increased recognition of the fact that individuals spend the greatest portion of their lives within the indoor environment. These energy cost-reduction practices will continue to be implemented in both the private and commercial sector, in part further motivated by limitations in the energy supply side in certain locations.

Since about one third of the heat loss in homes during the heating season is attributable to air exfiltration, the escape of heated air and its replacement by cold infiltrating air, attempts to reduce that loss may increase the occupant's exposure to internally generated pollutants. In many commercial, public, and industrial buildings (for example, hospitals, office buildings, etc.), not only is there a concern for the extent of total air infiltration but also for the distribution of that ventilation within the many floors of naturally ventilated buildings or between the heating, ventilating, and air-conditioning (HVAC) zones of buildings equipped with such systems.

To quantify the extent of air infiltration in buildings, one of two techniques generally have been used, either the conservative tracer approach or a building pressurization technique; a review of both methods is provided elsewhere [2]. Briefly, the tracer approach determines the infiltration rate as it normally exists in the building by measuring either the decay of the tracer concentration (if only an initial quantity is injected) or the steady state concentration (if a continuous known tracer release rate is used) or the tracer emission rate (if the tracer concentration is held constant) [3]. The pressurization method requires a blower assembly to be installed, and the total flow rate developed by the blower when the house or small building is brought to a specified pressure is related to the expected normal exfiltration rate through the use of a complex empirical model [4]. This latter method was never intended for larger, more complex buildings, and now it is generally being conceded that, even in the case of small, single-zone homes, the pressurization method is not giving a reliable measure of the air exfiltration rate under normal conditions.

Although tracer techniques provide the most reliable approach to determining air infiltration rates and rates of air exchange between zones in buildings, most methods either have been costly to field implement or have provided only brief (1 to 4h) measures of the rates. Because of the need for a simple, yet reliable, tracer technique, a kit was developed coined the Brookhaven National Laboratory Air Infiltration Measurement System (BNL/AIMS). The field components—miniature perfluorocarbon tracer (PFT) permeation sources and passive samplers—are quite inexpensive and reusable, require no trained field personnel, and can provide integrated measurements over days or months [1,5]. With the use of a programmable multitube sampler or a portable real-time analyzer, short-term (for example, hourly) variations also can be determined.

The BNL/AIMS is based on the applicable steady state assumption for a home considered as a single, well-mixed zone such that the average tracer concentration in that home is equal to the emission rate of the tracer source divided by the air exfiltration rate. Knowing the source rate and by measuring the average concentration with the passive sampler, a means to calculate the approximate average air exfiltration rate is thereby established. Extending this technique to a multichamber concept, in which a different type of PFT source is deployed in each chamber of a building, allows the calculation of not only the infiltration rates in each chamber but also the air exchange rates between chambers as well. Since both the perfluorocarbon tracer (PFT) source and the passive sampler—a miniature capillary adsorption tube sampler (CATS)—are about the size of a cigarette, inexpensive, and reusable, the BNL/AIMS is a very cost-effective means for determining these air exchange rates.

BNL/AIMS makes use of the Brookhaven PFT measurement capability that has been under development and applied to long-range atmospheric tracing for the past 7 years [6, 7]. The technology for the sampling and analysis of PFTs is well-established, and, for long-range atmospheric tracing, PFTs have supplanted the use of sulfur hexafluoride (SF_6) [7].

This paper provides the necessary details for other potential users to duplicate the system, which consists of field components (the miniature PFT sources and passive samplers) and a laboratory component (an electron capture gas chromatographic analyzer). Intercomparisons with other researchers' methods are presented as well as results from field use in homes. A simple model is presented for applying the technique in two- and three-zone cases, which are demonstrated. Some results of the effect of wind speed and inside-outside air temperature differences on the whole house air exfiltration rate also are presented.

Experimental

In this section, the details on the manufacture, testing, and calibration of the PFT sources and passive samplers will be provided as well as the scheme for the gas chromatographic analysis of the samplers when they are returned for the laboratory.

The Tracer Source

Fully fluorinated organic compounds of the perfluoroalkylcycloalkane family were chosen as the class of PFTs because they have a high electron capture detector (ECD) response (nearly comparable to that of SF_6), a lower than SF_6 atmospheric background (see Table 1 for concentration units; SF_6 background is about 900 fL/L), are harmless to health and the environment

TABLE 1—*PFT source rates and lifetimes.*

PFT[a]	Vapor Pressure at 25°C, atm	Background Ambient Concentration, fL/L[b]	Liquid Density, g/mL	Molecular Weight	Permeation Rate at 25°C, nL/min	Lifetime,[c], years
PDCH	0.046	25.6	1.85	400	12 to 20	7.2 to 4.3
PMCH	0.14	3.6	1.79	350	24 to 35	4.0 to 2.7
PMCP	0.44	2.8	1.70	300	40 to 55	2.6 to 1.9
PDCB	0.50	0.35	1.67	300	36 to 50	2.9 to 2.1

[a]PDCH, PMCH, and PMCP are available from Manchem, Inc., Princeton, N.J.; PDCB is available from PCR Research Chemicals, Gainesville, Fla.

[b]Concentration units: fL/L represents femtoliters per liter (that is, parts per quadrillion or 10^{-15}); pL/L represents picoliters/liters (that is, parts per trillion or 10^{-12}); nL represents nanoliters/liter (that is, 10^{-9} liters/liter).

[c]Based on an initial liquid PFT content of 0.4 mL.

[7,8], are modest in cost (about $100/kg), and have extreme chemical stability. This characteristic is very necessary since the analysis scheme includes chemical processing of the recovered constituents from the air samples in order to destroy and remove ECD-sensitive interfering components such as ambient chlorofluorocarbons, which are present in the air at concentrations orders of magnitude higher than that of the PFT.

The PFT source is a small permeation device which, at a known temperature, emits a constant rate of PFT vapor through a silicone rubber plug connected to a source of the PFT liquid. Aluminum shells (E. I. duPont and Co., Inc., Wilmington, Delaware, No. S-140) 32 mm (1.25 in.) long by 6.6 mm (0.26 in.) inside diameter (ID) are flared slightly to facilitate the insertion of the oversized silicone rubber plugs. The shells are then lightly lubricated (swabbed with a solution of 5% silicone grease in ethyl acetate) and air-dried in an inverted position to concentrate the grease near the openings. A code number is engraved onto the aluminum shells for identification of the PFT source, silicone rubber plug type, and the number of the source.

Placed upright into a small holder, about 20 of the shells are filled in succession with exactly 0.4 mL (1000 L = 1 m^3) of the appropriate PFT liquid using an automatic pipette (Scientific Manufacturing Industries, micropipettor). Table 1 lists the presently used PFTs, which are all liquids at room temperature (boiling points from 45 to 102°C); with four PFT types, a building with as many as four zones can be characterized (see Theory section). The precut plugs, 12.7 mm (0.5 in.) long by 7 mm (0.275 in.) outer diameter (OD), are inserted, pressed flush to the end, and crimped (duPont, Pompton Lakes, New Jersey, Lab Model Crimper) into the shell. Both the aluminum shells and the crimper were previously used in an electric blasting cap tagging program [8]. About 500 sources can be made per person-week. Figure 1 gives a schematic diagram of a typical source.

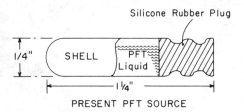

FIG. 1—*Diagram of the PFT source configuration.*

A subset of about 1 PFT source for every 50 made is kept in a constant (25°C) temperature chamber and periodically (for example, monthly) weighed on a high precision balance to determine the rate of emission. Using the gas law constant and the molecular weight, the gravimetric rate can be converted to a volumetric rate which can be compared to that determined chromatographically when a source is placed in a known flow rate of air (at a known temperature) and the PFT concentration measured on a calibrated gas chromatograph.

The extent of the effect of temperature on the PFT source rate is determined by measuring the volumetric rate chromatographically when the source temperature is varied from 25 to 37°C. In addition, several sources were placed in a 37°C oven for gravimetric determination of the effect of temperature as well.

A word of caution. As will be shown, the concentrations to be measured in homes and buildings are quite low, typically only a few parts per trillion. Thus, it is very important to keep the PFT containers, any source preparation, and the sources themselves well separated (that is, in ventilated hoods or a separate building) from any sampling and analysis equipment.

The Tracer Samplers

Two types of PFT samplers have been used, a passive sampler designed and fabricated at Brookhaven and a programmable sampler conceived at Brookhaven and now commercially available. The former will be described in detail, but the latter will only be briefly mentioned because it can be purchased.

Passive Sampler—The sampler is a glass tube about the size of a cigarette with an adsorbent in the middle. The device samples tracer vapors by the principal of passive diffusion. Subsequent thermal desorption and analysis gives the desired concentration results. Originally coined the capillary adsorption tube sampler (CATS) because of a capillary tube on one end [2], the present configuration is shown in Fig. 2. A glass tube, 6.4 mm (0.25 in.) OD by 4 mm (0.156 in.) ID by 6.4 cm (2.5 in.) long with a 45° taper ground at the ends to about one third the wall thickness (to prevent cutting of O-rings in the

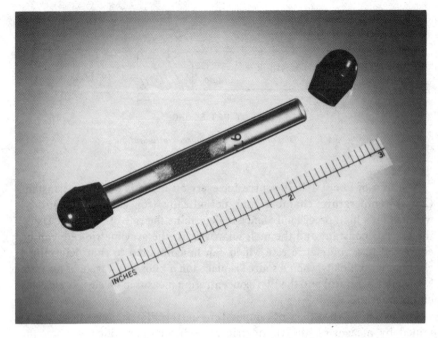

FIG. 2—*Passive sampler with polyurethane rubber caps.*

desorption apparatus), is cut from conventional pyrex glass tubing selected to have an ID within ±1.5% of the design value; the length is cut to within ± 0.8 mm. This tolerance is necessary to keep the sampling rate, which is proportional to the cross-sectional area and inversely proportional to the length from the mouth of the glass tube to the surface of the adsorbent bed, within ±3% precision [2].

Screens to retain the adsorbent material are fabricated by punching 9.5-mm (3/8-in.)-OD disks from 150 mesh stainless steel wire cloth (Newark Wire Cloth, Newark, New Jersey) and then shaping them into a cup by pressing the disk through a 4.1-mm (0.16-in.) hole in a 8-mm-thick brass plate with the back of a 3.6-mm (No. 28) drill bit mounted in a drill press. The screen cups then are washed in a degreasing solvent, a detergent, and finally distilled water in an ultrasonic bath.

The charcoal-like adsorbent, Ambersorb (Type 347, Rohm and Haas, Inc., Philadelphia, Pennsylvania) is boiled in distilled water three times, decanting away any fine dust floating on the surface. Next, since the adsorbent is in the form of small beads, the material is dried and then rolled down a very shallow inclined plane to separate any shapes that are not nearly perfect spheres (much of this nonspherical material was found to be compacted particles of Ambersorb dust). Finally, it is boiled again until the decanted fluid is clear, dried, and sieved to a 30 to 50 mesh size. Coconut charcoal, which can be used in place of Ambersorb, is treated in the same way excluding rolling.

Once the glass tubes have been cleaned using detergent solution and an identification number has been either hand-engraved using a diamond-tipped vibrator (Acme Burgess, Grayslake, Illinois, Model 74) or fired into the glass using powdered lead glass black numbered decals (Whale Apparatus Co., Hellertown, Pennsylvania), a cupped screen then is pressed into one end of the tube to a depth of 2.75 cm. Then the glass tube is filled with 64 mg of the prepared adsorbent and a screen placed in the other end. A small cup holding exactly 64 mg (0.11 cm³) is used for rapid filling of the tubes.

Whether for initial bakeout or for thermal desorption and recovery of sampled PFTs, a special rack with 23 positions was built as shown in Fig. 3. The resistance heating wire element consists of about 10 turns of 0.8-mm-OD (20 gage) nichrome wire (approximately 23 cm in length) such that 4.2 Vac (≈ 8.5 A or 36 W) heats the CATS tube to 450°C in 0.5 min and 1.9 Vac (≈ 3.8 A or 7 W) holds that temperature for another 0.5 min to effect the sample recovery; power is supplied from a transformer with a secondary rated at 6.3 Vac and 10 A (Essex/Stancor No. P-6308). The tubes are placed into the rack by

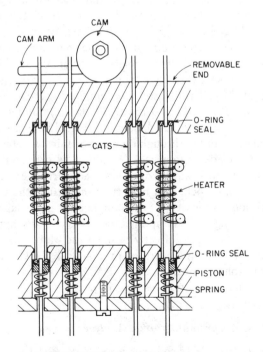

THERMAL DESORPTION APPARATUS

FIG. 3—*Passive sampler thermal desorption rack.*

slipping through the heating coil (with one rack end removed) until they contact the spring-loaded O-ring seal pistons; the removal end, a 25-mm (1-in.) aluminum square stock, is replaced and the eccentric cam compresses the tube ends against the spring-loaded seals. The open 1.59-mm ($^1/_{16}$-in.) tubing ends are connected to a 24-position Scanivalve rotary valve assembly (Gilian Instrument Corp., Wayne, New Jersey) which has an electrical rotary switch to bring the desorption power to the proper tube.

An alternatively designed desorption rack has different tube seals. A double O-ring seal is accomplished by the tube slipping through two O-rings, 9.5 mm (0.375 in.) OD by 6.4 mm (0.25 in.) ID, trapped in each end of the aluminum square stock; other aspects remain the same.

After initial fabrication of the CATS passive sampler, it is made ready for its first use by flushing with distilled water and then thermally desorbing at 425 to 450°C for about 20 min. The ends then are sealed with specially fabricated polyurethane rubber caps (Girard Rubber Co., Elmsford, New York, U103B-PU).

Sampling commences when the rubber cap near the numbered end is removed. Since the rate of sampling is proportional to the tracer diffusivity in air, the theoretical effective air sampling rates for each tracer are 214 mL/day for perfluorodimethylcyclobutane (PDCB) and perfluoromethylcyclopentane (PMCP); 201 for perfluoromethylcyclohexane (PMCH); and 188 for perfluorodimethylcyclohexane (PDCH) [2]. Rates are confirmed with standards and simultaneous programmable sampler measurements.

Programmable Sampler—The commercially available sampler (Gilian Instrument Corp., Model RD113) contains a lid and a base assembly, which together weigh just 7 kg. The lid assembly contains 23 stainless steel sampling tubes, 3.2 mm (0.125 in.) OD by 0.15 mm (0.006 in.) wall by 15.2 cm (6 in.) long, filled in the center with 150 mg of the Ambersorb adsorbent. Connected to a common inlet and outlet through the same Scanivalve rotary valve assembly used for the CATS desorption rack, each tube adsorbs all the PFTs in the air pulled through them at a rate, duration, and start time controlled by the pump, 7-day calendar clock, and battery all housed in the base assembly. Thermal desorption for recovery of the sample back in the laboratory occurs by direct ohmic heating of the sampling tubes. A low voltage high current (1.3 Vac at about 15 A) is passed directly through the wall of the stainless steel tube, which attains a temperature of over 400°C. This unit, coined the Brookhaven atmospheric tracer sampler (BATS), has been used in many atmospheric and home infiltration tests [2,6,7].

The Laboratory Gas Chromatographic Analyzer

The determination of PFTs collected via either the passive or programmable samplers is accomplished with a gas chromatograph (GC) system (Varian Instrument Corp., Floral Park, New Jersey, Model 3700 GC with a Model

CDS-111 integrator-controller) modified at Brookhaven. The scheme includes thermal desorption, chemical and physical processing, chromatographic separation, and ECD determination of the quantity of tracer recovered.

Because the analysis system is unique and necessarily complex, a detailed description is beyond the scope of this paper. Here, a brief description will be given with reference to the schematic diagram and the sequencing of events. Before the sample is thermally desorbed, the sampler tube is purged with carrier gas (5% H_2 in N_2) for a short period of time to remove any traces of oxygen which otherwise would react with the PFTs during the 400°C desorption recovery. The sample is purged through the precut catalyst (Table 2), the dryer to remove water vapor, and the two precut columns before entering an adsorbent trap. The 10-cm-long catalyst bed in the presence of the hydrogen in the carrier gas reduces any chlorofluorocarbon compounds, as well as any remaining oxygen, to their hydrogenated forms, thus rendering these interfering compounds nonelectron-capturing. After the surviving PFTs elute from the precut column, heavier molecular weight constituents still within the column are purged to the atmosphere by reversing the direction of flow. Meanwhile, the eluted PFTs are reconcentrated within a 10-cm-long Porapak QS adsorbent trap.

The purpose of the QS trap on the gas chromatograph (GC) is two-fold. First, by not opening the trap until the first PFT eluting from the precut column arrives, some lighter constituents are discarded. Second, after the precut column is backflushed, the trap remains open for 1 min to further purge away light-interfering gases and then is closed. When the Porapak QS trap has been heated to 200°C and opened, the PFTs are flushed through the

TABLE 2—*GC specification and conditions. All columns (including catalyst beds and adsorbent trap) are made with 3.2-mm (0.125-in.)-OD stainless steel tubing.*

Main column	1.2 m (4 ft) long packed with 0.1% SP-1000 on Carbopack C (Supelco, Inc., Bellefonte, Pa.)
Precut columns	1.2 m (4 ft) long Porasil F followed by 0.3 m (1 ft) long of 0.1% SP-1000 on Carbopack C
Column oven	140°C
Precut catalyst	10.1 cm (4 in.) long packed with palladium (Pd) (1%) on polyethylenimine/SiO_2-Royer Pd catalyst (Strem Chemicals, Inc., Newburyport, Mass.); 200°C
Main catalyst	3.2 cm (1.24 in.) long packed similarly; 200°C
Carrier gas	5% H_2 in N_2 at 25 and 20 mL/min, respectively, through the precut and main columns
Porapack QS trap	10.1 cm (4 in.) long packed with Porapak QS
Permeation dryer	1.2 m (4 ft) long Nafion dryer (Permapure Products Inc., Oceanport, N.J., Model MD-125-48S) located in the top of GC (~35°C)
ECD	180°C

main catalyst (see Table 2) for final cleanup before entering the main column for separation of the PFTs prior to detection in the ECD. While this is occurring, the next sample tube can be thermally desorbed and loaded onto the QS trap once it has sufficiently cooled (about 50°C), thus almost halving the overall PFT sample recovery and analysis time by overlapping the stages. Automation of the sequential analysis of all 23 tubes in either a CATS desorption rack or a BATS lid is accomplished by using the BATS base timing capability to initiate the GC timing sequence as each new tube steps in place. Each analysis, including reporting of the peak areas, takes 10 min; 23 tubes are analyzed in just under 4 h.

Figure 4 shows the detailed plumbing and valving used to effect the automated chemical and physical processing during the analysis of the PFT samples. Automation occurs through the use of eight external events contained within the integrator-controller. As shown in the footnote of Table 3, one event starts and stops the recorder paper, four events operate the four valves, and three events control the heating of the sampler tube and the Porapak QS trap. Three 6-port (Valco Instrument Co., Houston, Texas, SSAC6T Shaft Seal) and one 4-port (Valco SSAC4UT Shaft Seal) valves with air operators

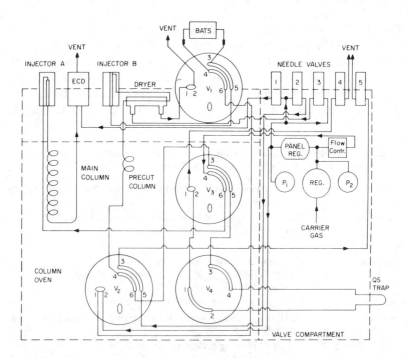

FIG. 4—*Schematic of laboratory GC analyzer. V_1 is the sample valve; V_2, the precut valve; V_3, the flow direction valve; and V_4, the Porapak QS valve. Each is shown in its "on" position; in its "off" position, the valve slots are rotated 90° counterclockwise.*

TABLE 3a—*Gas chromatograph[a] sequence of events.*

Event Time, min	Event Code	Event	Event Status
0.00	. . .	system steps to next sample tube; starts event clock	. . .
0.01	0.01	recorder starts	off
0.01	0.14	QS/sampler heating relay switches to QS trap	on
0.02	0.10	desorption power turned on	on
0.02	0.12	high power position	on
0.35	0.13	low power position	off
0.50	0.08	sample in QS trap injected (that is, V_4 on)	on
1.60	0.09	V_4 off	off
1.60	0.11	desorption power turned off	off
1.62	0.15	QS/sampler relay switches to sampler	off
2.30	0.06	V_3 on	on
4.95	0.04	V_2 on	on
5.00	0.02	V_1 on	on
5.00	0.10	desorption power turned on	on
5.00	0.12	high power position	on
5.40	0.13	low power position (not used for BATS tubes)	off
5.70	0.08	V_4 on	on
7.30	0.11	desorption power turned off	off
7.60	0.09	V_4 off	off
7.70	0.07	V_3 off	off
7.75	0.03	V_1 off	off
7.80	0.05	V_2 off	off
8.01	0.00	recorder off	on

[a]TABLE 3b—*External events designation and codes.*

| Item | Recorder | Valves | | | | Heating | | |
		Sample, V_1	Precut, V_2	Flow Direction, V_3	QS, V_4	Desorption Power	High Low	QS Sampler
Event on	0.00	0.02	0.04	0.06	0.08	0.10	0.12	0.14
Event off	0.01	0.03	0.05	0.07	0.09	0.11	0.13	0.15

are used. Vespel cone seals are preferred to the Teflon-filled ceramic type because the latter have been found to bleed contaminants at temperatures above 100°C. With the exception of the sample valve, they are mounted within the GC oven.

When the recorder shuts off at 8.01 min, the analysis is complete and the report of the peak areas, which is proportional to the quantity of each tracer, is printed as well as transmitted to a magnetic tape, which can then be processed on a Tektronix 4052 desk top computer. The GC is ready for the repeat of the cycle on a 10-min frequency.

Gas standards for calibrating the GC were prepared in the concentration range from 1 to 10 000 pL/L by first preparing 1000 ppm primary standards in helium (He) either gravimetrically or volumetrically and verifying on a thermal conductivity GC that was calibrated with pure PFT vapors. These primary standards then were successively diluted with ultra pure air (Scientific Gas Products, Plainfield, New Jersey) in Spectra-Seal aluminum cylinders (Airco Industrial Gases, Riverton, New Jersey). Regular steel cylinders were found to adsorb significant amounts of the higher boiling point tracers (PMCH and PDCH), especially at concentrations of 1 and 10 pL/L, but the Spectra-Seal cylinders showed no adsorption losses [7].

Calibration of the GC was performed by setting flow rates of 5 and 50 mL/min on the gas cylinder standards and passing the flow through consecutive BATS tubes for different durations. Quantities of from 0.05 to 5000 pL of tracer then were analyzed to calibrate the GC response for each tracer.

Theory

Numerous researchers have proposed models and methods for using tracer gases in the solution of those models for determining the air infiltration rate into a home or building considered as a single, well-mixed chamber or zone [2,3,9]. Recently, however, it has been recognized that many larger, more complex buildings, especially those with multiple-zoned HVAC systems and even one- and two-story homes with basements, realistically can only best be represented by models which recognize the building as multiple-connected zones, each of which is well-mixed [5,10–12].

In a series of tests, Maldonado demonstrated that the concentration of a tracer was very uniform in a conventional, 2.44-m (8-ft) ceiling, rooms such as living rooms, bedrooms, and basements, generally to within ±1 to 3% [13]. Furthermore, the variations between rooms on the same floor was generally within ±10%, indicating that an entire floor of a house could be considered as reasonably well-mixed. This had been demonstrated also by Dietz and Cote [2]. Only between floors was there a significant difference in concentration of as much as 30 to 60%, indicating that different floors should each be considered as separate, well-mixed zones, with finite rates of mixing between those zones. Unusual rooms in the Maldonado test house, such as the greenhouse, which was an open space from the basement level to the second floor, as well as the stairwell, showed evidence of nonuniform mixing in the vertical, that is, stratification [13].

The consequences of assuming a truly two- or three-zone building as a one-zone case can be significant for ventilation, indoor air quality, or energy load assessments. If, for example, a building is comprised of three equal-volume zones, each with its own HVAC system, but one is improperly functioning at an air infiltration rate of 0.2 h^{-1}, while the other two are at 1.1 h^{-1}, the overall average considered as a single zone is 0.8 h^{-1}; but the occupants of the first zone might be significantly more uncomfortable than those in either of the other two zones. Similarly, the air quality might be several times poorer in that zone, and the heating and cooling loads might be poorly distributed.

In another case, consider a two-story house with a basement. If it is treated as a single zone, then the concentration of any pollutant from an indoor source would be computed to be the same on all floors. However, because of the stack effect in houses in the winter time, there is generally a net-flow upwards within two- and three-level houses [5]. Thus, a pollutant source in the basement (for example, radon from ground soil) would be highest in the basement and generally half as much or so on the first and second floors. For a source on the first floor (for example, carbon monoxide (CO) from a kitchen range), the concentration would be highest on the first floor, somewhat lower on the second floor, but much less in the basement if the stack effect is evident. Finally, from, for example, an artist's studio on the second floor, the paint fumes would be highest on that floor and progressively significantly less on the first floor and in the basement.

Although the BNL/AIMS is a powerful technique for simply and inexpensively determining the air exfiltration rate in a single-zone building, its real potential is in application to the determination of air exfiltration rates from each zone and air exchange rates between zones in multizoned homes and buildings. The models for one-, two-, and three-zone cases are presented here.

One-Zone Case

For a building considered as a single, well-mixed zone of known volume, V, containing one type of tracer of known emission rate, $R_s(t)$, such that a tracer concentration, $C(t)$, is measured throughout the house which has an air exfiltration rate of $R_E(t)$, a simple material balance gives

$$V \frac{dC(t)}{dt} = R_s(t) - R_E(t)C(t) \tag{1}$$

where

$V =$ volume of the building (constant), m^3,
$R_s(t) =$ total tracer source rate (variable), nL/h,
$C(t) =$ average tracer concentration in the building (variable), $nL/m^3 \equiv$ pL/L, and
$R_E(t) =$ air exfiltration rate (variable), m^3/h.

Equation 1 is a general solution in which it is assumed that the tracer source rate, the tracer concentration, and the exfiltration rate can vary with time; it also was assumed that the tracer concentration in the ambient air, that is, the infiltrating air, is negligible, which is always the case for PFTs. Equation 1 then can be solved for various modes of tracer experiments including tracer decay, constant concentration, and constant emission rate [2,3].

The PFT sources are designed to provide a constant emission rate source in the building. About 5 to 10 h after deployment, the tracer concentration will become more or less constant, dependent only on slow changes in the exfiltration rate due either to mechanical ventilation or weather changes [2]. For these steady state assumptions [that is, $dC(t)/dt \approx 0$], Eq 1 becomes

$$\frac{1}{n} \sum_{t=1}^{n} \frac{R_s(t)}{C(t)} = \frac{1}{n} \sum_{t=1}^{n} R_E(t) = R_s \frac{1}{n} \sum_{t=1}^{n} \frac{1}{C(t)} \qquad (2)$$

assuming that the source rate is constant, that is, $R_s(t) = R_s$, over n periods of concentration. But

$$\frac{1}{n} \sum_{t=1}^{n} \frac{1}{C(t)} = \frac{1}{n} \left(\frac{1}{C(1)} + \frac{1}{C(2)} + \ldots + \frac{1}{C(n)} \right)$$

$$= \frac{1}{n} \left(\frac{C(2)C(3)\ldots C(n) + C(1)C(3)\ldots C(n) + \ldots + C(1)C(2)\ldots C(n-1)}{C(1)C(2)\ldots C(n)} \right)$$

$$\approx \frac{1}{n} \left(\frac{n\bar{C}^{n-1}}{\bar{C}^n} \right) \approx \frac{1}{\bar{C}}$$

The second term in Eq 2 is the average infiltration rate, $\bar{R}_E$. Thus

$$\bar{R}_E \approx \frac{R_s}{\bar{C}} \qquad (3)$$

The approximation in Eq 3 is because it was shown that the reciprocal of an average concentration, $\bar{C}$, which is the quantity that the passive sampler determines, is close to but not identical to the average of reciprocal concentrations. Consider two simple cases in which for each of five consecutive intervals of time a constant concentration truly prevails. As shown in Table 4, assuming a source rate of 1500 nL/h, Case 1 assumes a small concentration change (1 nL/m³) per period and Case 2 a larger value (5 nL/m³). The true exfiltration rates for each period are calculated as are the true averages for each case. Lastly, the average R_E calculated from the average concentrations, which are identical in both cases, are computed from Eq 3. As shown in Case 1, for small changes in concentration (that is, exfiltration rate), the true value is very close to that from Eq 3. The difference, less than 1%, is an order of magnitude less than the relative standard deviation of the measurement; thus, the results are statistically identical.

For Case 2, the calculated exfiltration rate is substantially less than the true average value by about 27%. But statistically the two values are identical

TABLE 4—*Effect of changing concentrations on calculated average exfiltration rate. Assume R_s is 1500 nL/h.*

Period	Case 1		Case 2	
	C, nL/m³	R_E, m³/h	C, nL/m³	R_E, m³/h
1	17	88.2	25	60
2	16	93.8	20	75
3	15	100.0	15	100
4	14	107.1	10	150
5	13	115.4	5	300
Avgerage	15 ± 1.6	100.9 ± 10.7	15 ± 7.9	137.0 ± 97.3
R_E, calculated[a]		100.0 ± 10.5		100.0 ± 52.7
Difference[b]		0.9 ± 15.0		37.0 ± 110.7

[a]Calculated from Eq 3.
[b]Difference between the true average R_E and that calculated by Eq 3.

since this difference is less than either's standard deviation. In addition, if in a real situation the true exfiltration rates varied from 60 to 300 m³/h, it would appear that an average of 100 is not even substantially different than 137 m³/h.

Thus, it is concluded that the BNL/AIMS technique, through the use of passive samplers which provide an average tracer concentration, gives a statistically valid indication of the average exfiltration rate, which is a flow rate. To obtain the more common quantity, air changes per unit time, the exfiltration rate must be divided by the volume of the house. For air quality purposes and for energy and material balances, the flow rate is actually a more valuable quantity.

Two-Zone Case

Examples of two-zone cases are a two-story house on a slab, a one-story (for example, ranch) with a basement or a crawl space, and any building which is ventilated with two separate HVAC systems.

Figture 5 depicts the model for a one-story house (Zone 1) with a basement (Zone 2). Air can infiltrate from outside the house into each zone (R_{I1} and R_{I2}) and exfiltrate each zone to the outside (R_{E1} and R_{E2}). In addition, air can exchange between the zones in both directions (R_{12} and R_{21}).

Assuming that a different tracer type is used in each zone (Tracer 1 in Zone 1, etc.), tracer material balances, assuming that steady state pertains and that there is negligible tracer in the outside air, give the following:

Zone 1

$$R_{21}C_{12} - R_{12}C_{11} - R_{E1}C_{11} = -R_{s1} \tag{4}$$

$$R_{21}C_{22} - R_{12}C_{21} - R_{E1}C_{21} = 0 \tag{5}$$

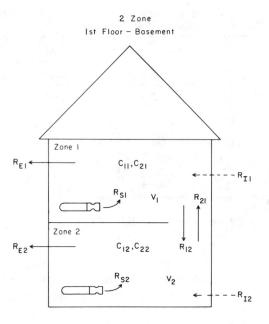

FIG. 5—*Model considered for a two-zone house.*

Zone 2

$$R_{12}C_{11} - R_{21}C_{12} - R_{E2}C_{12} = 0 \qquad (6)$$

$$R_{12}C_{21} - R_{21}C_{22} - R_{E2}C_{22} = -R_{s2} \qquad (7)$$

where

R_{12}, R_{21} = air exchange rates from Zone 1 to Zone 2 and Zone 2 to Zone 1, m³/h,

R_{E1}, R_{E2} = air exfiltration rates from Zones 1 and 2, m³/h,

R_{s1}, R_{s2} = rates of tracer sources in each respective zone, nL/h, and

C_{11}, C_{21}, C_{12}, C_{22} = concentration of Tracer 1 in Zone 1, etc., nL/m³ ($\equiv$ pL/L).

The concentrations are measured with the passive samplers, and the tracer source rates are known. Thus, the four unknowns, two air exchange rates and two exfiltration rates, can be solved from the four simultaneous equations. The rate of infiltration for each zone then can be calculated from air mass balances:

$$R_{I1} = R_{E1} + R_{12} - R_{21} \tag{8}$$

$$R_{I2} = R_{E2} + R_{21} - R_{12} \tag{9}$$

The solutions to Eqs 4 to 7 can be obtained by solving as two sets of simultaneous equations, noting that R_{21} can be solved from Eqs 4 and 5 and R_{12} from Eqs 6 and 7. Then R_{E1} and R_{E2} can be obtained from Eqs 5 and 7, respectively. The solutions, which are given in the Appendix, also can be obtained by any standard matrix inversion routine for use on a desktop computer [14]. This is especially useful when the number of zones increases to three or four.

Once all the flow rates have been determined, simple material balances then can be performed for pollutants in the same building. The following equations

$$R_{21}C_{p2} + R_{I1}C_{pa} - R_{12}C_{p1} - R_{E1}C_{p1} = -R_{p1} + k_1 V_1 C_{p1} \tag{10}$$

$$R_{12}C_{p1} + R_{I2}C_{pa} - R_{21}C_{p2} - R_{E2}C_{p2} = -R_{p2} + k_2 V_2 C_{p2} \tag{11}$$

where

C_{p1}, C_{p2}, C_{pa} = concentration of pollutant in Zone 1, Zone 2, and the ambient outside air, respectively,
R_{p1}, R_{p2} = rate of the pollutant source in each zone,
k_1, k_2 = rate of pollutant scavenging in each zone, and
V_1, V_2 = volume of each zone.

would then give the pollutant net source strength in each zone of the building. For radon, one would expect a positive term for the basement and a near-zero result for the main floor, since the radon source is generally from soil gas entering a basement [15]. For nitrogen dioxide (NO_2) from a gas range, the source term should be positive on the first floor and zero in the basement; NO_2 removal on the first floor may be moderate ($k = 0.5 \ h^{-1}$) and perhaps larger in the basement, due to scavenging being a dominant mechanism in that zone [16]. Thus, the multizone modeling would provide for unique identification and quantification of these processes.

Three-Zone Case

A typical example of a three-zone building is a two-story house with a basement. Again, assuming that a different tracer source is used in each zone and that the steady state assumption applies, a set of nine tracer material balance equations can be developed to solve for nine unknown flow terms (three exfiltration flow rates, one from each zone, and six air exchange rate terms, two leaving each zone). A set of three air mass balance equations would provide the three unknown infiltration rates.

The solutions to the tracer and air material balance equations are given in the Appendix. It is apparent that as the number of zones increases, the matrix solution approach with computer assistance is the only manageable way.

N-Zone Case

It is apparent, then, that for N zones, a set of N^2 tracer material balance equations can be written to solve for N^2 unknown flow terms (N exfiltration flow rates, one from each zone, and $N(N-1)$ air exchange rates, that is, $N-1$ leaving each zone to flow to another zone). Also, a set of N air mass balance equations would provide the N unknown infiltration rates.

Field Deployment

In order to avoid contamination, the PFT sources are shipped separately from the passive samplers. When going from house to house during deployment, it is convenient to carry the samplers in a container mounted under the hood of the vehicle, that is, in the engine compartment, which is effectively outside, and the samplers within the vehicle. An alternative would be to place the sources in a zip lock plastic bag along with a small satchel of charcoal (for example, activated coconut or aquarium charcoal), which will keep the concentration of PFT vapor at zero. When a large number of homes are being surveyed, it is generally wise to retain two or three passive samplers as controls, that is, unopened, in order to verify the absence of contamination during shipment, deployment, and storage.

Since the single and multizone models assume that the tracer is well-mixed within each zone, it is desirable to deploy the sources in a manner which provides uniform emission in a zone. Typically, one source is deployed for every 46.5 m^2 (500 ft^2) of living area, in order to establish steady state concentrations of about 10 to 20 pL/L. Thus, in a single story house, for example, a small ranch house, one source is placed in each extreme end of the house (for example, the living-dining room area and the master bedroom). In a two-story house, two sources are deployed on the main floor (for example, the living room and family or dining area) and two upstairs (for example, the master bedroom and one other bedroom). The doors to all rooms should remain open. If the house has a basement, one or two sources should be deployed in that zone. Ignoring the basement, as will be discussed later, will result in errors in the determination of a pollutant source strength term if it is truly located in the basement.

For a single zone type of measurement, the same type of PFT source should be used on each floor. In houses with basements, the whole house rate may be correctly determined, but the living area infiltration rates and corresponding actual pollutant concentration distributions will not be determinable. For a complete understanding with a multizone approach, a different type of tracer should be used on each floor. If a computer system is used to interpret the results, there is essentially no difference in cost with BNL/AIMS to perform a multizone measurement compared to a single zone measurement, assuming the same number of sources and samplers are used; thus, the approach selected should be governed by the physical arrangement of the building or house and the subsequent use of the data.

The sources are used as received; they are always emitting tracer, there is nothing to open or uncover, and they may be placed in any orientation. Generally, a PFT source is placed within a meter or so of an outside wall. For example, it can be taped onto the leg of a table or end table or even on a lower portion of a hanging chandelier. Since the source is sensitive to temperature, it should not be placed near a heating or cooling source nor in direct sunlight or other drafty location such as a window. The average temperature of the source must be recorded; the average room temperature taken from a room thermostat is usually adequate for this purpose, even in the case of one or more daily temperature setback cycles.

Although it is assumed that the tracer concentration is uniform throughout a zone and thus only one passive sampler need be deployed per zone, it is accepted practice to obtain at least two sample measurements per zone to verify that assumption, if the cost can be justified. The principal cost in this method is, of course, the number of analyses made per home. The samplers are usually deployed in the same room as the sources but at least 2 to 3 m from any source and usually near an inside wall location (but at least 0.5 m from any wall, floor, or ceiling). They also can be placed on a table or taped to the leg of a chair or table. The samplers have a rubber cap on each end. To initiate sampling, only *one* cap must be removed (usually the one near the numbered end). The sampler number, location, and the time and the date sampling commenced must be recorded. At the end of the designated sampling period (for example, 1 day, 1 week, 1 month, etc.), the sampler is capped and a record made of the time and date sampling ceased. If it is desirable to compute air changes for the house, then the volume of each zone should be recorded.

In large, multistory, multizone buildings equipped with HVAC systems, it may be simpler to deploy the appropriate number of sources [for example, as little as 1 per 465 m² (5000 ft²)] directly at the entrance to each distribution blower, thereby establishing adequate concentrations of about 1 pL/L. The air entering the distribution system is in part recycled return air and in part fresh outside air. Thus, in principle, the concentration of tracer in the distribution air is related to the intentional rate of addition of fresh air and also should be identical to the tracer concentration throughout the rooms in that zone. Since the building is further being exchanged with fresh air by natural infiltration, in practice the room tracer concentrations will be less than that in the distribution system. However, the average room tracer concentrations throughout the zones can be used to compute the total exfiltration rate from each zone plus the zone-to-zone air exchange rates. Models are being developed and tested to demonstrate how the PFT method can be used to distinguish natural infiltration from forced ventilation is large buildings and also to determine the efficiency of ventilation systems with respect to stratification.

Results and Discussion

To aid in the acceptance of this simple passive tracer source and sampler air infiltration measurement technique, the reliability and validity of each component is documented here and comparisons and applications of the methodology are presented.

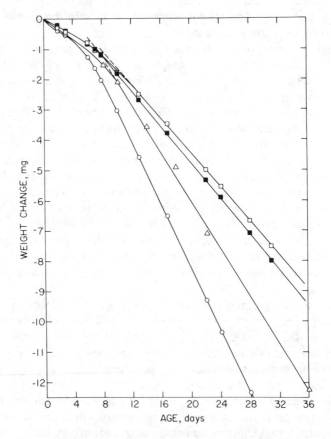

FIG. 6— *Time required for new sources to attain a steady emission rate. Two upper curves (□, ■) are PDCH sources with 60-durometer silicone rubber plugs (S60); the next (△), PMCH (S60); the last (0), PMCH (S80).*

Performance of the Tracer Source

Initial Performance—Usually the sources are fabricated and then set aside for a period of time to allow them to achieve a steady rate of emission. As shown in Fig. 6, the PFT sources are ready for use in just 10 to 12 days after manufacture.

Long-Term Performance—Three of the four tracer types given in Table 1 were fabricated into PFT sources and the gravimetrically determined emission rates determined over two different time periods for silicone rubber plugs of "quoted" 40 (Table 5) and 70 (Table 6) durometer hardness. With the exception of an occasional outlier, the emission rates for each group of six sources were comparable to within ±1 to 3%. The rates were determined over a 3-month period at the end of 1982 using an electrobalance and again in the

TABLE 5—*Stability of PFT source rates with time, determined gravimetrically at 25°C.*

PFT Type	Code[a]	Permeation Rate and Standard Deviation, nL/min		$\dfrac{1983}{\text{Ratio: } 1982}$
		Nov. 1982 to Jan. 1983[c]	May 1983 to Sept. 1983[d]	
PDCH	3-1-S40	19.43 ± 0.29	20.27 ± 0.11	1.043 ± 0.022
	2	19.83 ± 0.09	19.81 ± 0.10	0.999 ± 0.010
	3	16.22 ± 0.19*	16.82 ± 0.08*	1.037 ± 0.017
	4	19.62 ± 0.08	19.84 ± 0.09	1.011 ± 0.009
	5	19.40 ± 0.32	20.30 ± 0.20	1.046 ± 0.028
	6	19.01 ± 0.27	19.85 ± 0.12	1.044 ± 0.021
	Avg[b]	19.46 ± 0.30	20.01 ± 0.25	1.030 ± 0.020
PMCH	2-1-S40	33.74 ± 0.16	33.55 ± 0.11	0.994 ± 0.008
	2	36.12 ± 0.21	35.92 ± 0.12	0.994 ± 0.009
	3	33.62 ± 0.16	33.35 ± 0.12	0.992 ± 0.008
	4	33.09 ± 0.16	32.92 ± 0.12	0.995 ± 0.008
	5	37.72 ± 0.21*	37.04 ± 0.06*	0.982 ± 0.007
	6	34.57 ± 0.16	34.35 ± 0.14	0.994 ± 0.009
	Avg[b]	34.23 ± 1.18	34.02 ± 1.18	0.992 ± 0.005
PDCB	1-1-S40	49.34 ± 0.18	48.98 ± 0.24	0.993 ± 0.009
	2	49.80 ± 0.21	49.66 ± 0.29	0.997 ± 0.010
	3	52.10 ± 0.18	51.74 ± 0.22	0.993 ± 0.008
	4	50.30 ± 0.24	49.98 ± 0.14	0.994 ± 0.008
	5	48.09 ± 0.21	47.96 ± 0.17	0.997 ± 0.008
	6	48.88 ± 0.21	48.53 ± 0.15	0.993 ± 0.007
	Avg	49.75 ± 1.38	49.48 ± 1.33	0.995 ± 0.002

[a]3-1-S40 means Tracer 3 (that is, PDCH), source No. 1, silicone rubber plug of 40 hardness.
[b]Asterisked values excluded from average.
[c]Perkin-Elmer electrobalance.
[d]High-precision analytical balance.

TABLE 6—*Stability of PFT source rates with time, determined gravimetrically at 25°C.*

| PFT Type | Code[a] | Permeation Rate and Standard Deviation, nL/min | | 1983 Ratio: 1982 |
		Nov. 1982 to Jan. 1983[c]	May 1983 to Sept. 1983[d]	
PDCH	3-1-S70	12.54 ± 0.05	12.69 ± 0.07	1.012 ± 0.010
	2	12.47 ± 0.08	12.61 ± 0.08	1.011 ± 0.013
	3	12.54 ± 0.07	12.66 ± 0.19	1.010 ± 0.021
	4	12.64 ± 0.08	12.80 ± 0.08	1.013 ± 0.013
	5	12.35 ± 0.09	12.55 ± 0.07	1.016 ± 0.013
	6	12.61 ± 0.08	12.84 ± 0.08	1.018 ± 0.013
	Avg	12.53 ± 0.10	12.69 ± 0.11	1.013 ± 0.003
PMCH	2-1-S70	25.75 ± 0.12	25.55 ± 0.25	0.992 ± 0.014
	2	24.19 ± 0.13	23.98 ± 0.11	0.991 ± 0.010
	3	24.84 ± 0.12	24.66 ± 0.12	0.993 ± 0.010
	4	30.26 ± 0.15*	29.90 ± 0.10*	0.988 ± 0.008
	5	24.14 ± 0.12	23.94 ± 0.12	0.992 ± 0.010
	6	23.70 ± 0.13	23.54 ± 0.12	0.993 ± 0.010
	Avg[b]	24.52 ± 0.80	24.33 ± 0.79	0.992 ± 0.002
PDCB	1-1-S70	35.10 ± 0.13	35.35 ± 0.28	1.007 ± 0.012
	2	35.50 ± 0.04	35.71 ± 0.25	1.006 ± 0.008
	3	36.55 ± 0.03	36.75 ± 0.27	1.005 ± 0.008
	4	36.21 ± 0.06	36.30 ± 0.18	1.002 ± 0.007
	5	35.64 ± 0.05	...	...
	6	37.53 ± 0.05	37.63 ± 0.18	1.003 ± 0.006
	Avg	36.09 ± 0.88	36.35 ± 0.90	1.005 ± 0.002

[a]3-1-S40 means Tracer 3 (that is, PDCH), source No. 1, silicone rubber plug of 40 hardness.
[b]Asterisked values excluded from average.
[c]Perkin-Elmer electrobalance.
[d]High-precision analytical balance.

middle of 1983 for a 5-month period with a different balance. The ratio of the rates for the two periods was essentially unity, indicating no aging effects.

A larger group of 20 PDCB sources with silicone 60 rubber plugs had the following emission rates for 19 of 20:

Avg: 47.88 ± 0.93 nL/min (±1.9%)
Median: 47.93 nL/min
Range: 46.68 to 50.08 nL/min
Outlier: 53.67 nL/min

Although gravimetric calibration is significantly more convenient and in essence more accurate and precise, several sources also were calibrated chromatographically as shown in Table 7. From the standard deviations, it is apparent that the precision of the gravimetric results is at least an order of

TABLE 7—*PFT source calibration; gravimetric versus chromatographic.*

Source Type	Source Code	Emission Rate at 25°C, nL/min		Gravimetric/ Chromatographic
		Gravimetric	Chromatographic	
PDCB	1-1-S70	35.4 ± 0.3	38.8	0.91
PMCH	2-1-S40	33.6 ± 0.1	31.1 ± 1.0	1.08 ± 0.04
PMCH	2-7-S60	35.7 ± 0.1	32.9 ± 1.2	1.09 ± 0.04
PDCB	1-1-S70	35.4 ± 0.3	38.1 ± 2.8	0.93 ± 0.07
PDCB	1-2-S70	35.7 ± 0.3	38.4 ± 2.9	0.93 ± 0.07
PDCB	1-1-S40	49.0 ± 0.2	49.7 ± 3.9	0.99 ± 0.08
PDCB	1-2-S40	49.7 ± 0.3	50.3 ± 3.7	0.99 ± 0.07
PDCB	1-7-S60	53.3 ± 0.1	55.1 ± 4.1	0.97 ± 0.07
PDCH	3-1-S70	12.7 ± 0.1	13.3 ± 2.8	0.95 ± 0.17
PDCH	3-2-S70	12.6 ± 0.1	13.2 ± 2.5	0.95 ± 0.16
PDCH	3-3-S70	12.7 ± 0.2	13.7 ± 2.7	0.93 ± 0.16
PDCH	3-1-S80	12.8 ± 0.1	12.6 ± 2.5	1.02 ± 0.17
				Avg = 0.98 ± 0.06

magnitude better than that for GC determinations. The average ratio of gravimetric to chromatographic was nearly unity within ±6%.

Effect of Temperature—Table 8 gives the activation energies found for several PFT sources fabricated with a range of rubber plug hardnesses. The immediate temperature effect measurements were determined over short periods of temperature change (<1 h) by GC. The long-term temperature effects were determined gravimetrically by placing sources in a 37°C oven and comparing the permeation rate with that found gravimetrically for the same or similar sources when stored in a 25°C oven.

Unfortunately, the quoted hardness of the rubber plugs was not always consistent with the actual hardness as determined by "feel." Thus, the entries into the table are arranged in increasing order of hardness as indicated by decreasing permeation rate, which ranged over less than a factor of 2, as did the activation energies (ΔH) for the range in hardnesses covered.

For PDCH, the short-term ΔH ranged from 4 to 7 kcal/mole and 2 to 4 kcal/mol for PDCB. But the long-term ΔH was essentially identical for all three PFTs, having an average value of about 8 ± 1 kcal/mol. The effect of ΔH on the source rate for a 3°C error in the source temperature estimate (the largest anticipated temperature error) is as follows:

ΔH, kcal/mol	Rate error for a 3°C temperature error, %
4	7.2
6	11.1
8	15.0
10	19.1

TABLE 8—*PFT source activation energy.*

Source Type	Source Code	Activation Energy, kcal/mol	Gravimetric Emission Rate, nL/min	
			At 25°C	At 37°C
		Immediate ($<$ 1 h) Temperature Effect[a]		
PDCH	3-2-S60	4.00 ± 0.14	20.1 ± 0.2	...
PDCH	3-4-S40	4.99 ± 0.15	19.8 ± 0.1	...
PDCH	3-1-S70	5.16 ± 0.13	12.7 ± 0.1	...
PDCH	3-2-S70	5.33 ± 0.24	12.6 ± 0.1	...
PDCH	3-3-S70	4.59 ± 0.11	12.7 ± 0.2	...
PDCH	3-9-S70	6.53 ± 0.24	11.9[a]	...
PDCH	3-1-S80	6.94 ± 0.20	12.8 ± 0.1	...
PDCB	1-7-S60	1.70 ± 0.02	53.3 ± 0.1	...
PDCB	1-1-S40	3.06 ± 0.05	49.0 ± 0.2	...
PDCB	1-2-S40	3.26 ± 0.05	49.7 ± 0.3	...
PDCB	1-1-S70	3.86 ± 0.04	35.4 ± 0.3	...
PDCB	1-2-S70	3.66 ± 0.03	35.7 ± 0.3	...
		Long-Term ($>$ 1 week) Temperature Effect[b]		
PDCH	TC-185	8.6 ± 1.5	16.6 ± 0.6	29.1 ± 0.8
PDCH	3-3-S70	8.7 ± 0.4	12.7 ± 0.2	22.4 ± 0.2
PMCH	2- -S80[c]	7.9 ± 1.3	29.9 ± 1.1	43.4 ± 0.4
PDCB	1-7-S60	6.2 ± 0.1	53.3 ± 0.1	79.8 ± 0.2
PDCB	1- -S80[c]	8.0 ± 1.2	38.8 ± 0.4	65.3 ± 1.2
Avg long-term ΔH		7.9 ± 1.0		

[a]Estimated from chromatographic measurements between 25 and 37°C.
[b]Placed in oven to obtain gravimetric rate at 37°C for comparison with rate at 25°C.
[c]Represents average from three sources.

Since all source rates are reported at 25°C, any use at other temperatures must be considered long-term changes. Thus, a 3°C error in temperature is likely to cause a 13 to 16% error in emission rate.

Performance of the Passive Sampler

Tightness of End Caps—When the caps are installed on the sampler (CATS) tube, it is important that the leakage rate be a very small percentage of the normal (one cap removed) sampling rate. This is necessary to prevent contamination with tracers during shipment and storage. As shown in Table 9, the original yellow vinyl cap as well as the subsequent Auster black rubber cap had leakage rates of about 0.5 to 0.8%. When a Girard black rubber cap (buna rubber; No. U103B) was used, the rate was 0.06%. Polyurethane rubber tubing had been previously selected for use in the programmable sampler because of its impermeability and lack of solubility towards PFTs, lack of contamination from desorbed rubber constituents, and its excellent clinging

TABLE 9—*Passive sampler (CATS) leakage rate with caps on.*

Type of Cap	Rate of Leakage, %
Vinyl (yellow)	~0.5
Auster (black)	0.6 to 0.8
Girard U103B	0.060
Girard U103B-PU	<0.0004

*a*Leakage rate as percentage of sampling rate.

or sticking tendency to smooth surfaces. Thus, when the Girard end cap was fashioned from polyurethane (U103B-PU), the leak tightness improved by more than two orders of magnitude to less than 0.0004% of the uncapped rate.

Effect of Temperature and Pressure—Theory states that there is no effect of barometric pressure on the sampling rate, and therefore no tests were conducted on that effect.

CATS were exposed to a PMCH/PDCH standard for about 200 min at temperatures of 25, 35, and 50°C. As shown in Table 10, the change in the average quantity of tracer sampled for 10°C change in temperature was less than 2%, in agreement with the theoretically expected change; but, within the standard deviation of the measurements, the change was not even discernible. Thus, normal room temperature changes will have no effect on the performance of the passive samplers.

TABLE 10—*Effect of Temperature on CATS.*

CATS No.	Temperature, °C	PMCH Measured	PMCH Expected	PDCH Measured	PDCH Expected
334	25	124.4		170.4	
335	25	122.6		169.4	
336	25	116.8		159.7	
340	25	127.4		174.5	
342	25	123.4		171.1	
		123 ± 4	123	169 ± 5	169
331	35	126.0		177.0	
332	35	126.4		172.0	
333	35	123.0		167.5	
		125 ± 2	125	172 ± 5	172
337	50	137.2		188.8	
338	50	136.8		183.6	
339	50	135.2		187.1	
		136 ± 1	128	186 ± 3	176

Tracer Response, Arbitrary Units

Comparison of CATS with BATS—Eight passive samplers were exposed for 45 min in a chamber containing PDCH during which time the three BATS tubes were collected at known sampling rates. The CATS concentrations averaged 136 ± 5 pL/L and the BATS, 119 ± 2 pL/L. Thus the CATS effective sampling rate for PDCH was about 14 ± 6% higher than that expected from the dimensions of the passive sampler and an empirically derived diffusion coefficient [2]. Additional tests are being conducted to verify the sampling rates for all four PFT types.

Reproducibility of Multiple CATS—As shown in Table 11, the concentrations of three PFTs sampled with 20 passive samplers at the same location in a

TABLE 11—*Reproducibility of Multiple CATS Sampling (sampling for 45.3 h).*

CATS Analysis No.	Tracer Concentration, pL/L			Tracer Concentration Ratios		
	PDCB	PMCH	PDCH	PDCB/PMCH	PDCH/PMCH	PDCB/PDCH
1	3.407	37.29	35.12	0.09134	0.9416	0.09701
2	3.518	38.34	36.17	0.09176	0.9435	0.09725
3	3.403	38.53	35.34	0.08831*	0.9170*	0.09630
4	3.503	39.04	36.60	0.08974	0.9377	0.09571
5	3.444	37.73	36.26	0.09128	0.9610	0.09498
6	3.612	39.54	36.51	0.09134	0.9234*	0.09892*
7	3.523	38.41	36.17	0.09170	0.9416	0.09738
8	3.629	39.27	37.18	0.09242	0.9469	0.09760
9	3.524	38.76	36.78	0.09093	0.9488	0.09583
10	3.541	38.85	36.80	0.09115	0.9472	0.09624
11	3.596	39.17	37.27	0.09179	0.9515	0.09647
12	3.502	38.19	35.97	0.09168	0.9419	0.09734
13	3.584	38.79	36.96	0.09242	0.9530	0.09697
14	3.591	38.79	37.11	0.09256	0.9566	0.09676
15	3.654	40.07	38.03	0.09117	0.9489	0.09609
16	3.592	39.04	37.92	0.09200	0.9714	0.09471
17	3.527	38.71	37.56	0.09111	0.9703	0.09390
18	3.577	38.64	36.74	0.09258	0.9508	0.09738
19	3.468	37.57	36.03	0.09231	0.9589	0.09626
20	3.413	38.38	36.81	0.08893*	0.9592	0.09271*
Avg	3.530	38.66	36.67	0.09133	0.9486	0.09629
Standard deviation	±0.075	±0.66	±0.76	±0.00115	±0.0133	±0.00141
Relative standard deviation	(±2.1%)	(±1.7%)	(±2.1%)	(±1.26%)	(±1.41%)	(±1.46%)
Avg[a]	...	...	...	0.09163	0.9517	0.09634
Standard deviation	...	...	...	±0.00072	±0.0096	±0.00102
Relative standard deviation	...	...	...	(±0.78%)	(±1.01%)	(±1.06%)

[a]Values of 2 points with asterisks excluded.

house which contained the three types of tracer sources was quite reproducible to within ±2%. The precision of the analyses can be estimated by ratioing one tracer to another since that ratio is independent of the sampler dimensions (that is, sampling rate). The last three columns showed that precision to be less than ±1.5%; with the exclusion of 2 out of 20 ratios, the precision was within ±1% for concentration in the 3 to 30 pL/L range.

Gas Chromatograph Performance

Six ambient air samples of about 25 L each, collected with the programmable sampler, were analyzed with the GC system. The chromatograms, two of which are shown in Fig. 7, show the elution of an unknown followed by a small peak representing PDCB, just ahead of a second unknown, which has been identified as ambient PMCP. This is followed by the PMCH peak and then three peaks representing three of the isomers of PDCH. The analysis results of all six samples are shown in Table 12. Since even the PDCB concentration at 0.35 fL/L was determined with ±10% precision with a 25 L sample, typical home concentrations of 3 to 30 pL/L, that is, 4 to 5 orders of magnitude higher, could be quantified with just a 2.5-mL air sample. For a passive sampler, that would be equivalent to about a 20-min exposure or sam-

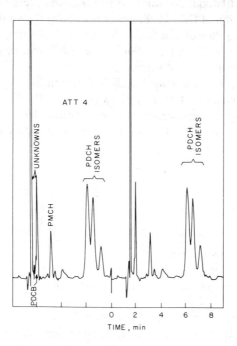

FIG. 7—*Chromatograms of two 25-L ambient air samples with the GC specifications shown in Table 2. The unknown peak after PDCB is PMCP.*

TABLE 12—*PFT analyses of six background air samples.*

Sample Volume, L	PFT Ambient Concentrations, fL/L[a]			
	PDCB	PMCP	PMCH	PDCH
24.94	0.373	2.76	3.72	26.8
24.36	0.340	2.76	3.57	27.4
24.88	0.359	2.68	3.53	24.9
24.11	0.329	2.69	3.47	23.6
23.37	0.290	2.59	3.50	25.5
22.11	0.383	2.79	3.70	25.5
Avg	0.346	2.71	3.58	25.6
	±0.034	±0.07	±0.10	±1.4

[a]fL/L is equivalent to 0.001 pL/L.

pling period. This accounts for the high analytical precision obtained for the not-quite two-day period results shown in Table 11.

At the 140°C column temperature, Fig. 7 demonstrated that three tracers could be clearly resolved, that is, PDCH, PMCH, and either PMCP or PDCB. In order to better resolve the latter two, the column temperature had to be reduced to about 100°C, at which temperature the PDCH peaks were not entirely eluted until about 28 min. Further research is needed to speed up the analysis time for four PFTs. Preliminary tests have shown that by temperature programming the column from 100 to 150°C, starting when the precut column is backflushed, the resolution of four PFTs can be completed in 13 min, including oven cool-down time.

A typical calibration curve for PDCH is shown in Fig. 8. Although the response is supposed to be linear up through nearly the first four orders-of-magnitude, a step or kink occurs at tracer volumes less than 1 pL for this constant current–type ECD. The response is supposed to follow the semitheoretical equation

$$v = \frac{a\,A}{1 - ab\,A} \tag{12}$$

where

v = the tracer volume, pL,
A = integrator area, kilocounts, and
a, b = product of fundamental rate constants.

Equation 12 would apply to an ECD operating in the constant frequency mode or the constant current mode when analyzing weakly electron-capturing compounds [17]. For the response shown in Fig. 8, the equation was modified empirically to give

$$v = \frac{a\,A}{1 - ab\,A\dfrac{t + A^q}{p + A^q}} \tag{13}$$

where

t, p, q = empirical constants.

Typical values for PMCH are

$a = 0.00266$
$b = 0.000753$
$t = 5.7 \times 10^6$
$p = 6.7 \times 10^4$
$q = 1.43$

From these values it can be shown that a 0.5% deviation from linearity occurs at just 0.079 pL of PMCH, a 5% deviation at 0.86 pL, and a 25% deviation at

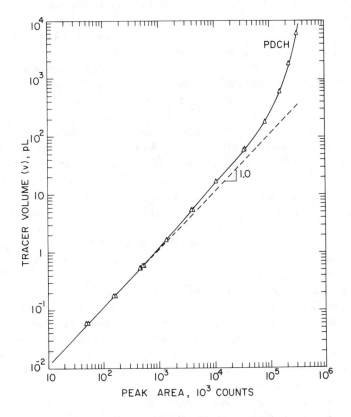

FIG. 8—*Response of the ECD-GC to PDCH.*

7.4 pL. Thus, typical biweekly measurements (about 2.8 L) in a home with tracer concentrations of 3 to 30 pL/L would have collected 8.4 to 84 pL and would be in this error range of more than 25% if the nonlinear response were not considered. Care must be taken to provide accurate calibration over the range of expected tracer quantities.

An ECD working in the constant frequency mode would not suffer from this nonlinearity in the early portion of the calibration curve but would have about a 100-fold reduction in dynamic range. This would be inadequate for infiltration-type measurements; the maximum dynamic range of the constant current ECD-mode has been needed on several occasions.

Field Use of BNL/AIMS

The PFT air infiltration measurement system has been deployed in more than 1000 homes with most of the measurements being single or two-zone types. In this section, examples of that use will be given showing the uniformity of the tracer concentration within a room and on a floor, comparison of the BNL/AIMS versus SF_6 tracer techniques, measurements of infiltration rates from groups of homes in the United States, Canada, and Sweden, correlation of infiltration rates with meteorological and other parameters, and demonstration of the multizone capability in homes.

Tracer Uniformity in a Room and on a Floor—A number of uses of this technique have demonstrated that the tracer concentration is generally quite uniform within a room and even on the same floor provided doors are not left closed.

Tests were conducted in the Brookhaven house, a passive solar-assisted house with a basement and two floors. As shown in Table 13, two PDCH sources were deployed on the first floor (one in the dining area and one in the family room) and two PMCH on the second floor (one each in the master bedroom and Bedroom 1). The first two CATS were located side by side; the PMCH concentrations were nearly identical (within ±0.3%) and the PDCH values nearly so (within ±1.5%). It was noted that the precision of PDCH analyses is typically five-fold poorer than that for PMCH because the former consists of three broader peaks compared to a single narrow peak for PMCH.

For the five samplers located in the dining-living area, a single large room, the tracer concentrations were quite uniform (within ±2.6%). For the five on the second floor there was more spread. CATS 584 gave a low PMCH value because there was no source in that room and the door was closed. The average of the other four samplers was within ±10% for the tracer deployed on that floor. It would appear that as long as bedroom doors are open, two samplers at different locations on the same floor should give a reasonable average of that zone's concentrations.

Subsequently, in September of 1983, with an additional tracer, PDCB, located in the center of the basement, PFT concentration measurements again

TABLE 13a—*PFT concentration distribution within the BNL House[a] (1/19/83 to 1/21/83).*

CATS Sampler No.	Location	Floor	Comments	PFT[b] Concentration, pL/L	
				PMCH	PDCH
577	living room (LR) coffee table	1st	next to No. 581	9.37	7.62
581	LR coffee table	1st		9.42	7.40
574	LR TV	1st	far from PDCH	9.12	7.85
585	dining area	1st	next to PDCH source	9.65	7.93
573	LR fireplace	1st		9.56	7.53
575	master bedroom	2nd	near door to hall	17.0	7.37
576	master bedroom	2nd	nearer PMCH source	22.0	7.07
584	Bedroom 2	2nd	door closed; no source	10.4	8.34
583	Bedroom 1	2nd	on dresser in sun	19.2	7.43
580	Bedroom 1	2nd	on dresser in shade	18.8	7.78

[a]House consists of basement and 1st and 2nd floors.

[b]TABLE 13b—*PFT sources were as follows.*

Floor volume, m³	PFT Source		PFT Location	Avg PFT concentration, pL/L	
	Type	Rate, nL/h		PMCH	PDCH
240	PDCH	2035	dining area and family room	9.42 ± 0.18	7.67 ± 0.20
215	PMCH	3749	master bedroom and Bedroom 1	19.2 ± 1.8	7.41 ± 0.25

were made at several locations on each floor as shown in Table 14. Even though the PMCH sources on the second floor were located, one each, in the two bedrooms, the concentration measured in the bathroom off the hall between the two rooms was only slightly less (about 10%) than that found in the bedrooms. This was also true for PDCH on the first floor; the kitchen, which had no source, had an identical concentration to that measured in the other rooms which contained the sources.

Thus, for the open nature of the first floor, the tracer uniformity was exceptionally good, indicating rapid mixing within that floor or zone. For the compartmentalized nature of the second floor, the tracer on that floor was only slightly less well-distributed as long as the doors were open (Table 14) but poorly so when a door was closed (Table 13) as expected. It was not apparent why the basement, which was completely open, showed a nonuniformity in the PDCB concentration distribution. Further, it was interesting to note that the PMCH concentration on the first floor was highest in the family room and lowest in the other end, the living room; the staircase to the second floor, where the PMCH sources were deployed, was located in the family room.

TABLE 14a—*PFT concentration distribution within the BNL House (9/16/83 to 9/30/83).*

CATS Sampler No.	Location	Floor	Comments	PFT[a] Concentration, pL/L		
				PMCH	PDCH	PDCB
925	master bedroom	2nd	PMCH source in room	52.9	17.8	5.77
816	Bedroom 2	2nd	PMCH source in room	53.6	17.9	5.46
944	bathroom	2nd	no source	47.9	17.1	5.49
Avg				51.5 ± 3.1	17.6 ± 0.4	5.57 ± 0.17
954	LR coffeee table	1st	PDCH source in room	16.4	21.9	6.40
838	kitchen range	1st	no source	17.2	21.6	6.83
935	family room counter	1st	PDCH source in room	18.9	20.7	6.29
Avg				17.5 ± 1.3	21.4 ± 0.6	6.51 ± 0.29
927	basement near stairs	basement	PDCB source in center of room	7.22	4.44	32.3
963	basement near furnace	basement	PDCB source in center of room	6.99	4.47	38.7
Avg				7.11 ± 0.16	4.46 ± 0.02	35.5 ± 4.5

[a]TABLE 14b—*PFT sources were distributed as follows.*

Zone	Floor	Floor Volume, m³	PFT Source		Location
			Type	Rate, nL/h	
1	2nd	215	PMCH	3941	master bedroom and bedroom 2
2	1st	240	PDCH	2115	dining area and family room
3	basement	204	PDCB	2004	center of basement

The extent of the floor-to-floor mixing also can be inferred from the data in Table 14. Since the PDCB concentrations on the second and first floors were nearly the same and since that tracer source was in the basement, then the rate of air exchange between the first and second floor must be fairly high. The PMCH concentrations were much higher on the first floor compared to the basement, and, since that tracer source was in the second floor, the air exchange between the basement and first floor is fairly low. Similarly, the PDCH concentrations on the second floor are four-fold higher than in the basement; hence the air exchange between those floors is quite low.

In conclusion, then, mixing between rooms on the same floor is generally good enough to consider each floor as being well-mixed. However, the mixing between floors is much lower, and hence each floor in a house can be considered to be a single, well-mixed, but separate zone in the home. Examples will be given in a later section.

Comparison of BNL/AIMS with Other Techniques—A study was conducted by the Lawrence Berkeley Laboratory (LBL) over the three-week period shown in Table 15. The 480 m^3 house was equipped with an automated SF$_6$ tracer decay system which measured the infiltration rate every 90 min. During this period, two PDCH sources, one in the living room and one in the basement, and four passive samplers (CATS), two on each floor, were deployed as shown in Table 15. Despite the single source in the living room, the concentration in the bedroom was not substantially less than that in the living room for two reasons: (1) the good mixing that generally occurs on a floor and (2) the presence of a uniform PDCH concentration in the basement that exchanges with the main floor.

Based on the average PDCH concentration of 10.8 $\pm$ 1.2 pL/L, the source rate (1632 nL/h), and the volume of the house (481 m^3), the average air infiltration rate of 0.31 h^{-1} was computed, in good agreement with the 0.33 h^{-1} value obtained from the average of 306 SF$_6$ decay measurements.

In another study, this one conducted by the University of Wisconsin[3], the BNL/AIMS was deployed in nine homes, for which the average infiltration rate was 0.39 $\pm$ 0.22 (Table 16). This result compared very well with the average obtained by a constant SF$_6$ release technique deployed in eight of the nine homes (0.37 $\pm$ 0.21 h^{-1}). When the SF$_6$ method was plotted versus the BNL/AIMS, the slope was close to unity (0.82 $\pm$ 0.16) with an intercept near zero (0.04 h^{-1}); thus, the methods appear to give very similar results.

Subsequently, the homes also were evaluated with a blower door technique [4], but, as shown in Table 16, the infiltration rate was much higher than that from either of the tracer methods. Correlation with the BNL/AIMS showed a very large intercept, and the slope had a significantly large standard deviation. This large discrepancy is in contrast to the generally observed agreement of $\pm 25\%$.

[3]Quackenboss, J., personal communication, 1983.

TABLE 15—*Multiple SF$_6$ tracer decays versus BNL/AIMS[a]*
(1700 6/10/82 to 1300 6/30/82), Chicago test home.[b]

SF$_6$ Measurements (LBL)
   306 measurements at 90 min each (459 of 476-h period)
   mean SF$_6$ air infiltration rate = 0.33 h^{-1}

PFT Measurement
   2 PDCH sources and 4 passive samplers
   measured PDCH concentrations were as follows:

CATS No.	Location	Floor	PDCH Source	Concentration, pL/L
258	Living room	1st	1	12.0
250	Bedroom	1st	...	8.7
262	Basement	basement	1	11.1
256	Basement	basement	...	11.3
Avg			1632 nL/h	10.8 ± 1.2

Mean PFT infiltration rate = 0.31 ± 0.04 h^{-1}

[a]Field measurements conducted by Lawrence Berkeley Laboratory.
[b]Single-story house with an unfinished basement (481 m^3 total).

TABLE 16—*Comparison of BNL/AIMS with SF$_6$ tracer and blower door tests.[a]*

Method	No. of Homes	Average ACH,[b] h^{-1}	Method versus BNL/AIMS	
			Slope	Intercept
BNL/AIMS	9	0.39 ± 0.22	...	...
Constant SF$_6$ rate	8	0.37 ± 0.21	0.82 ± 0.16	0.04
Blower door	9	1.36 ± 0.45	1.01 ± 0.69	0.96

[a]Field tests conducted by the University of Wisconsin.
[b]ACH represents air changes per hour.

As a result of these two tests, it would appear that the BNL/AIMS gives results in good agreement with the conventional SF$_6$ techniques when both are conducted properly, but at significantly reduced costs and manpower requirements. A laboratory chamber validation of BNL/AIMS versus carbon dioxide (CO$_2$) tracer decay measurements demonstrated the precision of duplicate sampling (±1 to 3%) and the ability to accommodate variations in infiltration rates and indoor temperatures in arriving at the correct average ventilation rate by this method [*18*].

A Sample of Home Air Infiltration Rates—Several groups of homes were evaluated for their air change per hour (ACH) rates using the BNL/AIMS. The frequency distributions for the nine homes in the University of Wisconsin study along with one for seven homes in a Canadian study and another for thirty homes in a Connecticut study are shown in Fig. 9. All were conducted

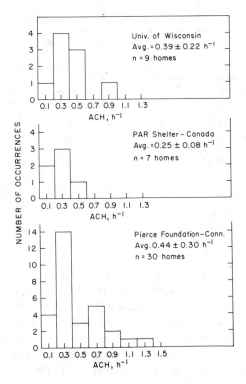

FIG. 9—*Histograms of ACH for three separate studies.*

during the February to March 1983 heating period and were generally two-week integrated measurement periods.

The averages for all three sets are quite close, between 0.25 to 0.44 h^{-1}, with two sets being nearly identical, the Wisconsin and Connecticut studies; the seven homes measured in Ottawa, Ontario, were the tightest (0.25 h^{-1}) as they were in a development of energy-efficient homes.

Reproducibility of Five Swedish Homes—Five Sparsam models of identical Swedish design were evaluated for air infiltration rate during April 1983; two homes were located in the city of Malmö and three in Stockholm. The two-story design had three bedrooms and a bathroom upstairs and a living room, kitchen, utility room, and foyer downstairs.

Four PDCH sources were deployed, two upstairs (Bedrooms 2 and 3) and two downstairs (living room and foyer). The four passive samplers were de-polyed in the same way, two upstairs (Bedroom 3 and hall) and two downstairs (living room and foyer). The PDCH concentrations found at each location and the average ACH for the whole house are shown in Table 17.

The two homes in Malmö and two of the three in Stockholm had essentially identical concentration distributions and air infiltration rates, with the latter

TABLE 17—*Tracer concentrations and air infiltration rates in five Swedish homes.*

House Code[a]	Sampling Period	PDCH Concentration, pL/L				Air Changes, h^{-1}
		1st Floor		2nd Floor		
		Foyer	Living Room	Bedroom	Hall	
M4	4/7 to 5/11/83	27.3	23.6	19.7	20.1	0.70 ($\pm16\%$)
M7	4/7 to 5/11/83	32.9	21.6	25.2	22.1	0.63 ($\pm21\%$)
S7	4/1 to 5/10/83	32.4	22.9	26.4	21.5	0.65 ($\pm19\%$)
S8	4/2 to 5/10/83	32.2	24.5	22.6	25.1	0.59 ($\pm16\%$)
S9	4/2 to 5/10/83	13.2	14.1	6.1	12.4	1.34 ($\pm32\%$)
Average:[b]		31.2 ($\pm8\%$)	23.2 ($\pm5\%$)	23.5 ($\pm13\%$)	22.2 ($\pm9\%$)	0.64 ($\pm 7\%$)

[a]*M* respresents city of Malmö and *S*, Stockholm.
[b]House S9 excluded from averages.

averaging 0.64 h^{-1} ($\pm7\%$) for the four homes and 1.34 h^{-1} for the outlier house, S9. Even the concentrations in the first four homes in the living room, bedroom, and hall were nearly identical at 23 pL/L ($\sim \pm10\%$) with the foyer higher, 31 pL/L ($\pm8\%$), because of the confined space at that location.

This Swedish home design was provided with ventilation ducting to help distribute the passive solar gain and, therefore, is not to be considered typical. Rather, the evaluation shows the consistency of the BNL/AIMS in making air infiltration measurements.

A Generalized Correlation for Parameters Affecting Air Infiltration Rates—It generally has been shown that air infiltration rates are approximately a linear function of the inside-outside temperature difference and also the wind speed; dependence on wind speed, u, has been shown to be between linear (that is, $u^{1.0}$) and quadratic (that is, $u^{2.0}$) [19,20]. In this section, correlations of these parameters as well as a terrain factor with infiltration rates will be presented. Since the BNL/AIMS gives integrated average infiltration rates, the temperature and wind data also will be periodically averaged values.

Studies of an NAHB house over monthly periods from Sept. 1982 to May 1983 are summarized in Table 18. The conventional comparison house, an electrically heated house located in Maryland, consisted of a single-story ranch house with a basement that had a sliding door opening to the backyard. The house was located in fairly open terrain, slightly sheltered by other homes nearby. For most of the periods, the measurements were conducted as a two-zone test; the air changes per hour figures are the total house infiltration rates divided by the total house volume.

The cold weather data from Oct. 1982 through Feb. 1983 were correlated successfully as shown in Footnote *b* of Table 18. The temperature dependence is shown graphically in Fig. 10, in which the ordinate is the ACH ad-

TABLE 18—*Modeled infiltration rates for the NAHB-CCH.*[a] *Effect of temperature difference and wind speed.*

Measurement Period	Avg Temperature Difference, °C	Avg Wind Speed, m/s	Average ACH, h⁻¹			
			Measured	Calculated[b]	Calculated[c]	Difference,[d] %
Sept. 1982	..	..	0.10	..	..	..
Oct. 1982	7.5	1.61	0.12	0.12	0.13	+7
Nov. 1982	11.5	2.06	0.18	0.18	0.19	+7
Dec. 1982	14.9	1.74	0.21	0.21	0.21	0
Jan. 1983	18.9	1.03	0.22	0.22	0.22	0
Feb. 1983	18.1	0.85	0.20	0.20	0.20	+2
March 1983	12.7	0.89	0.21	0.15	0.15	−28
April 1983	9.4	2.46	0.24	0.18	0.19	−19
May 1983	7.2	1.16	0.37	0.10	0.11	−72
Averages	16.2[e] ±2.9	1.1[e] ±0.4	0.18[f] ±0.05			±9%[f]

[a]National Association of Home Builders conventional comparison house.
[b]Calculated ACH, h^{-1} = $-(0.01 \pm 0.01) + (0.0108 \pm 0.0005)\Delta t + (0.0236 \pm 0.0024)u^{1.5}$.
[c]Calculated ACH, h^{-1} = $L(0.006 \Delta t + 0.03u^{1.5}/c)$, where $L = 1.70 \pm 0.08 (\pm 4.7\%)$ and $c = 2.3 \pm 0.23$ (slightly shielded terrain).
[d]Difference is between the second calculated and the measured values.
[e]Average temperature and wind speed was from December to March.
[f]May values excluded from averages.

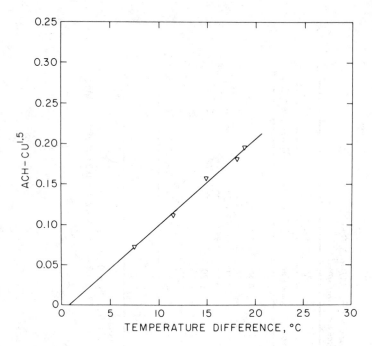

FIG. 10—*Dependence of air infiltration rate on inside-outside temperature difference.*

justed for the wind speed effect; the good correlation with Δt is quite apparent. When the temperature effect is subtracted from the ACH and the result is plotted versus wind speed as in Fig. 11, the data show a reasonably good fit with either $u^{1.5}$ (solid line) or u^2 (dashed line); the 1.5 exponent is preferred based on other experiences.

A generalized correlation, shown in Footnote c of Table 18, has the following form

$$\text{ACH} = L\left(0.006 \, \Delta t + \frac{0.03}{c} \, u^{1.5}\right) \tag{14}$$

where

$\quad$ ACH = average air changes per hour or infiltration rate, h^{-1},
$\quad\quad$ L = generalized house leakiness factor ($1 < L < 5$),
$\quad\quad$ c = terrain sheltering factor ($1 < c < 10$),
$\quad\quad$ Δt = average inside-outside temperature difference, °C, and
$\quad\quad$ u = average wind speed, m/s.

Equation 14 was developed from this plus an evaluation of other home infiltration measurements, some of which will follow. The leakiness factor tends

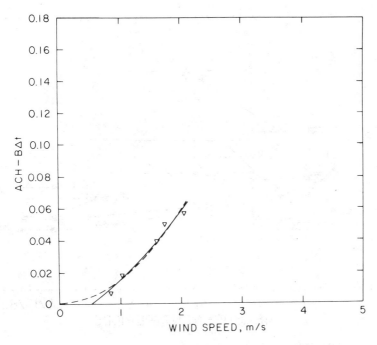

FIG. 11—*Dependence of infiltration rate on wind speed to the 1.5 or 2.0 power.*

to classify a home as to whether it is already reasonably airtight ($L < 1$ to 1.5) or is leaky and would benefit from weatherizing corrective action ($L > 2.5$ to 3). Similarly, an empirical terrain factor, c, has values for open terrain ($c \approx 1$), moderately sheltered terrain ($c \approx 3$), and highly sheltered terrain ($c \approx 10$).

For the conventional comparison house (CCH) house in Table 18, the leakiness factor, L, was found to be 1.70 ± 0.08 ($\pm 4.7\%$), indicating a moderately leak-tight home; the terrain factor, c, of 2.3 ± 0.23, was indicative of the slightly sheltered terrain. The calculated infiltration rates were lower in March, April, and May than the measured values, presumably from the springtime opening of windows.

Similar studies of the seven Canadian homes discussed earlier were conducted over five measurement periods from mid-February to mid-May 1983. From the seasonal trends of all Apple Hill homes, shown in Fig. 12, it appeared that there were two sets of three houses each that behaved similarly, with the seventh having the highest average infiltration rates. During the three coldest periods, when the infiltration rate dropped from one period to the next for one house, it did so for all seven.

Using the generalized correlation given by Eq 14, the data for all seven homes were used to find the best fit for the leak tightness constant, L, and the

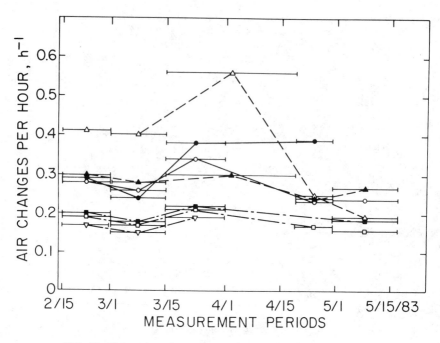

FIG. 12—*Seasonal trends in infiltration rates for seven Canadian houses.*

terrain factor, c. As shown in Table 19, the correlations for the cold weather gave calculated air change rates within a few percent of the measured rates; in the warmer weather, the calculated rate was usually less than the measured rate as in the NAHB test house.

The L values for three of the houses ranged from 1.3 to 1.5, indicating that they were quite tight; two had values of 1.9 to 2.0; and two had values of about 2.3, indicating that they might benefit from some weather stripping.

The terrain factors, c, ranged from 3 to 21 in Table 19, but the location for all seven homes provided nearly identical terrain, that is, moderately sheltered ($c = 3$), due to the number of homes in the area. The average c of 13 $\pm$ 9 for all seven appears to be high because the average wind speed data reported was quite high and appears to be in error by a factor of 2 to 2.5, based on the average Maryland (Table 18) and Long Island (Table 20) winds, which would have reduced c by three- to four-fold to a range of about 1 to 5, consistent with the model.

Three Long Island homes had multizone PFT infiltration measurements conducted from Oct. 1983 to April 1984 on about a semimonthly basis (the multizone nature of the measurements will be discussed in the next section). As shown in Table 20, the measured ACH were fitted to Eq 14 with an overall average relative standard deviation of ± 9 to $\pm 12\%$. The best values for L and c, given in Footnote c, indicated that the Dietz and Brookhaven houses

TABLE 19—Modeled infiltration rates for seven Canadian homes versus temperature difference and windspeed.

House Code	L	c	2/15 to 2/28/83			2/28 to 3/15/83			3/15 to 3/30/83			4/19 to 4/29/83			4/29 to 5/17/83		
			Mea-sured	Calcu-lated[a]	Differ-ence, %	Mea-sured	Calcu-lated	Differ-ence, %	Mea-sured	Calcu-lated	Differ-ence, %	Mea-sured	Calcu-lated	Differ-ence, %	Mea-sured	Calcu-lated	Differ-ence, %
08	1.93 ± 0.12	7 ± 3	0.28	0.29	+3	0.26	0.28	+6	0.34	0.34	0	0.24	0.23	−3	0.24	0.17	−31
10	1.47 ± 0.03	21 ± 12	0.19	0.20	+3	0.17	0.17	0	0.21	0.21	0	0.17	0.14	−17	0.16	0.10	−40
20	2.27 ± 0.28	3 ± 1	0.41	0.41	+1	0.40	0.45	+12	0.56	0.55	−2	0.25	0.38	+54	0.19	0.29	+54
28	1.27 ± 0.02	16 ± 6	0.17	0.17	+2	0.15	0.15	+2	0.19	0.19	−1	0.30	0.13	−58	...	0.09	...
32	2.00 ± 0.33	8 ± 13	0.29	0.29	+1	0.24	0.28	+15	0.38	0.34	−11	0.39	0.23	−41	...	0.16	...
34	1.53 ± 0.03	19 ± 10	0.20	0.21	+3	0.18	0.18	0	0.22	0.22	+1	...	0.15	...	0.19	0.10	−47
39	2.28 ± 0.17	18 ± 16	0.29	0.31	+6	0.27	0.27	0	0.30	0.33	+11	0.24	0.22	−7	0.27	0.15	−43
Avg Difference, %					±3			± 5			± 4			±30			±43
Avg Temperature Difference, °C					20.9			17.0			21.1			13.9			9.1
Avg wind speeds, m/s					3.2			4.5			5.1			4.2			3.8

[a]Calculated ACH, $h^{-1} = L(0.006 \Delta t + 0.03 u^{1.5}/c)$.

TABLE 20—Air changes per hour in three Long Island homes versus temperature difference and wind speed.

Approximate Measurement Period[a]	Approximate Temperature Difference, °C[b]	Approximate Wind Speed, m/s[b]	Average ACH, h^{-1}								
			Dietz House			Brookhaven House			Goodrich House		
			Measured	Calculated[c]	Difference, %	Measured	Calculated[c]	Difference, %	Measured[e]	Calculated[c]	Difference, %
Oct. 1983 (1)	7.2	1.7	...	...	...	0.13	0.13	1	...	...	...
(2)	11.2	1.9	0.17	0.16	−6	0.17	0.19	13	...	...	...
Nov. 1983 (1)	11.7	1.7	0.13	0.15	14	0.16	0.19	20	0.53	0.41	−22
(2)	10.2	2.6	0.18	0.17	−6	0.20	0.21	2	0.59	0.47	−20
Dec. 1983 (1)	12.7	2.6	0.17	0.20	15	0.21	0.23	12	0.64	0.57	−12
(2)	20	2.4	0.23	0.25	11	...	...	...	0.74	0.74	0
Jan. 1984 (1)	18	2.0	0.23	0.22	−4	...	...	...	0.72	0.69	−5
(2)	21	1.6	0.23	0.23	−2	...	...	...	0.70	0.70	0
Feb. 1984 (1)	16	2.2	0.20	0.19	−4	0.29	0.25	−13	0.54	0.60	11
(2)	15	2.7	0.22	0.24	9	0.28	0.25	−13	0.53	0.57	8
March 1984 (1)	18.0	2.8	0.29	0.27	−8	0.30	0.30	−2	0.63	0.72	14
(2)	13.7	2.4	0.21	0.20	−5	0.27	0.22	−16	0.62	0.56	−10
April 1984 (1)	11.0	2.8	0.21	0.21	−1	0.20	0.22	9	...	...	...
(2)	8.4	2.4	0.19	0.15	−21	0.16	0.16	5	...	...	...
Averages	18.0[d] ±2.3	2.3[d] ±0.4	0.21 ±0.04		±9%	0.22 ±0.06		±12%	0.62 ±0.08		±12%

[a]Numbers in parentheses represent 1st and 2nd half of the month.

[b]The approximate temperature differences and wind speeds were generally within ±1°C and ±0.1 m/s, respectively, of the actual measurements for each house; exact values were used in the calculation.

[c]Calculated ACH, h^{-1} = $L(0.006 \Delta t + 0.03 u^{1.5}/c)$:

House	L	c
Dietz	1.58 ± 0.18 (±12%)	2.5 ± 0.8
Brookhaven	1.68 ± 0.34 (±20%)	1.9 ± 0.6
Goodrich	4.47 ± 0.60 (±14%)	3.0 ± 1.6

[d]Average temperature and wind speed was from mid-December to mid-March.

[e]Living zone (1st and 2nd floor) ACH was used because of nonrepresentative condition in the three-zone measurements.

were quite tight (L of 1.6 to 1.7) and did not need further weatherizing; the Goodrich house was three-fold leakier (L of 4.5), indicating a significant weatherization need. The terrain factors determined were representative of the actual siting conditions. The Dietz house was located in a rural development with a lightly wooded landscape ($c = 2.5$); the Brookhaven house, an experimental building, was located in an open area with woods on the north side only ($c = 1.9$); the Goodrich house, in a more urban setting, was sheltered by homes on both sides and behind ($c = 3.0$).

The general weatherization correlation represented by Eq 14 would appear to adequately correlate the infiltration rates of homes, requiring only a single measurement period in which ACH, Δt, and u are measured and c is estimated based on the siting status, from $c = 1$ (flat and open terrain) to $c = 10$ (very hilly and/or heavily wooded or crowded), to determine an estimate of L, the house leakiness factor. Determining L before and after weatherization would then provide a direct measurement of the effectiveness of the weatherization effort in reducing air infiltration. Two or more measurements before and after weatherization would provide an independent determination of the terrain factor, c. It would appear that this technique should be capable of determining changes in L due to weatherization of greater than about 10 to 15%. The uncertainty can be reduced to about 5 to 10% if the passive samplers from the before and after weatherization periods are analyzed at the same time, thereby eliminating any GC calibration errors.

Based on the seven Canadian, one Maryland, and three Long Island homes, the leakage factor, L, for ten energy-efficient homes (that is, all but the Goodrich house) ranged from a low of 1.27 to a high of 2.28 with an average of 1.77 ± 0.34; excluding the Canadian homes, for which unreasonably high average winds were reported, the average terrain factor, c, was 2.4 ± 0.5 with a range of 1.9 to 3.0, also consistent with the model. Equation 14 also shows that in the winter period (mid-December to mid-March) on Long Island, the temperature difference accounts for 72% of the ACH and wind, 28%, based on a terrain factor, c, of 2.5. During the warmer weather, the correlation always underpredicted the ACH because of the opening of windows by the occupants; this was different in the unoccupied Brookhaven house (see Table 20). At the extreme, during the summer months, the ACH climbed to 1.5 to 2.0 h^{-1} for the Dietz and Goodrich houses; thus, attempts at establishing the weather correlation must be done under a consistent position for doors, windows, vents, etc.

Examples of Multizone Flow Determination in Homes. Applications of the BNL/AIMS technique to the multizone modeling presented earlier provides a simple and convenient way to determine the complete infiltration and air exchange picture for a house [5] or building [21]. In this section, some detailed discussion of the results obtained in four houses will be shown for the purposes of demonstrating the capability of the technique and the proper way to deploy sources and samplers for the information desired. This information is that which is sufficient to calculate, for example, pollutant concentrations in different locations within the house for pollutant sources at different locations or heat balances around a home for sizing and zoning the heating system [22].

As an example, for one type of pollutant source in a three-zone house, material balances around each zone give the following

$$-(R_{E1} + R_{12} + R_{13})C_{11} + R_{21}C_{12} + R_{31}C_{13} = -R_{s11} \qquad (15)$$

$$R_{12}C_{11} - (R_{E2} + R_{21} + R_{23})C_{12} + R_{32}C_{13} = -R_{s12} \qquad (16)$$

$$R_{13}C_{11} + (R_{23}C_{12} - (R_{E3} + R_{31} + R_{32})C_{13} = -R_{s13} \qquad (17)$$

where

$R_{s11}, R_{s12}, R_{s13}$ = rate of source Type 1 in Zone 1, etc., nL/h, and the other terms are similar to those defined in the section entitled "Two-Zone Case." These equations assume that steady state applies (that is, the pollutant rate is constant) and that there are no reactive losses. Radon would be an example of a pollutant meeting these assumptions; NO_2 from a combustion source would require the addition of a first-order decay term ($k_{11}V_1C_{11}$) to the right-hand term of each equation and quite possibly time-dependent solution.

Since all the rates of exfiltration, R_E, and rates of air exchange, for example, R_{12}, were determined from the tracer measurements (see Appendix), Eqs 15 to 17 can be used in two ways: (1) if the pollutant concentrations in the three zones are measured, the source rates can be computed, and (2) if the source rates are known or assumed, the concentrations in the three zones can be solved from the three simultaneous equations. The latter will be demonstrated to examine the variability in zone concentrations with source location, to demonstrate the best procedure for determining the total infiltration rates in multizone homes using a single, constant emission rate tracer source such as SF_6 [23], popular because of the simplicity of the sampling and analysis equipment, and to indicate the information that is not available with simplified approaches.

Consider a three-zone house (for example, second floor, first floor, basement) in which a simple, single tracer approach is to be used. An overall material balance gives

$$R_{E1}C_{11} + R_{E2}C_{12} + R_{E3}C_{13} = R_{s1} \qquad (18)$$

Equation 18 can be solved for the total exfiltration rate, R_{ET}, which is the sum of the individual exfiltration rates, if those rates are equal (a situation which will be shown not to be the case) or if the concentrations in each zone are equal (that is, $C_{11} = C_{12} = C_{13} = \bar{C}$). Then Eq 18 becomes

$$R_{ET}\bar{C} = R_{s1} \tag{19}$$

that is, a single tracer is applicable. Because this approach is popular, the question to be addressed here is under what circumstances are the concentrations in each zone of a two-story house with a basement equal and, if not, what are the extents of the errors. Replacing each of the concentration terms in Eqs 15 to 17 with $\bar{C}$ gives

$$R_{I1}\bar{C} = R_{s11} \tag{20}$$

$$R_{I2}\bar{C} = R_{s12} \tag{21}$$

$$R_{I3}\bar{C} = R_{s13} \tag{22}$$

Thus Eqs 20–22 show that in a multizoned structure, to attain a uniform tracer concentration within the entire building requires a source strength in each zone in proportion to the infiltration rate in each zone, which is the principal of the automated constant concentration approach [24]. Manual deployment of properly sized sources in each zone would, of course, require prior knowledge of the individual zone infiltration rates to achieve constant concentration in the entire building; the magnitude of errors associated with determining the total infiltration rate using equal source strengths will be demonstrated for three previously discussed Long Island homes. But first, a consideration of attics and crawl spaces will be made.

The potential effect of an attic and crawl space on the indoor air quality (IAQ) within the living zone are demonstrated for the energy efficient test house belonging to the University of Illinois, a one-story ranch home. The flow results, shown schematically in Fig. 13, were calculated from the PFT concentration data shown in Table 21. That the attic, main floor living zone, and crawl space are three separate zones is clear from the different concentrations of each PFT found in each zone; note also that the tracer concentration was the highest in the zone in which it was deployed, a necessary but not sufficient condition for all flow rates to be computed as positive values. The standard deviation of the living zone concentrations for PFT 2, which was deployed in that zone, was quite high, indicating that uniform tagging of that zone was not achieved.

Figure 13 shows that there is almost as much air exchange between the living zone and the attic, contrary to I'Anson's results [11], as there is between the living zone and the outside air, indicating that the attic considered as a zone can help to distinguish leaks in the ceiling from those in the walls such as door and window penetrations, important in weatherization studies. It should be mentioned that the large standard deviation associated with the attic concentrations could lead to large errors in the flow rates. A method is currently under development to calculate these errors.

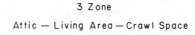

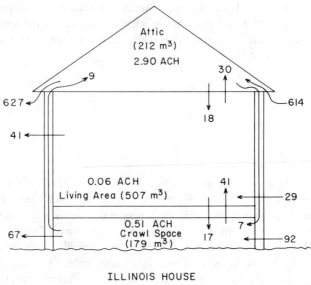

FIG. 13—*Three-zone flow rates determined for a ranch house.*

Table 22 shows the expected concentrations in the three zones for a 1000-nL/h source located alternatively in each zone. When located in the crawl space (Case 1), the concentration in the living zone (4.39 nL/m³) is 35% of the value when the source is in the living zone (12.41 nL/m³). With the source in the attic, the proportion is only 3.2% (0.40 divided by 12.41 nL/m³). Since attics do not generally contain any significant pollutant sources and, further, since they are usually well-ventilated (for example, nearly 3.0 ACH in this case, which is typical [11]), there is no need to consider attics in usual IAQ studies.

On the other hand, crawl spaces can be a significant source of soil gas containing radon [15]. If radon concentrations in the living and crawl zones were measured in the proportion of 4.39 to 9.27, then the entire source of radon would have been located in the crawl space; if the ratio were higher, then Eqs 15–17 could be used to find the source strength in both zones. A positive source in the living zone usually can be traced to radon in the domestic water supply. Further, as shown in Fig. 13, the crawl space contributed a greater flow of air into the living zone than did the outside walls, which is important to know for weatherization programs.

TABLE 21—BNL/AIMS results for several three-zone house tests. Measured PFT concentrations.

| House | Zone | Volume, m³ | Source Rate, nL/h | Average Tracer Concentrations,[a] nL/m³ | | | Exfiltration Rate, m³/h | Infiltration | | Effective ACH, h⁻¹ | Exchange Rates,[d] m³/h from Zone to Zone | | |
				PFT 1	PFT 2	PFT 3		Rate, m³/h	ACH,[b] h⁻¹		1	2	3
Illinois (3/14 to 4/11/84)	1. Attic	212	1578	2.45 ± 2.06	1.72 ± 1.15	0.92 ± 0.49	627.0	614.0	2.90	3.04	...	29.7	8.7
	2. Living area	507	2906	0.62 ± 0.11	36.07 ± 8.85	13.11 ± 0.17	40.5	28.6	0.06	0.16	18.2	...	40.8
	3. crawl space	179	2989	0.25 ± 0.06	5.50 ± 1.16	27.70 ± 2.00	66.8	91.7	0.51	0.60	7.3	17.4	...
	Totals	898					734.3	734.3	0.818[e]				
Dietz (2/1 to 2/22/84)	1. 2nd floor	255	1319	19.22 ± 1.50	23.51 ± 0.29	9.08 ± 0.19	19.6	7.2	0.03	0.27	...	116.6	0.1
	2. 1st floor	250	3045	9.12 ± 2.39	24.99 ± 0.39	9.63 ± 0.23	103.5	69.9	0.28	0.49	104.3	...	46.6
	3. basement	123	1153	0.17 ± 0.02	0.44 ± 0.06	25.30 ± 4.29	−0.8	45.1	0.37	0.37	0.1	0.7	...
	Totals	628					122.3	122.2	0.195[e]				
BNL (2/1 to 2/15/84)	1. 2nd floor	215	3208	26.64 ± 2.18	10.76 ± 0.21	4.34 ± 0.19	89.4	21.1	0.10	0.56	...	211.7	16.4
	2. 1st floor	240	1544	15.78 ± 1.96	12.41 ± 0.69	4.21 ± 0.31	26.3	75.5	0.31	0.52	148.1	...	40.7
	3. basement	204	1356	5.54 ± 0.14	3.44 ± 0.08	11.55 ± 0.00	74.2	93.3	0.46	0.58	11.8	26.2	...
	Totals	659					189.9	189.9	0.288[e]				
Goodrich (2/1 to 2/15/84)	1. 2nd floor	122	1743	10.49 ± 5.72	17.03 ± 0.91	2.50 ± 0.06	154.7	−18.5	−0.15	1.36	...	234.5	−1.9
	2. 1st floor	272	3477	2.14 ± 0.70	15.55 ± 1.37	2.34 ± 0.53	51.2	155.8	0.57	0.82	58.4	...	75.0
	3. basement	153	1471	0.08 ± 0.02	0.34 ± 0.08	7.07 ± 2.18	136.4	205.1	1.34	1.36	0.9	3.6	...
	Totals	547					342.3	342.4	0.626[e]				
Goodrich (modified)	1. 2nd floor	122	1743	10.5	15.5	2.5	152.4	14.3	0.12	...	...	185.1	3.7
	2. 1st floor	272	3477	2.1	17.0	2.6	63.0	127.1	0.47	...	49.7	...	74.5
	3. basement	153	1471	0.08	0.34	7.1	129.9	203.9	1.33	...	0.9	3.3	...
	Totals	547					345.3	345.3	0.631[e]				

[a] Average concentration for 2 or 3 CATS in each zone. PFT 1 was deployed in Zone 1, etc.

[b] The infiltration ACH was the zone infiltration rate, m³/h, divided by the zone volume, m³.

[c] The effective ACH was the zone source rate divided by the source concentration in that zone and by the zone volume.

[d] Air exchange rate example for the Illinois house: the rate from Zone 1 to Zone 2, R_{12}, was 18.2 m³/h.

[e] The total house ACH was the total infiltration rate divided by the total volume.

TABLE 22—*Expected zone concentrations in the Illinois house*
for a source in different locations.

	Source Rate, nL/h, and Location			Calculated[a] Zone Concentrations, nL/m³		
Case	Attic	Living	Crawl	Attic	Living	Crawl
1	...	...	1000	0.32	4.39	9.27
2	...	1000	...	0.59	12.41	1.89
3	1000	...	...	1.55	0.40	0.16

[a]By normalizing the measured concentrations in Table 21 with the known source strengths or by Eqs 15 to 17 using the flow rates in Table 21.

Infiltration ACH and effective ACH values are given in Table 21. The first is an indicator of the amount of fresh air entering each zone directly from outside; it is simply the infiltration rate divided by the zone volume. The second ACH, labeled the effective ACH, is an indicator of the total fresh air coming from outside and effectively coming from the other zones; it is simply the rate of a source in that zone divided by the concentration in that zone and the volume of the zone, that is, the apparent single zone infiltration rate. For example, the source rate in the living zone of the Illinois house (2906 nL/h, Table 21) divided by the concentration (36.07 nL/m³) gives an effective infiltration rate of 80.57 m³/h which, divided by the zone volume (507 m³), gives the effective ACH (0.159 h⁻¹) shown in the table.

The effective or single zone infiltration rate can be used to compute effective source strengths from measured concentrations. From the 12.41-nL/m³ value in Table 22 (Case 2), multiplying by the effective infiltration rate of 80.57 m³/h gives the effective source rate of 1000 nL/h. However, for Case 1, using the 4.39-nL/m³ concentration, the effective source rate in the living zone is computed to be 353.7 nL/h, which is equivalent to the actual crawl space source rate of 1000 nL/h times the portion of crawl space air entering the living zone (40.8 m³/h) relative to the total air leaving the crawl space (116.3 m³/h), that is

$$1000 \times \frac{R_{32}}{(R_{32} + R_{31} + R_{E3})}$$

Thus, the effective or single-zone ACH can be used to determine an effective pollutant source strength, but it cannot be used to quantify the actual source strength if it is located in another zone. This can only be done with the multiple tracers approach using the material balance equations such as Eqs 15–17 for a three-zone case.

The three Long Island houses had an unheated basement and two floors that were heated. The Goodrich house, built in 1952, was a New England cape cod style that had substantial additions to the first floor. The Dietz house, built in 1972, was a colonial model, also one of a number in a development. The unoccupied Brookhaven (BNL) house, completed in Sept. 1980, for energy conservation research, was specially equipped to reduce air infiltration. For each house, the basement was isolated from the first floor by a door which was closed at all times; the first and second floors were connected by an open staircase. Oil-fired hot water convective heating was used in the Goodrich and Dietz houses, supplemented by an airtight wood-burning stove in each first floor; forced hot air was provided to the first floor of the Brookhaven house with vents in the ceiling to provide natural draft to the second floor where the return air grill was located.

Table 21 gives the measured test results for a Feb. 1984 winter period, which were representative of the entire heating season results, and Fig. 14 shows the schematic of the flow patterns in the three houses. For the Dietz and Brookhaven houses, the concentrations were highest in the zones in which the source was deployed. The test failed in the Goodrich house; for the source deployed on the first floor, its concentration was higher on the second floor (17.0) compared to the first floor (15.6 nL/m^3). This was determined to be due to one of the first floor sources being placed on an inside wall in the living room near the staircase to the upstairs; apparently the airflow to upstairs carried most of the tracer from that source up the stairs instead of mixing within the room. As indicated earlier in the instructions, it is important to place the sources near outside walls. The result of this error was the calculation of a significantly large negative infiltration rate (-18.5 m^3/h in Table 21) on the second floor (note that the flow information in the table is slightly different than in the figure because of a correction made after the drawing was completed). Modifying the Goodrich concentrations slightly by reversing the concentrations of PFT 2 on the first and second floor gave the new results shown in Table 21. All the flow terms were now positive as anticipated; note that the total ACH remained essentially the same as did most of the other flow rates. This shows that small ($\sim 10\%$) errors in the measured concentrations could readily account for the negative flow rates; the previously mentioned error analysis routine will quantify the impact of those errors. Further details on the flow pattern differences between the three houses are given elsewhere [25].

The concentrations expected in each zone of the three homes for a 1000-nL/h source alternatively located in each of the zones are shown as Cases 2 to 4 in Table 23. The concentration differences are interesting; for Case 2, the concentration is much higher on the second floor in the Dietz house compared to the others because it had little infiltration and exfiltration from that zone. Also note the low concentrations in the basement for the Dietz and Goodrich homes because of the little flow into the basement from either the second or

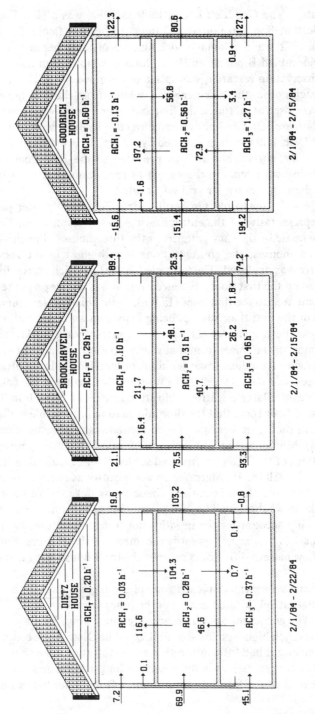

FIG. 14—*Three-zone flow rates determined for the periods indicated in the three Long Island houses. All flow rates are in m^3/h; the ACH values are the infiltration rates divided by the zone volumes.*

TABLE 23—Evaluations of multizone houses as single-zone buildings. Expected zone concentrations for one type of source in different locations.

House	Case	Calculation Basis	Source Location and Rate,[a] nL/h			Calculated[b] Zone Concentrations, nL/m³					Total Infiltration		Living Zone Infiltration	
			2nd	1st	Bsmt	2nd	1st	Bsmt	$\bar{C}_{21B}$	$\bar{C}_{21}$	Rate, m³/h	ACH, h⁻¹	Rate, m³/h	ACH, h⁻¹
Dietz (2/1 to 22/84)	1	3-zone results	…	…	…	…	…	…	…	…	122.2	0.195	93.1	0.184
	2	Source on 2nd floor	1000	…	…	14.6	6.9	0.1	…	10.74	…	…	125.6	0.249
	3	Source on 1st floor	…	1000	…	7.7	8.2	0.1	…	7.96	…	…	123.5	0.244
	4	Source in basement	…	…	1000	7.9	8.3	21.9	12.71	8.10	78.7	0.125	…	…
	5	Equal source rates (3)	333	333	333	10.0	7.8	7.4	8.42	…	118.8	0.189	…	…
	6	Equal zone concentration (3)	60	571	369	8.2	8.2	8.2	8.18	…	122.2	0.195	…	…
	7	Equal source rates (living zone)	500	500	…	11.1	7.6	0.1	…	9.34	…	…	107.0	0.212
	8	Equal zone concentration (living zone)	60	940	…	8.1	8.1	0.1	…	8.13	…	…	123.0	0.244
BNL (2/1 to 15/84)	1	3-zone results	…	…	…	…	…	…	…	…	189.9	0.288	…	…
	2	Source on 2nd floor	1000	…	…	8.3	4.9	1.7	…	6.61	…	…	151.2	0.332
	3	Source on 1st floor	…	1000	…	7.0	8.0	2.2	…	7.50	…	…	133.3	0.293
	4	Source in basement	…	…	1000	3.2	3.1	8.5	4.94	…	202.3	0.307	…	…
	5	Equal source rates (3)	333	333	333	6.2	5.4	4.2	5.22	…	191.4	0.290	…	…
	6	Equal zone concentration (3)	112	397	491	5.3	5.3	5.3	5.27	…	189.9	0.288	…	…
	7	Equal source rates (living zone)	500	500	…	7.6	6.5	2.0	…	7.06	…	…	141.7	0.311
	8	Equal zone concentration (living zone)	240	760	…	7.3	7.3	2.1	…	7.29	…	…	137.2	0.301
Goodrich (2/1 to 15/84)	1	3-zone results	…	…	…	…	…	…	…	…	345.3	0.631	…	…
	2	Source on 2nd floor	1000	…	…	6.0	1.2	0.1	…	3.61	…	…	276.7	0.702
	3	Source on 1st floor	…	1000	…	4.5	4.9	0.1	…	4.67	…	…	214.0	0.543
	4	Source in basement	…	…	1000	1.7	1.8	4.8	2.77	…	360.8	0.660	…	…
	5	Equal source rates (3)	333	333	333	4.1	2.6	1.7	2.78	…	359.5	0.657	…	…
	6	Equal zone concentration (3)	41	368	591	2.9	2.9	2.9	2.90	…	345.3	0.631	…	…
	7	Equal source rates (living zone)	500	500	…	5.2	3.1	0.1	…	4.14	…	…	241.3	0.612
	8	Equal zone concentration (living zone)	82	918	…	4.6	4.6	0.1	…	4.59	…	…	218.0	0.553

[a] The source rates for Cases 6 and 8 were calculated from Eqs 15 to 17 by letting all 3 (Case 6) or the 2nd and 1st floor (living zone—Case 8) zone concentrations be equal and the sum of the source rates be 1000 nL/h.

[b] Calculated from Eqs 15 to 17 using the flow rates given in Table 21. $\bar{C}_{21B}$ is the avg concentration for 3 zones and $\bar{C}_{21}$, for the 2nd and 1st floors (living zone).

first floors; in contrast, the BNL house had a modest basement concentration from a source on the second floor because of significant flows from the first and second floors into the basement (see Fig. 14).

CO from an unvented gas or kerosene space heater represents an example of a steady-state source on the first floor. For this Case 3, the relationship between second and first floor concentrations is about the same in all three homes, that is, slightly lower on the second floor compared to the first floor, despite the large differences in flow patterns. It would appear to be a general conclusion that for a source deployed on the first floor of any two-story house and, for that matter, for a source deployed in the basement (Case 4), the concentration on the second floor will be about 91 ± 4% of the value on the first floor. Thus, someone sleeping in a bedroom on the second floor will be exposed to a not-much-lower level than on the first floor. Of course, the modeling assumption here is that the first floor is a well-mixed zone such that the concentration is everywhere the same, including the first floor room containing the pollutant source. In many homes, the open nature of the first floor will lend towards good mixing; in others, a somewhat isolated room with the source might properly be treated as a separate zone from the balance of the first floor. In any event, the concentrations upstairs for nonreactive pollutants will not be significantly less than in the balance of the first floor.

Radon from soil gas penetration into basements is a form of steady-state source exemplified by Case 4 in Table 23. For all three homes built on the same soil and assuming the same source strength term (for example, 1000 nCi/h), the radon concentration would be much higher in the Dietz basement (21.9 nCi/m^3 or 21.9 pCi/L), by about a factor of 3 to 5, compared to the other two basement values for Case 4 (8.5 and 4.8 pCi/L). The same ratio holds for the living zone radon concentrations.

A closer comparison of the Dietz and BNL houses with respect to the supposed basement radon source is revealing. Assuming both had the same source rate of 1000 nCi/h and having measured the whole house infiltration rates as 0.195 and 0.288 h^{-1}, respectively (shown as Case 1 in Table 23), one would expect whole house concentrations (Case 6) of 8.2 and 5.3 pCi/L, respectively, for the Dietz and BNL houses, a ratio of about 1.5 to 1. Instead, the "measured" concentrations (Case 4) of 8.3 and 3.1 pCi/L, respectively, were in a proportion of 2.7 to 1, a significant difference. This is a good example of living zone radon concentrations correlating poorly with whole house, that is, single zone, infiltration rates. Even the ratio of the average radon concentrations in the whole house ($\bar{C}_{21B}$), 12.71/4.94 or 2.6 to 1, indicated poor correlation with the whole house ACHs.

The reason can be seen in the basement flow patterns as revealed by the three-zone BNL/AIMS results (see Fig. 14). For the Dietz house, the portion of basement air entering the living zone is 100% because there is no exfiltrating air ($R_{E3} = -0.8$ m^3/h). However, in the BNL house the portion is

$$\frac{40.7 + 16.4}{40.7 + 16.4 + 74.2} = 0.43$$

or only 43%. Thus, the BNL house radon source term is effectively much less. This cannot be explained with anything less than basement–living zone two-zone tracer measurements.

Built on the same soil with the same basement structure exposed to the soil, the BNL/AIMS flow patterns reveal a potential for further exacerbation of the potential radon problem in the Dietz house compared to the others. The zero exfiltration rate from the Dietz basement implies the existence of a significant subatmospheric pressure in the basement, which, of course, can mean a larger driving force for soil gas penetration than in a basement with a high exfiltration rate such as in the other two houses. This can be further seen by the very large basement to first floor stack effect (see Fig. 14), that is, the flow up (46.6) divided by the flow down ($0.7 \, m^3/h$) or 67 to 1; for the BNL basement, the stack effect is only 1.6 to 1, and for the Goodrich basement, 21 to 1. It is expected that such multizone measurements will significantly extend our understanding of this important IAQ concern.

How to perform single-zone measurements in multizone houses is also revealed in Table 23. Although, as just discussed, such measurements miss a lot of important information, many researchers prefer the single-zone approach because they have only one tracer source, usually SF_6. A first and simple approach is to uniformly divide the source strength between each floor (Case 5), remembering that the true infiltration rate can only be obtained when the concentration in each zone is equal (Case 6). Indeed, for equal source rates in each zone (Case 5), there was a significant difference in the concentration in each zone and in that distribution for the three houses. Comparing the average whole house concentration ($\bar{C}_{21B}$) for Case 5 with the true average (Case 6) shows that, for the Dietz house, the result is 2.9% high; for the BNL house, 0.9% low; and for the Goodrich house, 4.1% low. It would appear that in general these errors are small enough to preclude concern for attainment of equal zone concentrations.

The actual source rate distribution required to attain equal zone concentrations are shown in Case 6. The results show that the distribution should be for the second floor, 4 to 11%; for the 1st floor, 37 to 56%; and for the basement, 37 to 59%. Obviously, a good compromise would be 50% on the first floor and 50% in the basement with no source on the second floor; the errors with this general approach would probably always be less than 1 to 2% in houses with natural convection. Further studies are needed in forced convection homes.

Single-zone measurements of the living zone of a two-story house also is demonstrated in Table 23. Case 7 assumes equal source strengths of the second and first floors, and Case 8 gives the source strength distribution for equal concentrations on the two floors. This is an important approach for researchers that have two tracers and want to tag the basement with one and the living zone of a two-story house with the other. For a 50-50 distribution on the second and first floors (Case 7), the error in the living zone average concentration ($\bar{C}_{21}$) compared to the true value (Case 8) is 14.9% high for the Dietz house; 3.2% low for the BNL house; and 9.8% low for the Goodrich house.

The actual source rate distribution required to attain equal concentrations on the first and second floors are shown in Case 8. Thus, the distribution is weighted heavily towards the first floor, even in houses with forced air convection such as the BNL house (76%), compared to natural convection (92 to 94%). Placing the living zone source entirely on the first floor (Case 3) gives errors of -2.1, 2.9, and 1.7%, respectively, for the three houses, and the requirement of a uniform concentration in the first and second floor for a source in the basement (Case 4), which is required for correct solution of this two-zone approach, is seen to be nicely approximated. Thus, this approach will give a correct picture of the interaction between a basement and the living zone; of course, it cannot give the correct second floor concentration for a source on that floor.

The choice of PFT source types with zone location is important in multizone structures. Because of the stack effect in all houses, a source placed on the second floor will have a very low concentration in the basement (Case 2 in Table 23). To improve the precision of its measurement in the basement, the second floor tracer selected should be one with the highest emission rate (see Table 1) and the highest detectability, that is, the earliest eluting tracer on the gas chromatograph (GC) column (Fig. 7). Thus the choice for the second floor tracer in a three-zone study is either PDCB or PMCP. The same reasoning extended to the other floors dictated that PMCH be used on the first floor and PDCH in the basement. The use of PDCB in one zone and PMCP in another zone in a three-zone building should be avoided because those two tracers elute very close to each other (Fig. 7) and are, therefore, difficult to quantify without using special GC conditions.

In stacked four-zone structures, when both PDCB and PMCP must be used, the correct choice for the uppermost zone is PDCB, followed by PMCP in the next lower zone. When two components elute next to each other, a small quantity of the first eluting component next to a large amount of the second component is always easier to detect than the reverse situation. Placing PDCB in the highest zone guarantees the proper peak size order in each zone except the uppermost zone; but, in that zone, the PMCP concentration will be also high because of the stack effect.

A significant diurnal effect on ACH exists in houses because of the large swing in outside temperatures between day and night. With passive sampler measurements over a period of a few days to weeks, this effect is not discernable but is adequately integrated to obtain an average infiltration rate [19].

Two programmable samplers collecting 4-h integrated samples for almost 4 days in the BNL house, one sampling upstairs (second floor) and the other downstairs (first floor) gave the computed infiltration rates shown in Fig. 15. The diurnal trend is clearly evident, with maxima and minima occurring at about 0300 and 1500 h, respectively. Such detailed measurements may be important in more comprehensive studies on IAQ and energy flow calculations.

Conclusions

From the detailed studies on the PFT sources, for which four types currently exist, it was shown that they can be manufactured with a very reproducible ($\pm 2\%$) and constant emission rate, essentially constant for the lifetime of the sources (2 to 7 years). By using silicone rubber plugs cut from extruded rubber cord, the reproducibility has been improved to within less than $\pm$ 0.5%. The current temperature sensitivity of the source rate, about 15%/3°C, is sometimes a problem in field studies. Further studies with other rubber materials may reduce that dependence; preliminary tests with Buna rubber show about one half that dependence, but the emission rates are 20-fold lower.

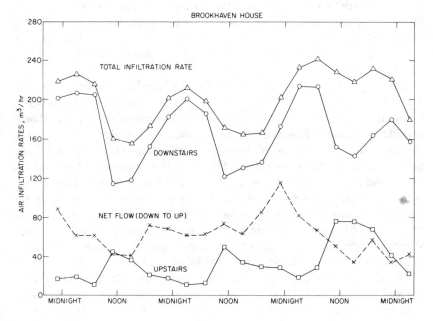

FIG. 15—*Diurnal effect on two-zone infiltration rates determined on a 4-h frequency using programmable samplers.*

The passive samplers (CATS) were simple to manufacture and very reproducible in their sampling rates, within ±2%.

Although the gas chromatograph analysis system for the passive samplers is complex, each step in the automated sequence is important. With temperature programming of the main column, multiple CATS can be analyzed for four PFTs on a 13-min cycle; new techniques are being explored to both improve the GC separation of the PFTs and to shorten the analysis time, primarily by separating the precut column from the main column and providing individually optimized temperature programming. Further work also should be done on improving the linearity of the electron capture detector in order to simplify the calibration procedures.

The field deployment of PFT sources in homes for the purposes of establishing a uniform tracer concentration on each floor required generally two sources per floor. Detailed studies in two-story houses showed that the concentrations were quite uniform (±3%) on the first floor, which is usually more open in structure than the compartmentalized nature of the second floor containing bedrooms, where variability was usually within ±10 to 15% when bedroom doors were always open but sometimes as poor as ±50% when bedroom doors were periodically closed. By placing sources near the outside walls, usually one at each extreme end of a floor, the flow dynamics provided good mixing. But the door to any room containing a source or being sampled must remain open. In multiple floor homes, the highest emission rate source type is preferred on the uppermost floor (that is, PDCB) and the lowest rate source in the basement (that is, PDCH). In cases where some bedroom doors are periodically closed, suspending the source in the hall, about 40-cm from the ceiling and near the bedroom doors may be preferable; tests are being conducted.

Sampling generally was done by placing the samplers near an inside wall. This allowed good mixing of the emitted PFT vapors with the room air before encountering the sampler. The exact siting of sources and samplers should consider the internal flow dynamics of the house. Warm air within a meter of the ceiling usually flows toward the outside walls where it is cooled, sinks, and returns inwardly toward the center of the floor (for example, to the hall). On the second floor, some of this returning air will flow down the staircase and pour out within a meter or so of the floor on the first floor. Flowing up the staircase will be a portion of the air on the first floor within a meter or so of the ceiling. Quite obviously, placing a source, meant to tag the first floor, near a staircase leading upstairs, might lead to short-circuiting of some of the tracer to the second floor. Such locations must be avoided.

The BNL/AIMS technique has been satisfactorily validated against SF_6 decay and constant source rate methods in homes and recently in a laboratory chamber versus CO_2 decay measurements [18]. The reproducibility of the system in identical homes located even in different cities was within ±7%.

Multizone measurements in a ranch house with an attic and a crawl space showed that considering the attic as a zone was unnecessary for IAQ studies. It was shown, however, that a significant portion of the living zone air can be exchanged with the attic, an important consideration in weatherization studies. Crawl spaces were shown to be important in both weatherization and IAQ studies because a significant portion of air entering the first floor of a house comes from the crawl space. This can have important implications on energy balances [22] and on IAQ studies, since such zones are the source of indoor radon.

Detailed studies in three two-story homes with basements showed both some extreme differences and similarities. In all three, for a source on the first floor, the concentration on the second floor was generally about 90% of that on the first floor. This provided the interesting observation that to tag the first and second floors to simulate a single, well-mixed zone, a source need only be distributed in the first floor. All three showed extreme differences in the interaction between the basement and the first floor and in the exfiltration patterns from the basements and the second floors, each of which would cause demonstrated differences in the expected indoor air quality for given pollutant source rates and locations.

A generalized weather correlation was successfully developed in which each house was characterized by a specific leakage factor, L, which was the whole house ACH normalized to a fixed function dependent only on inside-outside temperature difference, the wind speed to the 1.5 power, and a terrain factor. For ten homes, L varied from 1.3 to 2.3, and, for one home built in 1952, its value was 4.5. With a subjective estimate of the terrain factor, a single measurement period would provide an indication of L; two or more measurements would give an independent measure of the terrain factor as well. Field tests of the applicability of this ACH weather correlation in quantifying reduction in air infiltration due to weatherization efforts are currently under way.

Although the tracer source and sampler are quite inexpensive, less than $5 each in quantity, the analysis system is complex and costly. Thus, only a few central laboratories should be established to provide the technique as an inexpensive service to users worldwide. It should be noted that the technology is patented [26] and the service will be available commercially [27].

Acknowledgment

To the researchers who performed many of the field experiments in homes and provided the meteorological data, appreciation is expressed. A special thanks is extended to G. Senum and T. D'Ottavio for contributing valuable suggestions and input along the stages of this study. Support from the U.S. Department of Energy Offices of Buildings and Community Systems and of Health and Environmental Research is gratefully acknowledged.

APPENDIX

The solution to the two- and three-zone infiltration models are provided in this appendix.

Two-Zone Case

$$R_{21} = \frac{R_{s1}C_{21}}{C_{11}C_{22} - C_{12}C_{21}}$$

$$R_{12} = \frac{R_{s2}C_{12}}{C_{11}C_{22} - C_{12}C_{21}}$$

$$R_{E1} = R_{21}\frac{C_{22}}{C_{21}} - R_{12}$$

$$R_{E2} = R_{12}\frac{C_{11}}{C_{12}} - R_{21}$$

R_{I1} and R_{I2} are calculated from Eqs 8 and 9 in the text.

Three-Zone Case

Let

$$[\ \ ] = [C_{11}(C_{22}C_{33} - C_{23}C_{32}) + C_{12}(C_{23}C_{31} - C_{21}C_{33}) + C_{13}(C_{21}C_{32} - C_{22}C_{31})]$$

Then

$$R_{21} = R_{s1}(C_{21}C_{33} - C_{23}C_{31})/[\ \ ]$$

$$R_{31} = R_{s1}(C_{22}C_{31} - C_{21}C_{32})/[\ \ ]$$

$$R_{32} = R_{s2}(C_{11}C_{32} - C_{12}C_{31})/[\ \ ]$$

$$R_{12} = R_{s2}(C_{12}C_{33} - C_{13}C_{32})/[\ \ ]$$

$$R_{13} = R_{s3}(C_{13}C_{22} - C_{12}C_{23})/[\ \ ]$$

$$R_{23} = R_{s3}(C_{23}C_{11} - C_{13}C_{21})/[\ \ ]$$

$$R_{E1} = R_{31}\frac{C_{23}}{C_{21}} + R_{21}\frac{C_{22}}{C_{21}} - R_{13} - R_{12}$$

$$R_{E2} = R_{32}\frac{C_{13}}{C_{12}} + R_{12}\frac{C_{11}}{C_{12}} - R_{23} - R_{21}$$

$$R_{E3} = R_{13}\frac{C_{11}}{C_{13}} + R_{23}\frac{C_{12}}{C_{13}} - R_{31} - R_{32}$$

$$R_{I1} = R_{E1} + R_{12} + R_{13} - R_{21} - R_{31}$$

$$R_{I2} = R_{E2} + R_{21} + R_{23} - R_{12} - R_{32}$$

$$R_{I3} = R_{E3} + R_{31} + R_{32} - R_{13} - R_{23}$$

The total ACH in a house is given simply by the sum of the exfiltration rates of all zones divided by the sum of the volume of all zones. (See section entitled "Two-Zone Case" of the text for definition of the terms.)

References

[1] Spengler, J. D. and Sexton, K., "Indoor Air Pollution: a Public Health Perspective," *Science*, Vol. 221, No. 4605, July 1983, pp. 9–17.

[2] Dietz, R. N. and Cote, E. A., "Air Infiltration Measurements in a Home Using a Convenient Perfluorocarbon Tracer Technique," *Environment International*, Vol. 8, No. 1–6, 1982, pp. 419–433.

[3] Kronvall, J., "Tracer Gas Techniques for Ventilation Measurements: a 1981 State of the Art Review" in *Studies in Building Physics*, A.-S. Anderson, Ed., Report TVBH-3007, Lund Institute of Technology, Lund, Sweden, 1981, pp. 81–94.

[4] Sherman, M. H. and Grimsrud, D. T., "Infiltration-Pressurization Correlation: Simplified Physical Modeling," LBL-10163, Lawrence Berkeley Laboratory, Berkeley, CA, 1980.

[5] Dietz, R. N., Goodrich, R. W., Cote, E. A., and Wieser, R. F., "Brookhaven Air Infiltration Measurement System (BNL/AIMS) Description and Applications," BNL-33846, Brookhaven National Laboratory, Upton, NY, Aug. 1983.

[6] Ferber, G. J., Telegadas, K., Heffter, J. L., Dickson, C. R., Dietz, R. N., and Krey, P. W., "Demonstration of a Long-Range Atmospheric Tracer System Using Perfluorocarbons," ERL ARL-101, NOAA Air Resources Laboratories, Rockville, MD, Apr. 1981.

[7] Dietz, R. N. and Dabberdt, W. F., "Gaseous Tracer Technology and Applications," BNL-33585, Brookhaven National Laboratory, Upton, NY, July 1983.

[8] Senum, G. I., Gergley, R. P., Ferreri, E. M., Greene, M. W., and Dietz, R. N., "Final Report of the Evaluation of Vapor Taggants and Substrates for the Tagging of Blasting Caps," BNL-51232, Brookhaven National Laboratory, Upton, NY, March 1980.

[9] *Building Air Change Rate and Infiltration Measurements*, C. M. Hunt, J. C. King, and H. R. Trechsel, Eds., ASTM STP 719, American Society for Testing and Materials, Philadelphia, PA, 1980.

[10] Hernandez, T. L. and Ring, J. W., "Indoor Radon Source Fluxes: Experimental Tests of a Two-Chamber Model," *Environment International*, Vol. 8, No. 1–6, 1982, pp. 45–57.

[11] I'Anson, S. J., Irwin, C., and Howarth, A. T., "Air Flow Measurement using Three Tracer Gases," *Building and Environment*, Vol. 17, No. 4, 1982, pp. 245–252.

[12] Perera, M. D. A. E. S., "Review of Techniques for Measuring Ventilation Rates in Multi-Celled Buildings," in *Proceedings*, EC Contractors' Meeting on Natural Ventilation, Brussels, 30 Sept. 1982, Building Research Establishment, Garston, England, 1982.

[13] Maldonado, E. A. B., "A Method to Characterize Air Exchange in Residences for Evaluation of Indoor Air Quality," Ph.D. dissertation, Iowa State University, Ames, Iowa, 1982.

[14] Ruckdeschel, R. F., *Basic scientific subroutines*, Vol. 1, Byte/McGraw-Hill, Peterborough, NH, 1981.

[15] Bruno, R. C., "Sources of Indoor Radon in Houses: a Review," *Air Pollution Control Association Journal*, Vol. 33, No. 2, 1983, pp. 105–109.

[16] Judekis, H. S. and Wren, A. G., "Laboratory Measurements of NO and NO_2 Depositions

onto Soil and Cement Surfaces," *Atmospheric Environment*, Vol. 12, 1978, pp. 2315-2319.

[17] Lovelock, J. E., "The Electron Capture Detector Theory and Practice," *Journal of Chromatography*, Vol. 99, 1974, pp. 3-12.

[18] Leaderer, B. P., Schaap, L., and Dietz, R. N., "Evaluation of the Perfluorocarbon Tracer Technique for Determining Infiltration Rates in Residences," *Environmental Science and Technology*, Vol. 19, No. 12, 1985, pp. 1225-1232.

[19] Wang, Sr., F. S. and Sepsy, C. F., "Field Studies of Air Tightness of Residential Buildings" in *Building Air Change Rate and Infiltration Measurements*, ASTM STP 719, C. M. Hunt, J. C. King, and H. R. Trechsel, Eds., American Society for Testing and Materials, Philadelphia, PA, 1980, pp. 24-35.

[20] Malik, S., "Field Studies of Dependence of Air Infiltration on Outside Temperature and Wind," *Energy and Buildings*, Vol. 1, No. 3, 1978, pp. 281-292.

[21] Dietz, R. N., Goodrich, R. W., Cote, E. A., and Wieser, R. F., "Application of Perfluorocarbon Tracers to Multizone Air Flow Measurements in Mechanically and Naturally Ventilated Buildings," presented at the ASHRAE seminar on Tracer Gas Measurements of Ventilation Rates in Mechanically Ventilated Buildings, Chicago, Jan. 30, 1985, BNL 35249, Brookhaven National Laboratory, Upton, NY, Aug. 1984.

[22] D'Ottavio, T. W. and Dietz, R. N., "Errors Resulting From the Use of Single Zone Ventilation Models on Multi-Zone Buildings: Implications for Energy Conservation and Indoor Air Quality Studies," to be presented at the ASHRAE Symposium on MultiCell Infiltration, Honolulu, June 1985, BNL 36186, Brookhaven National Laboratory, Upton, NY, Feb. 1985.

[23] Tolzke, D., Quackenboss, J., Kaarakka, P., and Flukenger, J., "A Modified Tracer Gas Infiltration Method for Use in a Residential Indoor Air Quality/Weatherization Study," in *Indoor Air*, Vol. 5, B. Berglund, T. Lindvall, and J. Sandell, Eds., Swedish Council for Building Research, Stockholm, 1984, pp. 459-464.

[24] Sinden, F. W., "Multichamber Theory of Air Infiltration," *Building and Environment*, Vol. 13, 1982, pp. 21-28.

[25] Dietz, R. N., D'Ottavio, T. W., and Goodrich, R. W., "Seasonal Effects on Multizone Air Infiltration in Some Typical U.S. Homes Using a Passive Perfluorocarbon Tracer Technique," presented at the Copenhagen '85 World Congress on Heating, Ventilating, and Air Conditioning, Copenhagen, 25-30 Aug. 1985, BNL 36151, Brookhaven National Laboratory, Upton, NY, Feb. 1985.

[26] Dempsey, J. C., "Method and Apparatus for Measuring the Rate at which Air Infiltrates into and out of Buildings," U.S. Patent No. 4,493,207, January 15, 1985.

[27] "Research Foundation Offers Builders New Low-Cost AIMS," *National Building News*, Vol. 1, No. 15, October 14, 1985, p. 10.

DISCUSSION

R. Gammage[1] *(written discussion)*—Please explain how your tracer technique has been used to study pollutant scavenging inside residences.

R. Dietz, R. Goodrich, E. Cote, and R. Wieser (authors' closure)—As an example, consider a ranch house as having two zones, a bedroom zone (Zone 2) and a living zone (Zone 1), with a source of NO_2 only in the living zone from a gas stove. Then the two-zone pollution equations (Eqs 10 and 11) can be solved for k_2 in the bedroom zone from Eq 11, assuming R_{p2} is zero and then

---

[1]Health and Safety Research Division, Oak Ridge National Laboratory, Oak Ridge, TN.

assuming $k_1 = k_2$, the pollutant source rate in the living zone, R_{p1}, can be solved from Eq 10. Thus, this technique can solve for both pollutant scavenging and source rates.

M. Sherman[2] *(written discussion)*—You stated that there is about a 15% error for a 3°C temperature change. If one relies on occupants or set points to determine the temperature, 3°C is likely a significant underestimate. But even if the temperature is measured as a function of time, changes in infiltration will correlate with the changes in temperature. Since the emission also correlates with temperature, how do you correct the result in cases like night setback, etc.?

R. Dietz, R. Goodrich, E. Cote, and R. Wieser (authors' closure)—The time-weighted average temperature is used to adjust the emission rates using an activation energy of 8 kcal/mol. This average value was shown not to cause any error in the determination of infiltration rates [*18*].

P. Lagus[3] *(written discussion)*—Are the perfluorocarbon tracers commercially available? If so, from what source or sources? What is the approximate cost of each?

R. Dietz, R. Goodrich, E. Cote, and R. Wieser (authors' closure)—The AIMS technique will be commercially available from the National Association of Home Builder's Research Foundation at some time in the early spring of 1986. Contact can be made with Larry Zarker at (301)762-4200 for more information on the availability and cost of the system. Most of the perfluorocarbon tracer compounds that are used to make the sources are available from Manchem, Inc., Princeton, N.J. (see Table 1).

E. Krutson[4] *(written discussion)*—(1) Regarding the source, could you determine the amount released by weighing before and after field deployment? (2) Regarding the sample, is the sampling rate constant, that is, does the Ambersorb saturate?

R. Dietz, R. Goodrich, E. Cote, and R. Wieser (authors' closure)—(1) The typical weight loss is in the range of 0.3 to 0.8 mg per day or 2 to 5 mg per week; this would be difficult to determine with the necessary accuracy after just 1 week of deployment; (2) even after one month of sampling, the total amount of tracer on the Ambersorb is only a few nanograms, orders of magnitude less than saturation; however, the influence of other adsorbed materials on the sampling rate should be confirmed as negligible.

P. Lagus (written discussion)—You seem to ignore the effects of a varying air change rate. What effect does a varying air leakage rate have on the accuracy of the sampling/emission technique?

R. Dietz, R. Goodrich, E. Cote, and R. Wieser (authors' closure)—The diurnal cycling of outdoor temperatures can cause temperature difference

---

[2]Lawrence Berkeley Laboratory, Berkeley, CA.
[3]S-Cubed, Box 1620, La Jolla, CA.
[4]U.S. Dept. of Energy, New York, NY 10014.

swings of as much as a factor of 2. Reference *18* has shown that the reciprocal of the average tracer concentration, which is the item measured by the passive sampler, is not identical to the average reciprocal tracer concentration, which is the item needed to compute ventilation rates. For wintertime measurements of several days or longer, it is estimated that this approach will underestimate the true ventilation rate by about 3 to 6%, a tolerable bias for this convenient technique.

David I. Jacobson,[1] *Gautam S. Dutt,*[2] *and*
Robert H. Socolow[2]

Pressurization Testing, Infiltration Reduction, and Energy Savings

REFERENCE: Jacobson, D. I., Dutt, G. S., and Socolow, R. H., **"Pressurization Testing, Infiltration Reduction, and Energy Savings,"** *Measured Air Leakage of Buildings, ASTM STP 904*, H. R. Trechsel and P. L. Lagus, Eds., American Society for Testing and Materials, Philadelphia, 1986, pp. 265–293.

ABSTRACT: House tightening has become an important component of residential energy conservation programs. The technique of pressurization as a means of improving the effectiveness and labor productivity of house tightening has been increasingly used. It would be desirable if the measurements taken as part of the house pressurization activity could be used to quantify the degree of tightening actually accomplished. Such measurements were taken both immediately before and immediately after a house tightening activity carried out, as part of the Modular Retrofit Experiment (MRE), in 98 single-family houses in seven sites in New Jersey and New York. We have reduced the pressurization data from 55 homes according to two prescriptions, one rooted in the airflows actually observed at a relatively high pressure (50 Pa) and one requiring the extrapolation to a low pressure (4 Pa) by means of a curve fit through and beyond the observations. The two prescriptions turn out to give very different answers to the question: By what percent has the average air infiltration rate been reduced? In a large fraction of cases, the process of house tightening leaves a signature in the pressurization data such that the percent reduction in airflow is greater at lower pressures; as a consequence, the prescription which involves extrapolating to 4 Pa gives much larger estimates of the percent reduction in air infiltration achieved by the tightening process. In the seven sites we examined, the estimated percentage savings for the 4-Pa extrapolation was over twice as large on the average. The differences in the interpretation of pressurization data also lead to wide discrepancies in the expected reduction in naturally induced air infiltration, which was not measured in the MRE. In a subsequent experiment, known as the Dual Infiltration Reduction Experiment (DIRE), tracer gas decay measurements before and after house tightening supplement pressurization data. This experiment helps to clarify the relationship between air leakage *reduction* as measured by the two techniques—an area that has not been explored in past research relating natural air infiltration and leakage reduction pressurization.

The natural air infiltration reduction can be interpreted directly in terms of energy savings. For the MRE houses, the air infiltration energy savings component is computed

[1]Graduate student, Dept. of Mechanical Engineering, University of Illinois, Urbana, IL 61801.

[2]Research fellow, University Nat. Auton., Mexico, c/o Marco Martinez, Insurgentes sur 4411, Edit. 9-404, 14430 Mexico 22, D.F., Mexico.

[3]Director, Center for Energy and Environmental Studies, Princeton University, Princeton, NJ 08544.

from estimates of natural air infiltration reduction. This component is compared with total savings in space heating energy use where available utility billing data permit the latter to be calculated.

KEY WORDS: Air infiltration, air leakage, blower door, tracer gas decay, pressurization

Air infiltration generally represents a significant part of the energy used to heat houses. Consequently, the reduction of air infiltration has featured strongly in many recent energy conservation programs. The development of methods to measure the natural air infiltration rates in houses and of devices to pressurize houses in order to exaggerate and quantify air leaks has improved greatly our understanding of air infiltration during the past decade [1]. Experiments with house pressurization soon revealed that windows and doors, originally believed to contribute most of the air leakage in a house, only account for a small part of the total [2-4]. Pressurization devices may be used to locate the less obvious air leaks and quantify their relative magnitude.

One offshoot of the research was the development of easy-to-use house pressurization devices called *blower doors*, which consist of a calibrated high flow fan mounted on a plywood frame, temporarily secured in an exterior doorway of a house. These devices can be used to find air leaks, and, while in place, many of the leaks can be sealed. This process of reducing air infiltration in houses using a blower door is generally referred to as "shell tightening." Besides being a convenient and rapid way of finding air leakage sites, the calibrated fan also permits the house air leakage to be measured both before and after a shell-tightening retrofit has been performed. This enables the effectiveness of the retrofit in terms of leakage reduction to be evaluated on the spot. However, in order to facilitate the leakage rate measurements using house pressurization, the house is subjected to much higher inside-outside pressure differences than would normally occur. Thus these measurements are not directly indicative of the natural air infiltration induced by the pressure effects created by wind and temperature differences. It is these natural air infiltration rates that determine the space conditioning energy requirements and the amount of ventilation available.

Various models have been developed to estimate natural air infiltration from pressurization data, for example by Shaw [5], Kronvall [6], and Sherman et al [7]. In a recent study, Linteris and Persily [8] compared the predictions of these models with natural air infiltration as measured by the tracer gas decay method. In that study, many of the difficulties in the use of the models were discussed, and the practical value of pressurization testing as a low-cost tool for measuring air leakage rate was questioned.

This paper examines data from two house retrofit experiments to determine whether reliable information about natural air infiltration can be obtained from pressurization testing. In the first experiment, leakage data were from house pressurization only and were used to estimate natural air infiltration reduction and corresponding energy savings. These energy savings then were compared with total measured energy savings resulting from the retrofits. In the second experiment, air leakage was measured using both pressurization and tracer gas decay before and after the retrofits in an attempt to understand the relationship between reduction in air leakage measured by the two methods.

The two experiments are called the Modular Retrofit Experiment (MRE) and Dual Infiltration Retrofit Experiment (DIRE).

Shell Tightening and the Modular Retrofit Experiment

The blower door and the "shell tightening" process are combined with other building energy diagnostics and conservation measures in the "house doctor" procedure. Infrared thermography is used in conjunction with the blower door to find many hidden thermal bypasses in the building envelope and to find "convective loops," both first observed at Twin Rivers [9]. A typical house doctor procedure may include a furnace tune-up to increase its efficiency as well as other measures to reduce space and water heating energy use. Thus, a house doctor procedure consists of an instrumented analysis accompanied by on-the-spot retrofits, some of which involve reduction in air leakage [10].

The MRE was designed to test the dissemination of the house doctor technology. The level of effort, energy savings, and cost effectiveness of house doctoring, when applied to a variety of housing styles, was evaluated in this experiment, carried out in collaboration with five New Jersey and New York gas utilities.[3] Princeton designed the experiment, trained utility staff as house doctors, and later evaluated the energy savings from the retrofits [11][4].

The experiment was carried out in groups of similar houses called *modules*, located within the same housing development. Each participating utility had one or two modules of 18 to 24 houses, and there was a total of seven modules in the experiment. Initially, 18 houses were chosen in each module and randomly assigned to three equally sized groups. Each of the houses in one group, the "house doctor" group, received a one-day visit by two house doctors. A second group, the "major retrofit" group, involved the "house doctor" treatment as well as additional retrofits performed by a contractor hired by the utility. The third group of homes was designated as "control" and received neither house doctor visit nor any subsequent retrofits. Details of differences in treatment among the groups, both designed and as implemented, are presented in the summary reports on the MRE [11,12]. One of

---

[3]Consolidated Edison of New York; Elizabethtown Gas Co., New Jersey Natural Gas Co., Public Service Electric and Gas Co., and South Jersey Gas Co., all of New Jersey.
[4]Similar experiments were carried out in Minnesota, Tennessee, and California but are not reported here.

the departures from design led to the addition of six more houses to the house doctor group in some modules.

Among the data collected during the house doctor visit were blower door measurements of building leakage for a range of pressure differences under pressurization and depressurization conditions. These leakage measurements were carried out both immediately before and immediately after the house doctor retrofits by utility personnel. Blower door measurements were not conducted following the major retrofits, nor were any blower door measurements conducted in the control houses.

In this paper, the leakage data from the seven modules are examined in order to understand the contribution of shell tightening to the total energy savings as determined from utility billing data. Our attention is focused on houses in the house doctor group listed in Table 1.

Leakage Data

Utility house doctors were instructed to carry out blower door measurements both immediately before and immediately after the retrofits. The measurements consisted of blower fan rpm and corresponding indoor-outdoor pressure differences (usually 12.5, 25.0, 37.5, and 50.0 Pa or equivalently 0.05, 0.10, 0.15, and 0.20 in. of water nominal) during house pressurization and depressurization.[5] Cellar doors were closed when directly accessible from the living space. These pressures (after being corrected for calibration differences) along with their corresponding fan rpms were used with the appropriate blower door calibration curves to generate flow rates [13]. The data for both pressurized and depressurized cases are separately fit to a curve of the form

$$Q = C(\Delta P)^n \qquad (1)$$

TABLE 1—*Location of houses in the Modular Retrofit Experiment.*

Module	Location	Utility
Y	Freehold, NJ	New Jersey Natural Gas Co.
Z	Toms River, NJ	New Jersey Natural Gas Co.
C	New Rochelle, NY	Consolidated Edison Co.
E	Edison, NJ	Elizabethtown Gas Co.
S	Oak Valley, NJ	South Jersey Gas Co.
P	Wood Ridge, NJ	Public Service Electric and Gas Co.
T	Whitman Square, NJ	South Jersey Gas Co.

[5]By *pressurization* we mean that the living space interior is at a higher pressure than the exterior.

where ΔP is the indoor-outdoor pressure difference, and C and n are constants.

Using a log-log least squares method, the values of C and n are determined. The r^2 values for these regressions were generally high, with 189 out of 220[6] tests at or above 0.98. Fits were about equally good for pressurization and depressurization modes, so that we have averaged the estimates from the two modes in the results described in following paragraphs.

Using these curve fits, flow rates at 50 Pa, $Q(50)$, were calculated. The values of $Q(50)$ were normalized by the volume of the living space (excluding the basement) and expressed as number of air changes per hour (ACH). Averages of values for pressurization and depressurization were used.

Another popular measure of leakage is Effective Leakage Area (ELA), defined by Sherman and Grimsrud [7] as

$$\text{ELA} = \frac{Q(\Delta P)}{\sqrt{(2\Delta P/\rho)}} \quad \text{at} \quad \Delta P = 4 \text{ Pa}, \quad \text{or}$$

$$\text{ELA} = 1.085 \ Q(4)$$

(2)

where ELA is in square centimetres, ΔP is in pascals and ρ is the density of air at room temperature (1.22 kg/m³). $Q(4)$ is the 4-Pa flow rate in m³/h from the curve fits obtained using Eq 1. ELA does not bear any simple relationship to physical opening areas in the building envelope but instead characterizes the total effect of all these openings. It is the opening area of an orifice with a discharge coefficient equal to 1. The ELA depends on which ΔP is used to calculate it. $Q(4)$, like $Q(50)$, differs for pressurization and depressurization, and mean values were used. Table 2 presents a summary of the pre- and post-retrofit estimates of 50-Pa flow rates (normalized to exchanges per hour) and 4-Pa flow rates (expressed as effective leakage areas) for the 55 houses. Also presented in this table are the specific leakage areas (SLA) expressed in cm²/m², which is the ELA normalized by the floor area.

Table 2 shows the percent reduction in $Q(50)$ and $Q(4)$, which one can associate with the house-tightening process. In 43 of the 55 houses, the percent reduction in $Q(4)$ is larger than the percent reduction in $Q(50)$. The average over the houses in each module is presented in Table 3.

The two methods of estimating seasonally-averaged air infiltration reduction and corresponding energy savings, presented in the next two sections of this paper, involve multiplication by a constant (for each house and each method), and hence the percent savings turn out to be identical to the percent reductions in $Q(4)$ or $Q(50)$. Thus, the systematically larger percent reduction in $Q(4)$ is of considerable importance for this analysis.

---

[6]We have reduced data for 55 houses, with four tests in each house: pre- and post-retrofit and with the house both pressurized and depressurized.

TABLE 2—Pressurization leakage data.

House ID	Floor Area, m²	50 Pa ACH[a]			ELA[b], cm²			SLA[c], cm²/m²		
		Pre	Post	% Reduction	Pre	Post	% Reduction	Pre	Post	Reduction
Y MODULE										
Y007	231.4	11.3	9.3	18.0	1505	1131	24.8	6.50	4.89	1.61
Y010	231.4	7.3	7.3	-0.1	709	475	33.1	3.06	2.05	1.01
Y018	231.4	11.4	10.0	12.3	1475	943	36.1	6.37	4.07	2.30
Y024	231.4	7.5	7.0	7.8	757	589	21.0	3.27	2.54	0.73
Y039	231.4	8.6	7.9	8.2	1090	860	21.1	4.71	3.72	0.99
Y044	221.4	10.6	8.9	16.7	1255	742	40.9	5.42	3.21	2.21
Y013	231.4	8.5	8.7	-2.6	876	588	32.8	3.78	2.54	1.24
Y038	231.4	10.4	9.2	11.2	1169	830	29.0	5.05	3.59	1.46
Y046	231.4	9.5	8.6	10.2	1384	954	31.1	5.98	4.12	1.86
Y002	231.4	8.8	7.5	13.8	1159	840	27.5	5.01	3.63	1.38
Y032	231.4	7.9	7.4	6.8	961	627	34.8	4.15	2.71	1.44
Mean		9.3	8.3	9.3	1122	780	30.2	4.85	3.37	1.48
Standard deviation		1.5	1.0	6.4	274	196	6.3	1.19	0.85	0.50
Z MODULE										
Z052	78.7	13.2	11.6	12.0	465	231	50.4	5.91	2.93	2.98
Z056	78.7	14.4	13.1	9.5	620	419	32.4	7.88	5.32	2.56
Z064	94.1	11.3	10.0	11.5	452	300	33.7	4.81	3.19	1.62
Z066	72.4	15.4	14.8	3.6	380	188	50.6	5.25	2.60	2.65
Z077	82.8	8.1	7.3	9.6	265	194	26.8	3.20	2.34	0.86
Z100	80.6	12.1	10.4	14.1	498	225	55.0	6.18	2.79	3.39
Z063	80.6	10.4	8.6	17.8	619	391	37.0	7.68	4.85	2.83
Z078	78.7	19.8	17.3	12.9	968	781	19.3	12.30	9.92	2.38
Z085	78.7	12.7	12.1	4.6	590	375	36.4	7.50	4.76	2.74
Z090	80.6	14.4	9.9	31.4	688	573	16.7	7.66	6.38	1.28
Z099	80.6	15.3	14.4	6.0	751	560	25.4	9.32	6.95	2.37
Mean		13.4	11.8	12.1	572	385	34.9	7.06	4.73	2.33
Standard deviation		3.1	3.0	7.7	192	189	12.8	2.44	2.34	0.77

C Module

C004	156.7	12.1	11.9	2.0	901	678	24.7	5.75	4.33	1.42
C018	111.9	11.3	9.2	18.5	658	315	52.2	5.88	2.82	3.06
C021	114.3	12.4	11.5	8.0	881	714	19.0	7.71	6.25	1.46
C025	163.5	19.6	17.5	10.5	1568	1454	7.3	10.76	8.89	1.87
C042	134.2	12.4	11.7	5.6	666	895	−34.4	4.96	6.67	−1.71
Mean		13.6	12.4	8.9	935	811	13.8	7.01	5.79	1.22
Standard deviation		3.4	3.1	6.2	372	416	31.6	2.32	2.32	1.77

E Module

E115	183.4	14.4	15.0	−4.1	1133	1101	2.8	6.20	6.00	0.20
E137	168.7	9.8	9.6	1.7	744	625	16.0	4.41	3.71	0.70
E151	153.7	16.8	14.4	14.5	1347	899	33.3	8.76	5.85	2.91
E156	153.3	14.0	12.8	8.9	888	718	19.2	5.79	4.68	1.11
E162	183.4	11.2	10.7	3.9	1256	835	33.5	6.85	4.55	2.30
Mean		13.2	12.5	5.0	1074	836	21.0	6.40	4.96	1.44
Standard deviation		2.8	2.3	7.1	252	182	12.9	1.59	0.96	1.13

S Module

S223	130.1	12.2	11.2	8.1	790	630	20.3	6.07	4.84	1.23
S225	130.1	13.8	13.1	5.0	774	808	−4.4	5.95	6.21	−0.26
S228	167.0	9.6	8.6	10.2	844	683	19.1	5.05	4.09	−0.96
S235	130.1	9.0	6.2	30.9	757	354	53.2	5.82	2.72	3.10
S236	130.1	10.0	9.0	9.9	612	555	9.4	4.70	4.27	0.43
S237	167.0	10.0	8.7	13.4	892	887	0.6	5.34	5.31	0.03
S240	167.0	7.9	7.2	8.3	709	594	16.2	4.25	3.56	0.69
S241	130.1	11.0	10.9	0.7	708	515	27.2	5.44	3.96	1.48
S246	130.1	12.2	11.2	8.0	850	623	26.7	6.53	4.79	1.74
Mean		10.6	9.6	10.5	771	628	18.7	5.46	4.42	1.04
Standard deviation		1.9	2.2	8.4	87	157	16.9	0.72	1.02	1.01

TABLE 2—Continued.

House ID	Floor Area, m²	50 Pa ACH[a]			ELA[b], cm²			SLA[c], cm²/m²		
		Pre	Post	% Reduction	Pre	Post	% Reduction	Pre	Post	Reduction
					P Module					
P111	169.6	17.3	16.1	6.8	1547	1725	−11.5	9.12	10.17	−1.05
P134	116.2	17.7	14.8	16.8	1090	1241	−13.9	9.38	10.68	−1.30
P136	127.3	14.0	11.7	16.3	888	777	12.5	6.97	6.10	0.87
P156	119.9	25.9	31.0	−19.9	1891	1418	25.0	15.77	11.83	3.94
P165	118.0	14.4	13.3	7.1	1089	779	28.5	9.23	6.60	2.63
P169	112.9	17.1	15.5	8.9	1778	1452	18.3	15.75	12.86	2.89
Mean		17.7	17.1	6.0	1381	1232	9.8	11.04	9.71	1.33
Standard deviation		4.3	7.0	13.4	414	384	18.4	3.76	2.77	2.18
					T Module					
T115	171.0	8.0	7.7	4.7	514	574	−11.8	3.01	3.36	−0.35
T128	178.3	9.1	8.0	12.9	761	654	14.1	4.27	3.67	0.60
T132	173.8	10.0	9.1	8.5	958	789	17.7	5.51	4.54	0.97
T136	171.9	11.2	10.2	9.3	858	785	8.5	4.99	4.57	0.42
T140	150.1	9.2	9.4	−2.2	443	431	2.7	3.85	3.75	0.10
T143	154.6	9.5	8.7	8.4	719	671	6.6	4.65	4.34	0.31
T150	112.9	10.0	8.5	15.4	1301	987	24.2	11.52	8.74	2.78
T151	215.6	8.2	8.3	−1.5	779	718	7.9	3.61	3.33	0.28
Mean		9.4	8.7	7.0	792	701	8.7	5.18	4.54	0.64
Standard deviation		1.0	0.8	6.3	266	164	10.8	2.68	1.77	0.94

[a] Average of pressurization and depressurization flow rate at 50 Pa obtained from each curve fit in ACH.
[b] ELA obtained from average of values from separate pressurization and depressurization curve fits using $Q = A\sqrt{(2\Delta P/\rho)}$ at $\Delta P = 4$ Pa.
[c] SLA is ELA normalized by living space floor area.

TABLE 3—*Percent reduction in Q(4) and Q(50) flow rates.*

Module	Reduction in $Q(4)$, %	Reduction in $Q(50)$, %
Y	30	9
Z	35	12
C	14	9
E	21	5
S	19	11
P	10	6
T	9	7

The greater percent change in $Q(4)$, as compared to $Q(50)$, is a manifestation of an underlying physical effect: the lower-pressure blower door readings are reduced by a larger percentage than the higher-pressure blower door readings, following the house doctor measures in these houses. This shows up in the estimates of the exponent n in Eq 1, which increases in value in 37 of the 55 comparisons with the house in the pressurization mode (the average over the 55 houses rising from 0.65 to 0.68) and in 38 of the 55 comparisons in the depressurization mode (the average rising from 0.71 to 0.77).

One might wonder, as well, about the process of extrapolation from the region of testing, above 12.5 Pa, to the low-pressure region at 4 Pa.

The data in Table 2 suffice to calculate the correlation between $Q(50)$ and $Q(4)$ across houses, in both preretrofit and postretrofit condition, which gives an indication, for example, of whether the houses perceived to be leakiest at 50 Pa are still leakiest at 4 Pa. The squares of the correlation coefficients are shown in Table 4. The curve-fitting process to relate $Q(50)$ and $Q(4)$ is seen to keep some but not all of the structure of the data within a module which places the houses on a single tightness scale.

In a recent study of blower door accuracy and repeatability, a wood-frame house was pressure tested many times over the course of a year [14]. $Q(50)$ was seen to have a measurement uncertainty of 1 to 2%, while $Q(4)$ had a 5%

TABLE 4—*Square of correlation coefficient (R^2) between $Q(50)$ and $Q(4)$.*

Module	R^2	
	Pre	Post
Y	0.85	0.44
Z	0.63	0.34
C	0.73	0.77
E	0.62	0.91
S	0.56	0.67
P	0.92	0.54
T	0.51	0.27

spread for the same set of blower door readings. Thus, the extrapolation of flow to 4 Pa introduces uncertainties which account for some of the differences in the flow reductions observed at 4 and 50 Pa.

Estimating Natural Air Infiltration

Air leakage as measured using a blower door occurs at artificially imposed, large pressure differences and does not correspond directly to air infiltration resulting from wind and temperature effects. It is the natural air infiltration that contributes to heat loss from the building. Since natural air infiltration depends on wind velocity and direction and interior-exterior temperature difference, it varies over time. Other factors which influence the variability include furnace operation and occupant effects such as door and window openings.

Various models for relating pressurization data to natural infiltration have been proposed. We picked two of these, a fluid-mechanical model developed at Lawrence Berkeley Laboratory (LBL) [15] and a simple empirical relationship observed by Kronvall and Persily [6,14]. These models are called the LBL and KP methods.

The LBL method is based on values of ELA which, as explained (see Eq 2), are directly proportional to $Q(4)$. This method uses a coefficient, "heating season average infiltration per unit ELA," which is house and climate specific, to obtain the seasonal average infiltration rate, I, from the ELA [15]. In the Appendix, we derive this coefficient for the MRE houses.

The KP method is based on an empirical relationship between air infiltration and air leakage under pressurization, discussed by Kronvall and Persily [6,14] and best understood in terms of Fig. 1. This figure plots $Q(50)$ against measured air infiltration rate (both in ACH) for a widely dispersed set of houses very different in levels of tightness. An approximate linear relationship is observed in this plot, which includes Kronvall's original 26 Swedish homes and a variety of homes in the Princeton, New Jersey area. The least squares fit to the data gives

$$\bar{I} = \frac{Q(50)}{18} - 0.08 \quad \text{with} \quad R^2 = 0.77 \qquad (3)$$

Where $\bar{I}$ is the natural air infiltration rate measured with a tracer gas. The scatter about the regression line (an average of 30%) is of the same order as the scatter exhibited by the more sophisticated predictive models [14]. The KP method explored here uses

$$\bar{I} = \frac{Q(50)}{20}, \qquad (4)$$

a rough approximation to Eq 3, to obtain $\bar{I}$ from blower door data. For the Freehold houses, where we supplemented the pressurization data with three

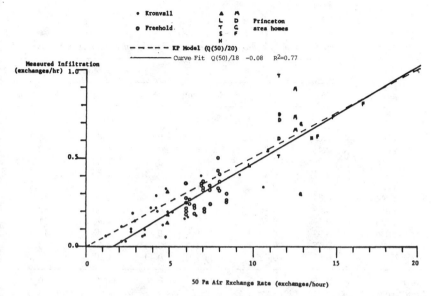

FIG. 1—*Infiltration rate versus air exchange rate at 50 Pa* [14].

air infiltration measurements (using a tracer gas) in each of 14 houses, the relationship expressed by Eq 4 is approximately correct for the *average* of the 14 houses [8]. Equation 4 also is plotted in Fig. 1.

The results of natural infiltration rates predicted by the LBL model and by Eq 4 for each house before and after house doctor retrofits are shown in Table 5. In general, the natural air infiltration rates and the absolute changes in natural air infiltration rates predicted by the LBL model are larger.

Although tracer gas measurements of natural air infiltration are not reported here, a number of these measurements were carried out in several houses in the Y module after the retrofits. Additional blower door data also were collected and used to predict natural infiltration using various models. This study is presented elsewhere [8].

When comparing the percent reductions in natural air infiltration from before to after house doctor treatments, we see that the LBL model predicts larger percent reductions for reasons discussed in the previous section entitled "Leakage Data." If we regress change in I(KP) versus change in I(LBL) across the houses in a module, we see relatively poor correlations: $R^2 = 0.38$, 0.23, 0.07, 0.39, 0.32, 0.55, and 0.49 in the Y, Z, C, E, S, P, and T modules, respectively. Since I(KP) is proportional to $Q(50)$ and I(LBL) is proportional to $Q(4)$, similar poor correlation would be seen between change in $Q(50)$ versus change in $Q(4)$. Thus, we cannot use the change in I(KP) to obtain a reliable estimate of the change in I(LBL), or vice versa. These results suggest that exercises to validate air infiltration models should include tests to com-

TABLE 5—*Predicted seasonally averaged air exchange rates (house volumes per hour).*

House ID	LBL Model			KP Model		
	Pre	Post	% Reduction	Pre	Post	% Reduction
			Y MODULE			
Y007	1.01	0.76	24.8	0.57	0.46	18.0
Y010	0.48	0.32	33.1	0.36	0.36	−0.1
Y018	0.99	0.64	36.1	0.57	0.50	12.3
Y024	0.51	0.40	21.0	0.38	0.35	7.8
Y039	0.73	0.58	21.1	0.43	0.39	8.2
Y044	0.84	0.50	40.9	0.53	0.44	16.7
Y013	0.59	0.40	32.8	0.42	0.43	−2.6
Y038	0.79	0.56	29.0	0.52	0.46	11.2
Y046	0.93	0.64	31.1	0.48	0.43	10.2
Y002	0.78	0.57	27.5	0.44	0.38	13.8
Y032	0.65	0.42	34.8	0.40	0.37	6.8
Mean	0.75	0.53	30.2	0.46	0.42	9.3
Standard deviation	0.18	0.13	6.3	0.07	0.05	6.4
			Z MODULE			
Z052	0.78	0.39	50.4	0.66	0.58	12.0
Z056	1.04	0.70	32.4	0.72	0.65	9.5
Z064	0.63	0.42	33.7	0.57	0.50	11.5
Z066	0.69	0.34	50.6	0.77	0.74	3.6
Z077	0.42	0.31	26.8	0.41	0.37	9.6
Z100	0.81	0.37	55.0	0.61	0.52	14.1
Z063	1.01	0.64	37.0	0.52	0.43	17.8
Z078	1.56	1.26	19.3	0.99	0.86	12.9
Z085	0.98	0.63	36.4	0.64	0.61	4.6
Z090	1.01	0.84	16.7	0.72	0.49	31.4
Z099	1.22	0.91	25.4	0.77	0.72	6.0
Mean	0.92	0.62	34.9	0.67	0.59	12.1
Standard deviation	0.31	0.30	12.8	0.15	0.15	7.7
			C MODULE			
C004	0.76	0.57	24.7	0.61	0.59	2.0
C018	0.75	0.36	52.2	0.56	0.46	18.5
C021	1.01	0.82	19.0	0.62	0.57	8.0
C025	1.26	1.17	7.3	0.98	0.88	10.5
C042	0.65	0.88	−34.4	0.62	0.59	5.6
Mean	0.89	0.76	13.7	0.68	0.62	8.9
Standard deviation	0.25	0.31	31.6	0.17	0.16	6.2

TABLE 5—*Continued.*

House ID	LBL Model			KP Model		
	Pre	Post	% Reduction	Pre	Post	% Reduction
			E MODULE			
E115	0.96	0.94	2.8	0.72	0.75	−4.1
E137	0.58	0.49	16.0	0.49	0.48	1.7
E151	1.37	0.91	33.3	0.84	0.72	14.5
E156	0.90	0.73	19.2	0.70	0.64	8.9
E162	1.07	0.71	33.5	0.56	0.54	3.9
Mean	0.98	0.75	21.0	0.66	0.62	5.0
Standard deviation	0.28	0.18	12.9	0.14	0.71	7.1
			S MODULE			
S223	0.95	0.75	20.3	0.61	0.56	8.1
S225	0.93	0.97	−4.4	0.69	0.66	5.0
S228	0.79	0.64	19.1	0.48	0.43	10.2
S235	0.91	0.42	53.2	0.45	0.31	30.9
S236	0.73	0.67	9.4	0.50	0.45	9.9
S237	0.83	0.83	0.6	0.50	0.44	13.4
S240	0.66	0.55	16.2	0.39	0.36	8.3
S241	0.85	0.62	27.2	0.55	0.54	0.7
S246	1.02	0.75	26.7	0.61	0.56	8.0
Mean	0.85	0.69	18.7	0.53	0.48	10.5
Standard deviation	0.11	0.16	16.9	0.09	0.11	8.4
			P MODULE			
P111	1.16	1.29	−11.5	0.86	0.80	6.8
P134	1.19	1.36	−13.9	0.89	0.74	16.8
P136	0.89	0.78	12.5	0.70	0.59	16.3
P156	2.01	1.50	25.0	1.29	1.55	−19.9
P165	1.17	0.84	28.5	0.72	0.66	7.1
P169	1.31	1.07	18.3	0.85	0.78	8.9
Mean	1.29	1.14	9.8	0.89	0.85	6.0
Standard deviation	0.38	0.29	18.3	0.21	0.35	13.4
			T MODULE			
T115	0.39	0.44	−11.8	0.40	0.38	4.7
T128	0.67	0.57	14.1	0.46	0.40	12.9
T132	0.72	0.60	17.7	0.50	0.47	8.5
T136	0.66	0.60	8.5	0.56	0.51	0.5
T140	0.51	0.49	2.7	0.46	0.47	−2.2
T143	0.61	0.57	6.6	0.48	0.44	8.4
T150	0.76	0.57	24.2	0.50	0.42	15.4
T151	0.56	0.52	7.9	0.41	0.42	−1.5
Mean	0.61	0.55	8.7	0.47	0.44	7.0
Standard deviation	0.12	0.06	10.8	0.05	0.04	6.3

pare measured changes in air infiltration (using a tracer gas) with model predictions.

Energy Savings

Having predicted air infiltration rates from the leakage data, one may calculate the winter space heating energy savings to be expected from the reduction in air infiltration.

The natural gas savings to be expected annually from air infiltration reduction in units of joules/year is given by

$$G = 1206 \times 24 \times V \times HD \times (\bar{I}_{pre} - \bar{I}_{post})/\eta \tag{5}$$

where

V = living space volume, m^3, excluding basement,
$\bar{I}_{pre,post}$ = winter average air infiltration rate before and after retrofit (ACH),
HD = heating degree days base 18.3°C, or 2707 degree days (based on a 9-year average at Newark, NJ), and
η = furnace seasonal efficiency, assumed to be 70% both before and after retrofits.

The numbers 24 and 1206 represent hours/day and the volumetric heat capacity of air (J/m^3 °C).

Space heating energy requirements and energy savings associated with air infiltration predicted by each method are shown in Table 6. Also shown are the measured total annual gas consumption,[7] before and after house doctor treatment, and the predicted savings based on a year of monthly meter readings in each case and corrected for weather to obtain normalized annual consumption (NAC) [12]. As just discussed, predictions of module-mean infiltration energy savings are smaller using the KP method than the LBL method. The module averages are 4.9, 3.8, 2.0, 6.3, 3.1, 3.8, and 1.1 times smaller for Y, Z, C, E, S, P, and T modules, respectively. Model predictions of air infiltration-related energy savings are all lower than the measurements of total energy savings accomplished by all the retrofits and any other factors influencing gas use during the 2- to 3-year period from beginning to end of the MRE.

The proportion of the total realized energy savings accounted for by the air infiltration energy savings varied, depending on the module and the model used to estimate infiltration energy savings (Table 7). Using the LBL model, an average 36% of the total savings were the result of air infiltration reduc-

---

[7]Most of the gas-heated houses in the MRE use natural gas for water heating, cooking, and clothes drying as well.

TABLE 6—*Predicted infiltration energy savings and estimated total energy savings.*

House ID	Measured Total Energy Use and Savings, GJ/year			Predicted Energy Use and Savings from Infiltration Reduction, GJ/year					
	NAC			LBL Model			KP Model		
	Pre	Post	Reduction	Pre	Post	Reduction	Pre	Post	Reduction
				Y MODULE					
Y007	192.9	130.5	62.4	64.1	48.2	15.9	35.9	29.4	6.4
Y010	175.0	162.2	12.9	30.3	20.3	9.9	23.0	23.0	0.0
Y018	207.7	165.7	42.1	62.9	40.2	22.7	35.9	31.4	4.4
Y024	165.3	144.4	20.9	32.3	25.4	6.8	23.8	22.0	1.9
Y039	195.5	181.2	14.2	46.5	36.6	9.8	27.1	24.9	2.2
Y044	204.9	202.3	2.6	53.5	31.7	21.8	33.7	28.0	5.6
Y013	192.0	160.5	31.5	37.3	25.1	12.2	26.8	27.4	-.6
Y038	224.7	186.4	38.3	49.8	35.3	14.5	32.7	29.1	3.7
Y046	154.3	113.4	40.9	59.0	40.6	18.4	30.2	27.1	3.1
Y002	182.6	165.2	17.4	49.4	35.8	13.6	27.6	23.8	3.8
Y032	153.8	99.8	54.0	41.0	26.7	14.2	25.1	23.3	1.7
Mean	186.2	155.6	30.7	47.8	33.2	14.6	29.2	26.4	3.0
Standard deviation	22.6	31.1	18.7	11.7	8.3	5.0	4.6	3.1	2.2
				Z MODULE					
Z052	100.6	95.9	4.7	16.7	8.3	8.4	14.1	12.4	1.7
Z056	105.9	104.1	1.8	22.3	15.1	7.2	15.5	14.0	1.5
Z064	80.5	74.6	5.8	16.2	10.8	5.5	14.6	12.9	1.7
Z066	90.5	82.9	7.5	13.6	6.8	6.9	15.2	14.7	0.5
Z077	112.6	107.6	5.0	9.5	7.0	2.5	9.1	8.3	0.8
Z100	87.8	73.7	13.9	17.9	8.0	9.8	13.4	11.5	1.9
Z063	130.2	114.2	16.0	22.3	14.0	8.2	11.5	9.4	2.0
Z078	144.5	139.4	5.2	34.7	28.1	6.6	22.2	19.3	2.8

TABLE 6—Continued.

House ID	Measured Total Energy Use and Savings, GJ/year			Predicted Energy Use and Savings from Infiltration Reduction, GJ/year					
	NAC			LBL Model			KP Model		
	Pre	Post	Reduction	Pre	Post	Reduction	Pre	Post	Reduction
Z MODULE (continued)									
Z085	72.6	78.5	−5.8	21.2	13.5	7.7	13.6	13.0	0.6
Z090	120.9	98.6	22.2	24.7	20.6	4.1	17.7	12.1	5.6
Z099	106.3	99.9	6.4	27.0	20.2	6.9	16.9	15.8	1.1
Mean	104.8	97.3	7.5	20.6	13.8	6.8	14.9	13.1	1.8
Standard deviation	21.6	19.6	7.5	6.9	6.8	2.0	3.4	3.0	1.4
C MODULE									
C004	138.4	129.4	9.0	32.4	24.4	8.0	26.0	25.4	0.5
C018	115.9	84.8	31.1	23.6	11.3	12.3	17.8	14.5	3.3
C021	203.9	183.6	20.3	31.7	25.6	6.0	19.4	17.9	1.5
C025	210.6	165.5	45.2	56.2	52.1	4.1	43.8	39.1	4.5
C042	179.4	157.7	21.6	23.8	32.2	−8.2	22.8	21.5	1.3
Mean	169.6	144.2	25.4	33.5	29.1	4.4	26.0	23.7	2.2
Standard deviation	41.2	38.5	13.5	13.3	14.9	7.7	10.4	9.6	1.7
E MODULE									
E115	171.9	140.5	31.5	45.8	44.5	1.3	34.2	35.6	−1.4
E137	116.5	108.7	7.8	25.3	21.3	4.0	21.4	21.0	0.4
E151	171.4	126.6	44.8	54.4	36.3	18.1	33.5	28.6	4.8
E156	178.3	162.6	15.7	35.9	29.0	6.9	27.8	25.4	2.5
E162	182.9	164.3	18.5	50.7	33.7	17.0	26.5	25.5	1.0

Mean	164.2	140.5	23.7	42.4	33.0	9.5	28.7	27.2	1.5
Standard deviation	27.1	23.8	14.6	11.8	8.6	7.7	5.3	5.4	2.4
S MODULE									
S223	146.2	102.9	43.3	31.9	25.4	6.5	20.6	18.9	1.7
S225	141.3	109.4	31.9	31.3	32.6	-1.4	23.3	22.1	1.2
S228	111.1	94.3	16.7	34.1	27.6	6.5	20.7	18.6	2.1
S235	79.9	58.9	21.0	30.6	14.3	16.3	15.1	10.5	4.7
S236	123.2	89.2	34.0	24.7	22.4	2.3	16.9	15.2	1.7
S237	105.4	76.2	29.3	34.3	35.8	0.2	21.7	18.8	2.9
S240	127.1	97.1	29.9	36.0	24.0	4.7	17.0	15.6	1.4
S241	154.6	111.8	42.8	28.6	20.8	7.8	18.5	18.3	0.1
S246	101.7	107.5	-5.9	34.3	25.2	9.2	20.5	18.9	1.6
Mean	121.2	94.1	27.0	31.1	25.4	5.8	19.4	17.4	1.9
Standard deviation	24.0	17.3	15.1	3.5	6.3	5.3	2.7	3.3	1.3
P MODULE									
P111	172.5	156.7	15.8	51.0	56.9	-5.9	37.9	35.3	2.6
P134	191.9	174.5	17.5	35.9	40.9	-5.0	26.7	22.2	4.5
P136	133.9	114.4	19.5	29.3	25.6	3.7	23.1	19.3	3.8
P156	166.5	141.4	25.1	62.3	46.7	15.6	40.2	48.2	-8.0
P165	129.9	109.2	20.7	35.9	25.7	10.2	22.0	20.4	1.6
P169	159.2	132.1	27.0	58.6	47.9	10.7	38.1	34.7	3.4
Mean	159.0	138.1	20.9	45.5	40.6	4.9	31.3	30.0	1.3
Standard deviation	23.7	25.0	4.4	13.7	12.7	8.9	11.4	11.4	4.7

TABLE 6—*Continued.*

House ID	Measured Total Energy Use and Savings, GJ/year			Predicted Energy Use and Savings from Infiltration Reduction, GJ/year					
	NAC			LBL Model			KP Model		
	Pre	Post	Reduction	Pre	Post	Reduction	Pre	Post	Reduction
				T MODULE					
T115	125.0	99.9	25.1	17.5	19.5	−2.0	17.8	17.0	0.9
T128	131.5	111.7	19.9	30.7	26.4	4.3	32.6	21.1	11.5
T132	118.5	93.9	24.4	32.6	26.8	5.7	22.5	20.6	1.9
T136	160.2	137.5	22.7	29.2	26.7	2.5	25.0	22.7	2.3
T140	96.1	79.1	16.9	15.1	14.6	0.4	13.7	14.0	−0.3
T143	134.3	123.5	10.8	24.4	22.8	1.6	19.0	17.4	1.6
T150	154.0	110.4	43.6	44.2	33.5	10.7	29.2	24.7	4.5
T151	160.8	125.2	35.6	31.4	29.0	2.5	22.9	23.2	−0.4
Mean	135.0	110.2	24.9	28.1	24.9	3.2	22.8	20.1	2.8
Standard deviation	22.6	18.9	10.4	9.2	5.8	3.8	6.1	3.6	3.7

TABLE 7—*Percentage of total energy savings accounted for by
air infiltration reduction.*

Module	LBL Model	KP Model
Y	47.4	9.6
Z	90.1	23.9
C	17.4	8.7
E	40.1	6.3
S	21.5	7.0
P	23.4	6.2
T	12.9	11.2
Mean	36.1	10.4
Standard deviation	28.6	6.2

tion, while only 10% of the total savings were explained by air infiltration energy savings calculated using the KP model. Numbers for individual modules varied considerably, especially for the LBL model predictions.

Another way to determine how closely the observed total gas energy savings are related to the air infiltration energy savings predicted by each model is to regress the former against the latter across the houses in a module. Regressions carried out were of the form

$$\Delta NAC_i = \alpha + \beta \, \Delta E_i^{1,2} \tag{6}$$

where i labels the house and
where

$\Delta NAC_i =$ total gas energy savings, as measured,
$\Delta E_i^1 =$ energy savings from air infiltration estimated using the KP method, and
$\Delta E_i^2 =$ air infiltration energy savings estimated using the LBL method.

Regression results are shown in Table 8. Of the fourteen regressions, six had R^2 less than 0.1, that is, show essentially no correlation, while only three are above 0.5. We note that the dimensionless coefficient β should be 1.0: a unit of energy saved through air infiltration reduction results in a unit savings in NAC. The standard error of estimate for the coefficient β is high, that is, it is poorly determined, and in half of the cases the range of estimates for β (± 1 standard error) excludes the value of 1.0. Thus, overall, these 14 regressions suggest that even if a large part of the total energy savings is the result of air infiltration reduction, the air infiltration savings estimates (by either model) do not provide detailed information about the total savings actually achieved in an individual house. Whatever the house doctor accomplished either has been captured poorly in the blower door data or has been masked by other retrofits that were included in the house doctor visit or by steps taken by the

TABLE 8—*Results of regression of total energy savings versus air infiltration energy savings estimates (see Eq 6).*

| Module | No. of Houses | Air Infiltration Model | Regression Coefficients[a] | | R^2 |
			α, 10^6 btu/year[b]	β, dimensionless	
Y	11	KP	23.73 (9.48)	1.92 (2.79)	0.050
		LBL	17.31 (17.68)	0.85 (1.22)	0.052
Z	11	KP	0.47 (2.65)	3.81 (1.22)	0.520
		LBL	9.11 (8.06)	−0.31 (1.22)	0.007
C	5	KP	7.18 (2.53)	8.06 (1.00)	0.956
		LBL	23.75 (7.88)	0.08 (1.01)	0.002
E	5	KP	19.64 (8.22)	2.75 (3.21)	0.196
		LBL	16.12 (11.65)	0.80 (1.00)	0.176
S	9	KP	33.96 (9.75)	−3.61 (4.31)	0.091
		LBL	32.56 (7.77)	−0.96 (1.02)	0.113
P	6	KP	21.50 (1.85)	−0.44 (0.42)	0.215
		LBL	18.80 (1.09)	0.44 (0.12)	0.780
T	8	KP	24.95 (5.00)	−0.03 (1.10)	0.000
		LBL	19.54 (4.23)	1.66 (0.88)	0.372

[a]Numbers in parentheses are the standard errors of estimate of α and β.
[b]1 Btu = 1055 J.

homeowner that alter the energy use during the course of the experiment or by a combination of these factors.

Dual Infiltration Reduction Experiment (DIRE)

The results of the MRE suggested additional research to better understand the relationship between the reduction in house leakage as measured by pressurization and actual reduction in natural air infiltration following retrofits. The experiment we designed involved both blower door and tracer gas decay measurements before and after a set of shell-tightening retrofits was completed.

The site of the experiment was a retirement community known as Crosslands in Kennett Square, Pennsylvania. The homes tested are attached single story apartments, about 85 m^2 (900 ft^2) in floor area, with electric baseboard heat. The units were being retrofitted by a house doctor service company whose objectives included significant air leakage reduction. Initially nine units were chosen out of a group of volunteer households. By the time the experiment began only five of the nine units remained to be retrofitted and thus available for pre-post comparisons. However, postretrofit data for the other four units were included in the data base.

Pressurization and Tracer Gas Data

Blower door tests were performed before and after the retrofits in the fall of 1982 and spring of 1983. The blower fan rpm and interior-exterior pressure differences were measured as in the MRE, except that fan speeds were set so that pressure differences were spaced evenly on a log (ΔP) scale instead of aiming for even spacing in ΔP. The nominal pressure differences were 12.5, 17.5, 25, 35, and 50 Pa or equivalently 0.05, 0.07, 0.10, 0.14, 0.20 in. of water. Measurements at 62.5 and 75 Pa (0.25 and 0.30 in. of water) also were obtained when it was possible to pressurize the unit to these levels. The results are presented in Table 9. Because of extremely windy conditions (gusts up to 11.1 m/s) during two of the pressurization tests, some of the data were poor. To remedy this, all the houses were retested in the winter of 1983–1984. These data also are presented in Table 9. It is interesting to note that four out of the five houses became tighter during the year.

The natural air infiltration measurements were done with the residents' co-operation using a tracer gas decay scheme. Each resident was given kits containing six (500-mL) polyethylene sample bottles with tightly fitting rubber seals, a smaller (250-mL) bottle containing approximately 8 cm^3 of sulfur hexafluoride (SF$_6$) tracer, a thermometer, and in some cases a wind gage. They also were given instructions on test procedure in a group meeting and were supplied with a set of written instructions. Samples were to be taken every half hour starting approximately one half hour after seeding the apartment with the SF$_6$ tracer. This bottle sampling procedure has been extensively (and successfully) used in earlier experiments [*8*].

Residents were generally given eight bottle sample kits, four for the preretrofit and four for the postretrofit measurements. Initial attempts to have the residents perform the tests concurrently failed because of scheduling problems. Data were taken at a variety of outside temperatures. Since it is harder for residents to determine wind conditions, no attempt was made to perform the before and after tests under similar wind conditions.

Results

A total of 39 tracer gas air infiltration measurements were analyzed. The results of the tests are presented in Table 10. A summary of the tracer gas and pressurization data comparisons is presented in Table 11. The tests are grouped according to weather conditions. From the before- and after-retrofit blower door data, we see a 33% reduction in average air infiltration rate at 50 Pa and 35% reduction in average SLA (or 4-Pa flow rate). Using the postretrofits measurements performed the next winter, we see a 37% reduction in average air infiltration rate at 50 Pa and a 47% reduction in the SLA. This latter comparison is similar to the results we saw in the MRE data; the 4-Pa flow rate and the SLA were reduced by a considerably larger fraction than the

TABLE 9—*Crosslands blower door data.*

Apartment No.	ACPH[a] 50 Pa	ELA[a,b], cm^2	SLA[a,c], cm^2/m^2	Outdoor Temperature, °C	Wind Speed, m/s
			PRE (1982)		
23	13.1/13.0	542/533	6.5/6.4	12.2	0
24	12.7/12.7	309/321	5.2/5.4	11.1	0
25	13.3/13.6	372/368	6.3/6.2	11.1	0
34	11.8/11.5	458/456	5.4/5.4	3.9	0
113	12.3/12.2	429/407	5.1/4.8	1.1	0
Mean	12.6	420	5.7		
Standard deviation	0.7	80	0.6		
			POST ONLY		
193	8.5/8.5	317/325	3.8/3.8	13.3	0
227	8.8/8.9	280/291	3.3/3.4	11.1	0
236	6.7/6.8	248/255	2.8/2.9	11.1	0
240	7.3/7.3	238/210	2.7/2.4	0	0
Mean	7.9	271	3.1		
Standard deviation	1.0	40	0.6		
			POST (Spring 1983)		
23	8.5	357	4.3	15.0	0 to 11.2 gusty
24	8.7/8.6	181/189	3.1/3.2	12.8	0 to 11.2 gusty
25	8.6	259	4.4	15.0	0 to 11.2 gusty
34	8.0/7.9	247/249	2.9/3.0	7.2	<2.2
113	8.3	292	3.5	6.1	<2.2
Mean	8.4	268	3.7		
Standard deviation	0.3	63	0.7		
			POST (Winter 1983–1984)		
23	8.0	288	3.5	8.9	0
24	8.2	180	3.0	8.9	0
25	8.6/8.7	201/181	3.4/3.1	8.9	0
34	7.2/6.7	189/179	2.2/2.1	−1.7	2.2 to 6.7 gusty
113	7.5/7.9	270/233	3.2/2.8	−1.7	2.2 to 6.7 gusty
Mean	7.9	219	3.0		
Standard deviation	0.6	48	0.5		

[a]When there are two numbers, tests were done twice by two people.
[b]ELA is defined as ELA $= Q(4)/\sqrt{(2\Delta P/\rho)}$.
[c]SLA is ELA normalized by floor area.

TABLE 10—*Crosslands tracer gas data.*

Apartment No.	Pre/Post	Air Infiltration	R^2	T(in), °C	T(out), °C	ΔT, °C	Wind Speed, m/s
23	pre	0.31	0.96	20.6	6.0	14.6	2
		0.71	1.0	20.6	−5.6	26.2	1
	post	0.58	0.98	22.2	5.0	17.2	7
		0.45	0.99	22.2	5.6	16.9	2
		0.43	0.89	22.2	19.4	2.8	1
24	pre	0.31	0.95	23.3	6.7	16.7	0
		0.43	0.99	21.7	−4.4	26.1	4
	post	0.20	0.98	23.3	18.9	4.4	3
		0.42	0.97	22.2	0.6	21.6	4
		0.11	0.88	22.8	0.0	22.8	0
25	pre	0.43	1.0	20.0	14.4	5.6	0
		0.44	1.0	22.2	−7.2	29.4	0
		0.53	0.98	22.8	−7.2	15.6	0
	post	0.47	0.94	21.7	7.8	13.9	0
		0.21	0.89	22.2	5.6	16.6	0
34	pre	0.24	0.88	22.2	8.3	13.9	0
		0.35	0.99	21.7	−6.1	27.8	0
	post	0.42	0.97	22.2	12.8	9.4	0
		0.24	0.89	22.2	5.6	16.6	3
		0.15	1.0	22.2	12.8	9.4	3
		0.34	0.99	22.8	0.0	22.8	4
113	pre	0.23	0.99	21.1	15.0	6.1	0
		0.36	0.97	21.1	−6.1	22.7	0
	post	0.44	0.95	22.8	−3.8	26.6	0
		0.20	0.98	23.3	5.6	17.7	0
227	post	0.14	0.95	21.7	12.2	9.5	0
		0.35	0.99	20.6	−6.1	26.7	0
		0.27	0.83	19.4	−2.7	22.1	0
193	post	0.17	0.88	21.7	7.2	14.5	0
		0.51	0.97	22.2	−7.2	29.4	0
		0.30	0.99	21.1	−1.1	22.2	0
236	post	0.26	1.0	20.6	−6.7	27.3	0
		0.27	0.99	22.6	−7.2	29.4	0
240	post	0.26	1.0	23.9	−4.4	19.5	0
		0.34	0.98	21.7	−7.2	28.9	0
		0.21	0.99	23.3	6.1	17.2	0

50-Pa flow rate. Because of the problems with excessive wind encountered during the first set of measurements, the second set is believed to be a better indicator of the true reductions in house leakage. From the before- and after-retrofit tracer gas data, we see a 19% reduction in the average air infiltration rate during cold weather $[T(\text{in}) - T(\text{out}) \geq 16.7°\text{C}]$ and almost no reduction in air infiltration based on the relatively few warm weather points $[T(\text{in}) - T(\text{out}) < 16.7°\text{C}]$.

TABLE 11—Summary of tracer gas and blower door data.

Group	Number of Houses	50 Pa Air Exchange Rate, Exchanges/Hour	Effective Leakage Area (ELA)[a], cm²	Specific Leakage Area (SLA)[b], cm²/m²	Air Exchange Rate Measured by Tracer Gas Decay, Exchanges/Hour[c]	
					Cold Weather[d]	Warm Mild[e]
Pre	5	12.6	420	5.7	0.43 (8)	0.30 (6)
Post[f]	5	8.4/7.9	268/219	3.7/3.0	0.35 (9)	0.31 (6)
Post only[g]	4	7.9	271	3.1	0.31 (9)	0.16 (2)[h]

[a]ELA $= Q(4)/\sqrt{2}\Delta P/\rho$.
[b]Specific Leakage Area is ELA normalized by floor area.
[c]Number of tests are shown in parentheses.
[d]$T(\text{in}) - T(\text{out}) > 16.7°C$.
[e]$T(\text{in}) - T(\text{out}) < 16.7°C$.
[f]Two sets of measurements were taken for each house. The numbers before the "/" refer to Feb.–April 1983 data and after the "/" refer to Dec. 1983 data.
[g]These are houses where only postretrofit data were collected, roughly at the same weather conditions as the preretrofit sample houses.
[h]Both measurements came from one house.

Data from the four apartments retrofitted at the beginning of the experiment are identified as POST-ONLY in Table 11. Both the blower door data and the cold weather tracer gas data here generally are consistent with the postretrofit measurements in the houses where we have both pre- and postretrofit data. For the two tests performed in mild weather in the post-only apartments, the air infiltration rate was much smaller than the average of the six values in mild weather for apartments for which we have data both before and after retrofits. A sample of two is too small to draw any conclusions.

A high percentage of the preretrofit tracer gas measurements were done during conditions of low wind speed (between 0 and 2.2 m/s). However, postretrofit tracer gas measurements often were made in very windy conditions (wind speed > 6.7 m/s) during late winter and early spring. Thus, the reduction in air exchange rate measured by tracer gas experiments before and after probably understates the actual reduction obtained.

Conclusions

Blower door data are frequently used to characterize the leakiness of houses in one of two ways—as ACH at a 50-Pa pressure difference, $Q(50)/V$, or as an effective leakage area, ELA. Both measures, determined before and after shell-tightening retrofits, have been used to quantify the effectiveness of the retrofits. For houses in the seven modules of the MRE reported here, percent reduction in $Q(50)/V$ was generally smaller than percent reduction in ELA, typically about half as much, though there was considerable variation in their relative magnitudes for individual houses. This difference was primarily the result of an interesting physical effect: shell-tightening reduced the flow rates through the blower door by a larger percentage when the house was less pressurized than when it was more pressurized.

Two models for estimating natural air infiltration rates from blower door data, the LBL model and the KP model, were found to disagree in their predictions of air infiltration reduction, the estimates from the LBL model being considerably higher.

To check and compare these predictions, the DIRE was designed. In five one-story attached apartments, both tracer gas decay measurements and blower door measurements were taken before and after shell-tightening retrofits. Unlike the MRE, blower door data expressed as percent reduction in leakage at 50 Pa and percent reduction in ELA (or leakage at 4 Pa) were quite comparable. Additionally, we noted that the percent reduction in natural air infiltration, measured using the tracer gas, was considerably lower than the percentage reduction in air leakage indicated by the blower door.

The DIRE was carried out in apartments which are not individually metered and thus provide no accurate means of obtaining the overall energy savings from the retrofits.

One question addressed in the analysis of the MRE data was: What fraction of house doctor energy savings is the result of air infiltration reduction? Total energy savings estimates based on utility billing data one year before and after the retrofits were compared to infiltration energy savings calculated using two methods. For each of the seven modules, a much larger portion of the energy savings was accounted for by air infiltration reduction calculated using the LBL method than by using the KP method. Averaged over all the modules, the former method explained 36% of the total energy savings while the latter explained only about 10%. Neither value is physically unreasonable. Additional tracer gas infiltration measurements together with energy savings estimates based on more detailed energy consumption data immediately before and after the retrofits will be necessary to assess the air infiltration component of total energy savings. Unfortunately, the DIRE apartments are not individually metered and so cannot provide this information.

One problem encountered in the DIRE was that it is unreasonable to expect residents to carry out more than a few tracer gas decay measurements before or after retrofits. Measurements done with automated tracer gas equipment are both much more costly and more intrusive. This limits the extent of data that can be calculated using our tracer gas decay methods. Since the air infiltration rate is very weather-dependent and consequently time-varying as well, an alternative method capable of providing long-term average measurements of air infiltration would be preferable. One such method is an inexpensive technique developed at Brookhaven National Laboratory which utilizes passive perfluorocarbon tracer (PFT) emitter and absorber. Measurement periods can extend from weeks to months and yield an average air infiltration rate for the period. Future retrofit experiments involving a comparison of pressurization leakage reduction and air infiltration energy savings might incorporate the PFT method of measuring long-term average air infiltration rates.

Acknowledgements

This research was partially supported by the U.S. Department of Energy Contract No. DE-AC02-77CS20062 (Building Systems Division, Office of Energy Research and Development, Conservation and Renewable Energy).

APPENDIX

Calculation of Natural Air Infiltration Using the LBL Model

Natural air infiltration depends on instantaneous weather conditions (that is, indoor-outdoor temperature differences and wind speed). However, seasonal averages are of interest in calculating winter heat loss rate due to infiltration. Grimsrud et al [15] have calculated the winter-average natural infiltration rate per square centimetre of ELA, for a reference house located in any of 59 cities which have Test Reference Year (TRY) weather data.

The reference house has the following characteristics:

1. Single story, height 2.5 m.
2. Leakage area of floor and ceiling are equal.
3. The total leakage area in the floor and ceiling equals that in the walls.
4. Terrain Class = III: rural areas with low buildings and trees.
5. Shielding Class = III: some obstructions within two house heights.

For houses with the same characteristics as the LBL reference house, the winter-average infiltration rate per unit ELA equals 0.32 $m^3/h/cm^2$ of ELA (see Table C-1 in Ref 15).

For some houses adjustments have to be made from the reference house case. The winter-average infiltration rate per unit ELA, Q_A^*/A, is given by

$$\left(\frac{Q_A^*}{A}\right)^2 = \left(\frac{Q_{wind}^*}{A}\right)^2 + \left(\frac{Q_{stack}^*}{A}\right)^2 \tag{7}$$

where

$$\frac{Q_{wind}^*}{A} = \frac{Q_{wind}^{ref}}{A} \cdot \frac{\alpha(H/10)^\gamma C'(1-R)^{1/3}}{0.1228}$$

$$\frac{Q_{stack}^*}{A} = \frac{Q_{stack}^{ref}}{A} \cdot \frac{(1+R/2)\sqrt{H}}{1.976}$$

Here, α, γ, C', and R are parameters, and H is the height of the house in meters. Here Q_{stack}^{ref}/A, and Q_{wind}^{ref}/A have the values for the reference house equal to 0.16 and 0.265 $m^3/h/cm^2$, respectively, at our location (New York and Philadelphia values were averaged). As an example, we will look at the Freehold houses, which are two story, but in which all the other specifications remain the same. For this case,

H = height of the house = 5 m,
R = 0.5,
α = 0.85,
γ = 0.2, and
C' = 0.240.

Hence

$$\frac{Q_{wind}^*}{A} = 0.265 \times 1.15 = 0.305 \text{ m}^3/h/cm^2$$

$$\frac{Q_{stack}^*}{A} = 0.16 \times 1.41 = 0.226 \text{ m}^3/h/cm^2$$

and

$$\frac{Q_A^*}{A} = 0.38 \text{ m}^3/h/cm^2.$$

References

[1] Blomsterberg, A. K. and Harrje, D. T., "Approaches to Evaluation of Air Infiltration Energy Losses in Buildings," *ASHRAE Transactions*, Vol. 85, Part 1, 1979, pp. 797-815.
[2] Harrje, D. T., Blomsterberg, A. K., and Persily, A., "Reduction of Air Infiltration Due to Window and Door Retrofits in an Older Home," Report No. 85, Princeton University Center for Environmental Studies, Princeton, NJ, 1979.
[3] Harrje, D. T. and Born, G. J., "Cataloguing Air Leakage Components in Houses," American Council for an Energy-Efficient Economy (ACEEE) Summer Study, Santa Cruz, CA, Aug. 1982.
[4] Caffey, G. E., "Residential Air Infiltration," *ASHRAE Transactions*, Vol. 85, Part 1, 1979, pp. 41-57.
[5] Shaw, C. Y., "A Correlation Between Air Infiltration and Airtightness for Houses in a Developed Residential Area," *ASHRAE Transactions*, Vol. 87, Part 2, 1981, pp. 333-341.
[6] Kronvall, J., "Testing of Houses for Air Leakage Using a Pressure Method," *ASHRAE Transactions*, Vol. 84, Part 1, 1978, pp. 72-79.
[7] Sherman, M. H. and Grimsrud, D. T., "Infiltration-Pressurization Correlation: Simplified Physical Modeling," *ASHRAE Transactions*, Vol. 86, Part 2, 1980, pp. 778-807.
[8] Linteris, G. T. and Persily, A. K., "Low-Cost Measurement of Air Leakage in Homes," American Council for an Energy-Efficient Economy (ACEEE) Summer Study, Santa Cruz, CA, Aug. 1982.
[9] *Saving Energy in the Home—Princeton's Experiments at Twin Rivers*, R. H. Socolow, Ed., Ballinger, Cambridge, MA, 1978. Also appeared as the entire issue of *Energy and Buildings*, Vol. 1, No. 3, 1978.
[10] Dutt, G. S., "House Doctor Visits—Optimizing Energy Conservation Without Side Effects," *New Energy Conservation Technologies and Their Commercialization*, Vol. 1, J. P. Millhone and E. H. Willis, Eds., Springer Verlag, 1982, p. 444-456.
[11] Dutt, G. S., Lavine, M. L., Levi, B. G., and Socolow, R. H., "The Modular Retrofit Experiment: Exploring the House Doctor Concept," Report No. 130, Princeton University Center for Energy and Environmental Studies, Princeton, NJ, June 1982. For a condensed version of this paper, see *What Works: Documenting Energy Conservation in Buildings*, J. Harris and C. Blumstein, Eds. American Council for an Energy-Efficient Economy (ACEEE), Washington, DC, 1984, pp. 95-109.
[12] Fels, M. F., Goldberg, M. L., Harwood, D., and Lavine, M. L., "The Modular Retrofit Experiment: Summary Scorekeeping Tables," Report No. 131, Princeton University Center for Energy and Environmental Studies, Princeton, NJ, June 1982.
[13] Gadsby, K., Linteris, G., Dutt, G. S., and Harrje, D. T., "The Blower Door," Report No. 124, Princeton University Center for Energy and Environmental Studies, Princeton, NJ, June 1981.
[14] Persily, A. K., "Understanding Air Infiltration in Homes," Report No. 129, Princeton University Center for Energy and Environmental Studies, Princeton, NJ, Feb. 1982.
[15] Grimsrud, D. T., Sherman, M. H., and Sonderegger, R. C., "Calculating Infiltration: Implications for a Construction Quality Standard," *Proceedings*, ASHRAE/DOE Conference on Thermal Performance of Exterior Envelopes of Buildings II, Las Vegas, NV, Dec. 1982.

DISCUSSION

M. Sherman[1] *(written discussion)*—The conclusions of this paper are weak. You are comparing spot tracer measurements made by untrained occupants with two models that were not intended to be used on the type of housing in which you made the measurements.

[1]Lawrence Berkeley Laboratory, Berkeley, CA.

D. Jacobson, G. Dutt, and R. Socolow (authors' closure)—Although the bottle sampling was done by community residents, they were not untrained. They were given detailed instructions—both verbal and written—on how to carry out these tests. These instructions had been tested in other experiments and have proven successful [8]. The quality of the data is readily verifiable and was done in this as in earlier experiments involving the tracer gas bottle sample technique. The verification procedure takes into account that there are five sample bottles for each run. A log-linear regression of tracer gas concentration with time is used to determine the validity of the data as well as to calculate the air infiltration rate. The correlation coefficient, R, had to be above a certain value or the data were discarded. Most of the R^2 values were 0.95 or higher.

Bottle sample tracer gas measurements are expected to give more reliable data than measurements where the analysis equipment is located within the house. In the former case, the analysis equipment never leaves the laboratory and can be calibrated immediately before and after analysis. Bottle samples by occupants permit much more data to be collected for each set of analysis equipment.

Contrary to the second of Dr. Sherman's comments, no model was applied for converting blower door data to natural air infiltration for attached houses. We were aware that the models were not appropriate for attached single story apartments. Our analysis was based on measurements of pressurization air leakage at 4 and at 50 Pa, expressed as effective leakage area (ELA) and ACH at 50 Pa. The calculation of these two numbers is routinely done for attached housing as was evident in other papers presented at the symposium. In our paper, we look at how each of these quantities captured the reduction in air leakage and made some comparisons with the reductions in natural air infiltration as measured by tracer gas decay. Admittedly, our data set was limited, but we believe that more comparisons of this kind are needed in order to understand the relationship between pressurization data and natural air infiltration.

M. Liddament[2] (written discussion)—I am interested in the widespread use of "blower doors" in the United States and Canada, including your own, and would like to know if the doors themselves are subjected to a performance standard. In other words, if each blower door was tested in the same enclosure, would they reproduce the same results?

D. Jacobson, G. Dutt, and R. Socolow (authors' closure)—Unfortunately, blower doors are produced by a number of different manufacturers who use a variety of designs. These different designs are not subject to any kind of performance standards at this time. Although not many comparisons have been reported, blower doors made by different manufacturers probably would not produce the same results if measuring the leakage rate of the same enclosure. Attempts are being made to develop standard calibration procedures and facilities, but the work is only in the preliminary stages.

[2]Air Infiltration Centre, Bracknell, Berkshire, Great Britain.

Jack D. Verschoor[1] *and John O. Collins*[2]

Demonstration of Air Leakage Reduction Program in Navy Family Housing

REFERENCE: Verschoor, J. D. and Collins, J. O., **"Demonstration of Air Leakage Reduction Program in Navy Family Housing,"** *Measured Air Leakage of Buildings, ASTM STP 904,* H. R. Trechsel and P. L. Lagus, Eds., American Society for Testing and Materials, Philadelphia, 1986, pp. 294–303.

ABSTRACT: The Department of Defense has an ongoing program to conserve energy at its installations. One method of energy conservation in residential units is the reduction of excessive air leakage by appropriate retrofits.

Under the sponsorship of the Office of Navy Family Housing, a demonstration of air leakage reduction was undertaken at the Great Lakes Naval Training Center. Two procedural documents were prepared in draft form: a manual for use by supervision and a handbook for the on-base mechanics doing the air leakage retrofits. The retrofits were designed to be incorporated at the time of change of occupancy, when routine interior maintenance and refurbishing are normally scheduled.

The demonstration consisted of measuring the "before" air leakage rate of each unit by the fan depressurization method. Major air leakage sites were noted. Retrofits were made in about half of the units, and the resulting reduction in air leakage was measured. Air leakage data are presented on a representative sample of 65 units of the housing inventory at Great Lakes.

KEY WORDS: energy conservation, air leakage, fan depressurization, infiltration, retrofit, residential housing

The Department of Defense has an ongoing program to conserve energy at its installations. As part of this program, the Office of Navy Family Housing undertook a demonstration of the potential for air leakage reduction in housing units at a major base. The purpose of the demonstration was to apply air leakage reduction methods from research type projects to the real world of family housing maintenance. A secondary purpose was to obtain actual air leakage data on a significant sample of family housing units at a base. If the

[1]Consultant, Verschoor Associates, Bailey, CO 80421.
[2]Research manager, Manville R & D Center, Denver, CO 80217.

demonstration program was successful on a pilot basis, air leakage reduction could be included as a standard maintenance procedure and expanded to other locations.

Normally, interior routine maintenance and refurbishing are scheduled at the time of change of occupancy of housing units. It was proposed to incorporate air leakage reduction as part of these procedures, before interior painting was completed.

A detailed manual and handbook for air leakage reduction were developed in draft form for implementation by base maintenance personnel. The air leakage manual was intended for use by base management and covers general objectives to be achieved and requirements. The handbook was designed for maintenance personnel and was written in language they would understand. It comprises background air leakage information and specific recommendations for materials, equipment, and procedures. It was felt that both documents were required because of the divergent information requirements of supervision and the mechanics actually doing the retrofits. Both manuals were designed to be self-explanatory, with no formal training sessions intended to instruct the users in how to follow the procedures described.

Supervisors' Manual

The air leakage management manual was prepared primarily for use by public works officials and facilities maintenance managers and planners. It details the technical aspects of air leakage, retrofit crew size and qualifications, and summarizes the steps in the retrofit procedure and the materials and equipment required.

The discussion points out that minimum air leakage is desirable from the standpoint of energy conservation. However, with too little ventilation there could be an undesirable buildup of pollutants. It was decided, with the current limited state of knowledge in this field, that an average of 0.5 air changes per hour (ACH) under naturally occurring conditions represented good present practice.

Where to set the desired air change rate under the induced test depressurization pressure of 50 Pa [0.20 in. water (H_2O)] was given considerable thought. There is wide local variation in the natural conditions causing infiltration (primarily terrain, shielding, wind speed and direction, and temperature difference factors). However, a mechanic requires a precise guide. As a preliminary specification, it was decided that the desired induced air change rate or retrofit goal (at −50 Pa) should be not more than 8 ACH, nor less than 5 ACH. As general knowledge is gained and specific locale requirements are found necessary, this general specification might well be changed.

The supervisors' manual is still in draft form; experience with its use at other Navy bases could dictate improvements.

Mechanics' Handbook

The handbook, designed for use by the maintenance superintendent, foremen, crew leaders, and mechanics, is in two parts. Like the supervisors' manual, it is also in draft form to facilitate future modifications.

Part I contains a discussion on why air leakage should be reduced, typical air leakage locations, and how to detect and correct excessive air leakage. Specific materials and methods are described. Equipment required and suggested crew are discussed.

Part II contains a detailed step-by-step procedure to be followed for air leakage retrofits. Numerous cautions are enumerated to insure minimum hazard to personnel and structure.

The objectives of the program caused certain simplifications to be made in writing the standard procedures: tests are conducted under negative pressure only (to facilitate leakage site detection), tests are made at only one differential pressure (50 Pa), and the living space volume (in cubic feet) is assumed to be eight times the gross floor area (in square feet). The use of infrared (IR) equipment would have been helpful for detection of air leakage locations. However, the cost of the equipment and the time and skill level required for proper IR scans ruled this out.

Tables of air flow rates at −50 Pa for the Navy blower doors are included in the mechanics' handbook. In addition, for those cases of very leaky units where the blower door does not have enough fan capacity to depressurize to −50 Pa, tables at lower pressures are included. The air flow rates in the reduced pressure tables were corrected to a pressure of −50 Pa using a value of the exponent n of 0.65.

To assist the mechanics in the field to remember the details of the procedures, a pocket-sized checklist was included (Fig. 1). A final feature of the procedures was the preparation of an air leakage retrofit report form for each unit (Fig. 2). This report will assist program managers in evaluating the current air leakage condition of the housing units and the effectiveness of the air leakage reduction energy conservation program. It was recognized that certain conditions may require more time for completion than would be available during a normal "change of occupancy" refurbishing. Space was provided on the report form for noting these conditions for futher follow-up.

Demonstration

The Great Lakes Naval Training Center (GLNTC) has 2089 family housing units. Sixty units for senior officers were constructed before World War II. All of the other units were built following World War II in various military construction financing programs. Because of the limited number of senior officer quarters, they were not included in this demonstration program.

NAVY FAMILY HOUSING - AIR LEAKAGE RETROFIT Checklist

Step 1 - Blower Door Installation
a. Snug in door frame.
b. Air leaks sealed with masking tape.
c. Level control panel.
d. Zero pressure gauge.
e. Connect electrical wire and pressure tubing.
f. Direction switch on "Off".
g. Fan speed control at "0".
h. SAFETY - Keep foreign objects out of fan.

Step 2 - Retrofit Report - Exterior Inspection
a. Enter unit location, type and features on report.
b. Calculate living space area and volume.
c. Inspect exterior caulking on windows and doors.
d. Inspect storm window and door condition.
e. Enter problem areas remaining on report for later repair.

Step 3 - Air Leakage Test Preparation
a. Disconnect furnace and hot water heater flue.
b. Close and latch windows and doors (except for blower door).
c. Close storm windows and doors.
d. Open interior doors except closet, cupboard and cellar.
e. Close fireplace damper (seal temporarily if defective).
f. Check water seal in plumbing traps.

Step 4 - "Before" Leakage Test
a. Adjust fan speed for 0.20 in. water pressure differential.
b. Readjust to 0.15 or 0.10 if lack of fan capacity.
c. Average 5 readings if gusty wind.
d. Calculate leakage volume and air change rate.
e. Record data on report.

Step 5 - Decision - Retrofit Required?
a. Object - as much less than 10 ach as possible, but not less than 5 ach.
b. Less than 5 ach - no retrofitting required.
c. 5 to 8 ach - minimum retrofits.
d. 8 to 12 ach - retrofit steps 6 through 9.
e. Greater than 12 ach - complete retrofit program.
f. Greater than 20 ach - look for major air leaks.

Step 6 - Vent Retrofits
a. Replace dryer vent.
b. Inspect/repair/replace other vents.
c. Note those with remaining problems on report.

Step 7 - Exterior Door Retrofits
a. True door if required.
b. Repair/replace weatherstripping.
c. Repair/replace threshold.
d. Weatherstrip sliding glass patio doors.

Step 8 - Electrical Retrofits
a. Seal main electric service box (power OFF).
b. Seal around ceiling light fixtures (do not seal recessed type).
c. Seal and gasket wall switches.
d. Seal and gasket receptacles, install safety caps.

Step 9 - Attic Inspection and Retrofits
a. Report type and thickness of attic insulation.
b. Repair and seal attic hatch.
c. Seal utility chase from attic side.

Step 10 - Interior Sealing Retrofits
a. Remeasure air leakage rate.
b. Do not continue retrofits that reduce rate below 5 ach.
c. Interior sealing areas: - walls
                           - windows and frames
                           - door frames
                           - heating system
                           - vents
                           - utility services
                           - other potential leakage areas

Step 11 - "After" Leakage Test
a. Test conditions same as "Before".
b. Adjust fan speed for 0.20 in. water pressure.
c. Calculate leakage volume and air change rate.
d. Look for additional leaks if greater than 10 ach.
e. Calculate percent improvement.
f. Record data on report.

Step 12 - Blower Door Removal
a. Remove blower door.
b. Retrofit that door (Step 7).

Step 13 - Furnace and Hot Water Heater
a. Check/reconnect/replace flue.
b. Relight pilots.
c. Check operation.

Step 14 - Retrofit Report
a. Check that completed fully.

FIG. 1—Pocket-sized checklist.

AIR INFILTRATION RETROFIT REPORT

Address_____Apt no._____Housing project_____

Type: Stories: Style: Mech. System: Fuel:
  prior '50_____   1 _____   single_____   furnace _____   gas   _____
  Wherry _____   2 _____   duplex_____   boiler _____   oil   _____
  Capehart _____   3 _____   twnhse_____   air cond._____   wood   _____
  Mil Con _____   basmt_____   flat _____   heat pump_____   elect. _____
  '59 - '69_____   split_____   other _____   base bd. _____   central_____
  1970 + _____   other_____   other   other   _____   other _____
Living space: area_____sq ft; volume_____cu ft

Exterior inspection: wind: speed_____MPH, direction_____
  window caulk_____door caulk_____other_____
  storm window_____storm door_____other_____

Attic Inspection: insulation_____avg. thick_____inches

Air Leakage retrofits:
  Vents: Exterior doors: Electrical service: Attic:
    dryer   _____   front   _____   main box   _____   flue   _____
    kitchen _____   kitchen_____   clg. lights_____   hatch   _____
    1/2 bath_____   side   _____   switches   _____   hatch seal_____
    bath #1 _____   patio   _____   receptacles_____
    bath #2 _____   rear   _____   t'stat   _____

Interior sealing:

Use code:		kitchen	din rm	liv rm	fam rm	1/2 bath	mast BR	MBR bath	BR #2	BR #3	bath #2	utility rm	basement	other
OK=alright	walls____													
NG=no good	baseboards__													
RPR=repair(ed)	windows___													
RPL=replace(d)	int. doors__													
S=sealed	heating___													
G=gasketed	vents___													
	TV/phone___													
	utilities__													
	other____													

  Special conditions_____

Future conservation steps recommended:
  Caulk exterior_____
  RPR/RPL storm window(s)_____
  RPR/RPL storm door(s)_____
  Attic insulation_____
  Other_____

Before work started: After work finished: Crew:_____
  Time   _____   Time   _____   _____
  Fan   _____RPM   Fan   _____RPM   _____
  Pressure_____In.H2O   Pressure_____in. H2O   (team leader)
  Leakage_____x1000 CFM   Leakage_____x1000 CFM   Date_____
  Change rate_____/ Hr   Change rate_____/ Hr   Improvement_____%

FIG. 2—*Typical air leakage retrofit report form.*

Results

The air leakage reduction demonstration was performed by regular GLNTC public works maintenance personnel during the period May–June 1983. As family housing units became available during normal occupancy change, air leakage tests and retrofits were scheduled. The air leakage rate was measured in the depressurization mode at -50 Pa (-0.2 in. H_2O) with a commercially available blower door assembly. Major leakage sites were noted.

Retrofits were attempted on about half of the units, and the "after" air leakage rate was measured. Some of the retrofits were of a temporary nature due to time exigencies. For example, defective bathroom exhaust back draft dampers were not replaced. Instead, the grill was covered with plastic film for the "after" test. Had time permitted a permanent retrofit, the air leakage reduction achieved would be expected to be similar to that reported.

The air infiltration retrofit report forms, as completed by the GLNTC mechanics doing the work, were analyzed. The air leakage data are summarized in Table 1.

The average "before" air leakage rates for the 65 units in the demonstration was 7.5 ACH. Figure 3 shows a histogram of the "before" test results.

For the 34 units with both "before" and "after" air leakage data, the "after" average was 7.1 ACH compared with 9.2 ACH "before." This represents an average reduction of 23% for those units retrofitted. Figure 4 shows a histogram of the retrofitted units.

The most frequently occurring air leakage sites found are noted in Fig. 5.

Analysis and Discussion

The retrofit report forms were not completely filled in for each family housing unit included in the demonstration. This made a detailed analysis of the

TABLE 1—*Air Leakage Retrofit Demonstration Results*
(air change at -50 *Pa differential pressure).*

	Average
All 65 units	7.5 ACH
34 retrofitted units:	
"Before"	9.2 ACH
"After"	7.1 ACH
Freqeuncy analysis of "before" data	
10 units	<5.0 ACH
32 units	5.0 to 7.9 ACH
18 units	8.0 to 11.9 ACH
5 units	>12.0 ACH

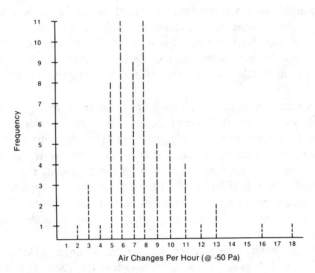

FIG. 3—*Air change rate of all 65 units tested.*

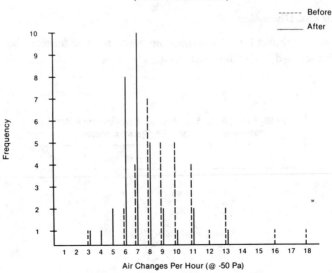

FIG. 4—*Air change rate for 34 retrofitted units.*

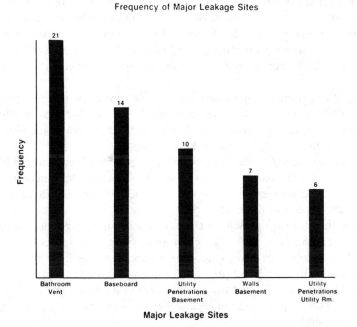

FIG. 5—*Major air leakage sites.*

data difficult. However, enough information was included to draw a number of interesting and valuable conclusions.

There were eight Wherry units included in the demonstration. These units were built in 1951 of concrete tilt slab construction. Originally they had single-glazed steel sash windows, which are very prone to excessive air leakage. In one of the recent Navy energy conservation programs, these units were replaced with very tight double-glazed horizontal slider and single-hung units. As a result, the Wherry units currently represent the "tightest" family housing units on base. Five of the eight had an air change rate of less than 5.0 ACH at −50 Pa. Several of the units inspected had evidence of mold growth in closets, baths, and bedrooms. Housing management personnel stated that they received frequent complaints from occupants of these units of "mustiness." Corrective measures for these units were outside the scope of this program. The authors are not aware of what action, if any, the Navy intends to take on these units.

Many of the units in the demonstration were constructed in 1960 and 1962 under the Capehart program. These units are town houses with a front-to-back split level configuration. The rear portion consists of the bedroom and bath level above a basement that is partially below grade. The latter contains the furnace, the domestic hot-water heater, provision for washer and dryer, and space that frequently had been made into a recreation area. The standard procedure called for all interior doors to be left open during the air leakage rate testing, except doors to closets and the basement. Even so, there were enough air passages connecting the basement to the living areas of these units that air leakage into the basement was an important factor in the leakage rate.

The Mil Con multifamily town house units were constructed in 1965 and 1969. These units have a central gas-fired boiler unit for each building. A common air leakage site in these units was related to the horizontal pipe chase connecting the boiler room to the housing units.

Several air leakage sites occurred with regularity. Frequently the backdraft damper in the bathroom exhaust vent was stuck in the open position. By contrast, the kitchen exhaust vent was not generally a problem area. Perhaps the grease present in the kitchen provides some lubrication for the damper, whereas the moisture present in the bathroom causes corrosion resulting in the damper tending to stick. Except for units with a brick veneer exterior, the lower level baseboards (slab-on-grade) were commonly leakage areas. Sliding patio doors were a frequent problem for units containing them.

Electrical receptacles and switches were not generally a significant air leakage site. With frequent interior repainting over the years, the plates were usually well sealed.

One unit was tested on two different occasions about three weeks apart. One member of the two-man crew was present both times. While the measured air leakage rate at −50 Pa was identical on both occasions, the living space area determined was slightly different, resulting in an apparent change in the air change rate.

Conclusions

In order to implement energy conservation in Navy family housing units, a draft retrofit procedure for reduction of air leakage was prepared. Two documents were written, a manual for use by supervision and a handbook for mechanics doing the retrofitting.

A demonstration of the air leakage reduction program was conducted at the GLNTC. The average "before" leakage rate for 65 units tested was 7.5 ACH at −50 Pa. For the 34 units retrofitted, the average leakage rate was reduced from 9.2 to 7.1 ACH. This is an improvement of 23%.

Frequent air leakage sites noted were bathroom vents, baseboards, utility penetrations in the basements and utility rooms, and basement walls.

Acknowledgment

The authors thank the Office of Navy Family Housing and the Naval Civil Engineering Laboratory for their initiation and financial support of this project and the public works personnel at the GLNTC for their cooperation and performance of the demonstration.

DISCUSSION

M. W. Liddament[1] *(written discussion)*—Several studies in Scandinavia have shown that dwellings constructed to a fabric airtightness of 3 ACH at 50 Pa are so tight that mechanical fresh air ventilation is essential. The 5 ACH at 50 Pa that you are aiming for is very close to this level. Therefore, what sort of provision is being made for fresh air ventilation?

J. D. Verschoor and J. O. Collins (authors' closure)—In this Navy program, 5 ACH at −50 Pa is the minimum accepted air leakage; the desired level is a range of 5 to 8 ACH. Based on present information, this range should provide sufficient ventilation for most occupancies. This survey of Navy family housing units also found that units with 3 ACH at −50 Pa were generally too "tight," as evidenced by moisture stress and mustiness complaints by the occupants. At this time, the authors have no information relative to any plans the Navy has to improve the ventilation in these tight units.

[1] Air Infiltration Centre, Bracknell, Berkshire, United Kingdom.

Richard D. Weimar[1] and Donald F. Luebs[2]

Field Performance of an Air Infiltration Barrier

REFERENCE: Weimar, R. D. and Luebs, D. F., **"Field Performance of an Air Infiltration Barrier,"** *Measured Air Leakage of Buildings, ASTM STP 904*, H. R. Trechsel and P. L. Lagus, Eds., American Society for Testing and Materials, Philadelphia, 1986, pp. 304–311.

ABSTRACT: A spun-bonded polyolefin air infiltration barrier (AIB) was installed immediately beneath the siding of a 5-year-old, ranch-style house [conventional comparison house (CCH)]. The AIB reduced the heating energy consumption by 24% during the first heating season and is expected to reduce the heating load by 28% over the remaining life of the house.

This test confirmed earlier field studies and allowed the development of the mechanism by which AIBs function and the recommendation of required AIB physical properties.

KEY WORDS: air infiltration barrier, AIB, heating energy conservation, AIB performance mechanism, AIB recommended physical properties

Objective

1. To determine the effectiveness of a spun-bonded polyolefin air infiltration barrier (AIB) sheet structure in reducing energy consumption when installed in a typical home.

2. To establish recommended physical properties required for AIBs used in typical construction.

Summary of Results

The heating energy consumption of a typical ranch-style, 111-m^2 (1195-ft^2) conventional comparison house (CCH), built by the National Association of Home Builders Research Foundation (NAHB-RF), was monitored accurately

---

[1]Christiana Laboratory, E. I. Du Pont de Nemours & Co., Wilmington, DE 19898.
[2]Director, Building Systems, National Association of Home Builders Research Foundation, Rockville, MD 20850.

for 5 years. The installation of an AIB reduced the consumption of energy in this CCH by 24% for the first heating season (1982–1983). This AIB is expected to reduce the cost of the heating load of living spaces in this house by 28% (compared to no AIB) over the remaining life of the house. These results were normalized for degree days and are based on the energy use history of the house for the 5 years immediately preceding the AIB installation.

Observations from this test installation, in addition to other field studies, suggested the recommendation of minimum physical property requirements for an AIB.

Definition—Air Infiltration Barrier

When installed, an AIB is a continuous envelope with an unbroken surface immediately beneath the siding (on the opposite side of the studs from a vapor barrier), has a gas permeability between certain upper and lower limits, and is sealed at the edges to the structure in such a manner as to ensure that air which transfers through the wall cavity must pass through the AIB.

Background

In Mt. Airy, Maryland, the NAHB-RF in 1977 built a standard ranch-style, three-bedroom house (CCH) with 111 m² (1195 ft²) of conditioned living space on the first floor and an equal space in the partially conditioned full basement. This house has been continuously occupied by the same family of four since February, 1978. The house is all-electric, and each service circuit has an individual meter. Accurate data on weather and energy consumption on each circuit have been kept on a monthly basis over the past 6 years for the CCH. This house was constructed using standard materials and practices with usual, but no special, attention to detail. The walls of the CCH were insulated with kraft-faced R-11 fiber glass batts and the ceiling with blown fiber glass to R-19 with a 0.10-mm (4-mil) polyethylene vapor barrier just above the gypsum board ceiling. CCH served as the control unit for the Energy Efficient Residence No. 1 (EER-1) that NAHB-RF constructed next door. Results of retrofitting EER-1 with an AIB will be reported at a later date.

Under contract to the DuPont Co., NAHB-RF removed from the CCH the existing brick veneer and aluminum siding, enclosed and sealed exterior walls on the first floor with a spun-bonded polyolefin AIB fabric, and replaced the brick veneer and aluminum siding.

Figures 1A and 1B present schematic drawings of the front and rear walls of the CCH after installation of the AIB. This concept is representative of the entire AIB installation. It should be emphasized that much care was taken to ensure that the AIB fabric was sealed at the edges and around openings (for example, windows, doors, and service penetrations).

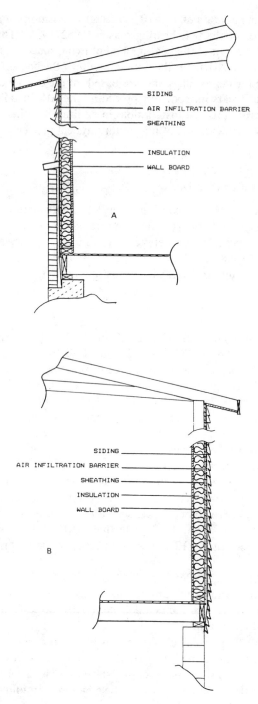

FIG. 1—(A) *Section at front wall of CCH;* (B) *Section at rear wall of CCH.*

The Mechanism by Which AIBs Function

An AIB works by controlling the movement of outdoor air through the wall as well as into and out of the wall cavity. A review of the function of the building envelope, of which the wall is a major and complex part, is useful in defining the function of an AIB in this envelope system.

The Function of Building Envelopes

For purposes of this paper, only the wall portion of the envelope will be addressed. Relative to comfort conditioning, the exterior wall serves two major functions:

1. Controls conductive heat loss/gain from the conditioned living space (insulation).
2. Controls leakage of unconditioned air into the conditioned living space or leakage of conditioned air from the living space (infiltration/exfiltration).

The major thrust on which the building industry has concentrated was reducing the cost of energy expended to condition the air inside a house. And, since the envelope (the wall) can be a principal source of loss of conditioned inside air, building walls tighter has been an important element in energy saving design and construction. Work on this aspect of reducing air transfer through the envelope was and is correct and should be continued.

The evolution of a wall system into today's technology has involved attempts to stop the movement of air mass into and through the wall, which includes siding, insulation, sheathing, vapor barriers, and caulking. Common methods used in the past to reduce the excessive envelope air infiltration include attempts to stop air infiltration completely. However, no air movement in a wall cavity also may lead to structural damage if moisture becomes trapped there. Liquid water in a wall cavity generally will require some air mass transfer for any significant rate of evaporation and removal of the water.

Function of an AIB

An air infiltration barrier functions to prevent localized high velocity air from moving through the envelope while allowing a controlled, very low velocity air mass exchange within the wall cavity. This is accomplished by:

1. The AIBs having a uniform air permeability, between specified limits, over its entire surface to control the air mass diffusion into and out of the envelope.
2. Having no unintended breaks in the surface of the AIB.
3. Sealing the edges of the AIB to the structure in such a way as to prevent air leakage into or out of the wall cavity at the edges.

The major advantage of an AIB is to allow a limited volume of air exchange between the wall cavity and the outdoors over a large area, eliminating high velocity air movement at localized points. This promotes evaporation of any moisture that may have condensed in the wall cavity and transfer of the moisture vapor out of the wall cavities. Thus, the AIB prevents excessive air mass transfer through the building envelope, which reduces the cost of conditioning inside air, while providing sufficient air mass transfer to ensure against accumulation of moisture vapor in the wall cavity.

Air Infiltration and Air Leakage in the CCH

Air Infiltration

At the time CCH was built, a series of SF6 tracer gas tests were run over several months while the house was still unoccupied. These tests established the average air infiltration rate to be 0.35 air changes per hour (ACH). After the AIB was installed in the CCH, a series of tests using a perfluorocarbon (PFT) tracer gas technique developed by Brookhaven National Laboratories (BNL) were conducted under occupied conditions over a 9-month period (September, 1982, to May, 1983). BNL developed a math model correlation between the SF6 tracer gas and PFT that indicates that the two sets of test results are directly correlatable. The PFT tests indicated an average infiltration rate of 0.22 ACH, a reduction of about 35% in air infiltration (Table 1).

Particularly interesting was the finding in the second series of tests that the rate of air exchange between the basement and the first floor was at least 15 times greater than that between the first floor and the outside air.[3]

TABLE 1—*BNL summary of CCH infiltration results.*

	Air Exchange Rates, h^{-1}		Air Infiltration Rates, h^{-1}		
Sampling Period	Basement to First Floor	First Floor to Basement	Basement	First Floor	Total
9/1 to 10/1/82	. . .	. . .	. . .	. . .	0.10
10/5 to 11/1/82	. . .	. . .	. . .	. . .	0.12
11/1 to 12/1/82	. . .	. . .	. . .	. . .	0.18
12/1 to 12/31/82	0.37	0.16	0.27	0.15	0.21
12/31 to 1/31/83	0.69	0.30	0.38	0.04	0.22
1/31 to 3/1/83	0.53	0.19	0.31	0.08	0.20
3/1 to 4/1/83	0.49	0.15	0.26	0.15	0.21
4/1 to 5/1/83	0.32	0.09	0.20	0.29	0.24
5/1 to 6/1/83	0.15	0.04	0.14	0.62	0.37

[3]Unpublished report from the Brookhaven National Laboratory to R. K. Yingling, National Association of Home Builders Research Foundation, 9 Feb. 1984.

Air Leakage

Air leakage values were determined for the CCH by blower door tests just before and just after the AIB installation. The results obtained are indicated in Table 2.

These results tent to confirm those of the tracer gas tests that the air exchange rate of this house was reduced by at least one third with the installation of the AIB. These results infer a significant reduction in heating energy demand due to the installation of the AIB.

Heating Energy Demand of CCH with an AIB

Figure 2 presents two energy consumption curves for CCH. The upper curve (circles) is the average heating energy consumed normalized for degree

TABLE 2—*Blower door test results for CCH. ACH.*

	Before AIB		After AIB	
	At 50 Pa	At 4 Pa	At 50 Pa	At 4 Pa
House pressurized	10.2	1.4	6.0	0.6
House depressurized	6.9	1.4	5.1	0.9
Average	8.6	1.4	5.6	0.8

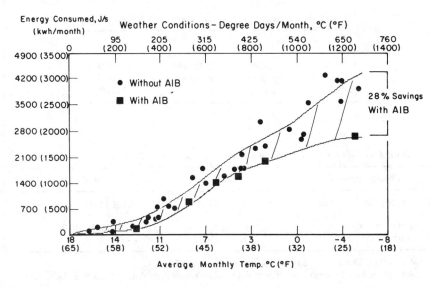

FIG. 2—*Energy consumption in the Mt. Airy house with and without AIB.*

days [base: 18.3°C (65°F)] on a monthly basis before the AIB was installed. The scatter about the average energy use rate curve is explained by variations in wind conditions about the CCH. As the wind increases about the CCH, the more conditioned indoor air will be forced out of the house at a given outdoor air temperature. Thus, various average monthly wind velocities can result in different amounts of energy consumed for a specified degree day month.

The lower curve (squares) represents data points for the first heating season of the CCH after installation of the AIB. Two observations should be noted about this curve:

1. All points on this curve are below all points on the upper curve (before the AIB was installed), which substantiates that the AIB resulted in a significant reduction in air infiltration.

2. All points lie close to the smooth curve, which indicates that most of the air mass passing through the envelope moved through the walls that the AIB now controls. If these points did not lie on a smooth curve, it would indicate that the air infiltration through the envelope was not controlled by the AIB.

The difference between the two curves represents a projected 28% energy savings for the CCH over the life of the house. For this particular heating season, the savings in energy consumption was 24%. The payback time on this low cost system (materials and labor) would be about two heating seasons for this house, assuming about $200 for labor and materials for installing the AIB on a new home.

TABLE 3—*Recommended air flow limits, m/s (ft/min.).*

Lower Limit		Upper Limit	
At 50Pa	At 4Pa	At 50Pa	At 4Pa
5.0E-4 (0.10)	1.0E-4 (0.02)	15E-4 (0.30)	3.5E-4 (0.07)

TABLE 4—*Minimum average strength properties recommended for sheet material ATBs.*

Physical Property	Min Value	Method
2.5-cm strip tensile: Strength	6.8 kg (15 lb)	ASTM D 1682-64 (1975)[a]
Elongation	15%	. . .
Elmendorf tear strength	0.3 kg (0.7 lb)	ASTM D 1424-83[b]
Hydrostatic pressure	25 cm (10 in.)	AATCC 127-77

[a]Methods for Breaking Load and Elongation of Textile Fabrics.
[b]Method for Tear Resistance of Woven Fabrics by Falling-Pendulum (Elmendorf) Apparatus.

Conclusion

As demonstrated in this test, an AIB, such as the spun-bonded fabric used, appears to offer a very cost-effective method to significantly reduce energy consumption in a conventionally constructed house.

AIB Physical Property Requirements

The principal physical property is limited uniform air permeability. Table 3 indicates AIB air permeability limits recommended for consideration.

In addition, for sheet material AIBs, the minimum average strength properties are recommended as shown in Table 4.

DISCUSSION

D. Saum[1] *(written discussion)*—Was the siding that was put up identical to the siding that was removed from the house?

D. Luebs and R. Weimar (authors' closure)—Yes.

T. Brennan[2] *(written discussion)*—During your slide sequence it was clear that you uncovered and sealed a variety of large openings through the band joist and around windows and doors. What would be the effect of sealing only those large holes by more conventional means (caulk, foam, polyethylene film) and ignoring the more circuitous paths through the sheathing and framing?

D. Luebs and R. Weimar (authors' closure)—The "variety of large openings through the band joist" to which you referred were not themselves sealed. Only the air infiltration barrier itself was sealed to the wall perimeters.

Sealing those "large holes" by conventional means would have brought the house to the original design specifications while reducing the air exchange rates in the house. The significant advantage of an air infiltration barrier is that its installation replaces having to correct errors, many of which may not be caught in the normal construction process.

[1]Infiltec, Waynesboro, VA.
[2]Red Wing, Rome, NY 13440.

Peter G. Giesbrecht[1] and Gary Proskiw[2]

An Evaluation of the Effectiveness of Air Leakage Sealing

REFERENCE: Giesbrecht, P. G. and Proskiw, G., **"An Evaluation of the Effectiveness of Air Leakage Sealing,"** *Measured Air Leakage of Buildings, ASTM STP 904*, H. R. Trechsel and P. L. Lagus, Eds., American Society for Testing and Materials, Philadelphia, 1986, pp. 312–322.

ABSTRACT: A field study was carried out to evaluate the effectiveness of air leakage sealing techniques for reducing air infiltration in houses. Presealing and postsealing air leakage tests were performed upon 82 single detached houses. All of the houses were located in Winnipeg or southern Manitoba, a region with an annual degree day value (Celsius) of about 5800. The sample group consisted of 56 conventionally constructed houses of varying size, style, occupancy, and airtightness and 26 nonstandard structures of smaller but identical size and age. This latter group was part of the Flora Place project.

All houses were placed under a negative pressure, and leakage sites were identified using smoke pencils. Windows and doors were weather-stripped and other unintentional openings caulked and sealed using specified materials and techniques.

Based upon the results of the study, the median reduction in airtightness of the conventional structures, defined using the equivalent leakage area at 10 Pa (ELA_{10}), was 31.6% with significant variations occurring both between houses of the same type and between different types of construction. When the houses are examined in groups according to type of construction, it is apparent that the greatest reduction in ELA (36.9%) was achieved in single-story houses. Houses constructed in somewhat more complicated fashion, such as split levels, exhibited less of a reduction. As a group, two-story houses showed the least reduction (24.4%), likely due to the indirect leakage between floors that could not be addressed properly. Within any group, houses with inaccessible air leakage points, such as in finished basement areas, showed the least reduction. The median reduction in the ELA_{10} for the Flora Place houses was 42.5%, again with significant variations between houses despite their near-identical construction.

Using the air leakage test data and a recently developed correlation model, an estimate was made of the naturally occurring air infiltration rates for all the test houses. This analysis indicated that the sealing produced a median reduction in the infiltration rate of 32.8% for the conventional houses and 46.1% for the Flora Place houses. Due to a lack of equipment, tracer gas tests were not conducted to confirm these values.

Note, however, that the results of this study likely are representative of houses constructed only in Manitoba and possibly in Saskatchewan and Alberta. Since houses in the prairie provinces tend to have low air infiltration rates, the effects of air leakage sealing on houses in other parts of the country could be different from those found in this study.

[1]Energy Engineer, ENER-CORP Energy Systems, Inc., Winnipeg, Manitoba, Canada R3JIN6.
[2]Mechanical engineer, UNIES, Ltd., Winnipeg, Manitoba, Canada.

KEY WORDS: air leakage, air infiltration, equivalent leakage area at 10 Pa, sealing measures

Air Infiltration in Houses

Air infiltration generally is acknowledged to represent a major component of the total heating load of houses. Depending upon the type of structure and its existing insulation levels, heat loss due to air infiltration may represent as much as 40% of the annual heating cost [1]. To the homeowner, this means an unwelcome expense that must be met every year. To the nation, it represents a significant component of the country's total energy needs. As a result, air infiltration represents both an existing liability and a potential opportunity for reducing energy costs. There is evidence [2] to support the fact that reducing the air change rate of a new house to less than 0.2 air changes per hour (ACH) may result in the buildup of unacceptable levels of indoor pollutants.

Purpose and Scope

The project described in this report was carried out to determine the effectiveness of air leakage sealing techniques for reducing air infiltration in houses. To quantify these results, presealing and postsealing air leakage tests were performed upon 82 houses, representing a broad cross section of age, style, construction, size, and occupancy. All were located in Winnipeg or southern Manitoba.

Interpretation of Results

Within the course of this project, a considerable volume of data was collected, refined, and subsequently analyzed with the most relevant information ultimately being reported within this document. However, to satisfy the study objectives, it was not considered possible to express these results using a single parameter. Therefore, to assist the reader in interpreting the study results, a few words of explanation are offered at this point.

First, air infiltration and air leakage should be defined. Within this report, air infiltration is used to describe the movement of outdoor air into the interior living space of the house occurring solely due to natural forces, that is, wind action and stack effect. This air, of course, has to be heated to prevent lowering of the interior air temperature. As air infiltrates into the structure, an equal amount must flow outwards from the interior to the outdoors. This air movement is termed air exfiltration. Air leakage, on the other hand, is used to describe the movement of outdoor air into the house due to the action of the depressurization (or pressurization) blower used in an air leakage test. Because many of the tests were conducted during the heating season, no tests

were conducted by pressurizing the houses. The accepted Canadian airtightness testing standard procedure [3] requires tests to be performed only under
depressurization conditions.

Airtightness (or air leakiness) generally is defined in terms of the equivalent
leakage area at 10 Pa³ (ELA_{10}). The primary value of such a parameter is that
it allows direct and easy comparisons of airtightness to be made between
houses since it is determined using standardized and accepted procedures.
Prior to introduction of the ELA_{10} parameter, many air leakage test results
were reported in terms of the number of ACH at various indoor-to-outdoor
pressure differentials (typically 4, 10, or 50 Pa). While these results had the
advantage of being easy to understand, they also were very prone to misinter-
pretation since many laymen thought they described the natural infiltration
rate. As a result, considerable confusion has occurred as to the actual air
infiltration rate of the typical house. To circumvent this problem, concensus
among those involved in air leakage testing in Canada has caused the adopta-
tion of the ELA_{10} [3] approach to eliminate any misunderstanding. As a
result, most air leakage tests, including those in this report, now are reported
in terms of the ELA_{10}.

It also was recognized, however, that the ELA_{10} does not provide explicit
information on the naturally occurring air infiltration rate, defined as the rate
of air exchange resulting solely from natural forces and not from the depressurization blower used in the air leakage test. For energy-estimating purposes, knowledge of the air infiltration rate is, of course, essential.

To provide this information, the air leakage test results were used to estimate the natural air infiltration rate using a recently developed correlation
model [4]. Testing this correlation on 25 houses in Canada and Sweden, this
model appears capable of predicting air infiltration rates within ±25% of
measured values.

To assist the reader, it is suggested that the air leakage test results, expressed using the ELA_{10}, be accepted as a means of comparing the airtightness of houses both within this and other studies. The predicted air infiltration rates, on the other hand, should be used to better appreciate the actual
effects of air infiltration produced under natural conditions, acknowledging
the accuracy limitations of the infiltration model. The ability of the model to
predict an infiltration rate not only is dependent upon a properly conducted
air leakage test but is also dependent on the outdoor temperature, wind speed
and direction, degree of shielding, and the correct calculation of the conditioned volume within the building envelope.

---

³One Pascal equals approximately 0.004 in. of water column.

Fundamentals of Air Infiltration

Causes of Air Infiltration

Air infiltration is caused by pressure differentials which exist across the house envelope and result in the uncontrolled movement of outdoor air into the structure. These pressure differentials can be produced by three different driving forces;

1. Stack effect,
2. Wind action.
3. Exhaust fan/ventilation system operation.

Stack Effect—Since indoor and outdoor air are at different temperatures during the heating season, their densities and resulting buoyancies will be different. In the winter months, these buoyancy differentials create negative indoor-to-outdoor pressure differentials over the lower portions of the house envelope and positive pressure differentials over the upper portions. As a result, the stack effect attempts to induce infiltration across the lower portions of the envelope and exfiltration over the upper portions.

Wind Action—The most obvious effects of wind action are well understood by most people. The wind blowing against a structure creates a pressure force on the windward side and a suction force on the leeward side which, if the walls contain any holes or cracks, causes air infiltration on the windward side and air exfiltration on the leeward side. In practice, the subtle dynamics of wind flow around buildings is considerably more complex. Distortions to these flow patterns caused by turbulence from adjacent structures, trees, etc., can result in air infiltration/exfiltration forces markedly different from those anticipated.

Exhaust Fan/Ventilation System Operation—Mechanical exhaust systems such as bathroom fans and dryer exhausts remove air from the building at high flow rates which may induce air infiltration over the entire house envelope. Because these systems are run intermittently, their contribution to the ELA and the predicted infiltration rate has not been included. Only unintentional openings in the building envelope were included in the air leakage tests.

The net pressure differential to which a house is exposed to and hence the net air infiltration that it experiences at any time will be the algebraic sum of the three driving forces just described. It is obvious that the pressure differentials and resulting air infiltration rates will vary throughout the year with outside temperature, wind speed and direction, and exhaust fan/ventilation system operation. In general, however, the average indoor-to-outdoor pressure differentials experienced by a house during winter operation generally will be less than 5 Pa [5].

Sources of Air Infiltration/Exfiltration

The locations of the most common sources of air infiltration in a conventional house are shown in Fig. 1 [6]. Contrary to popular belief, windows and doors are not the major sources, usually contributing only about 25% of the total. Rather, joints between the main walls and the floor system, electrical outlets on exterior walls, and ceiling penetrations for light fixtures, attic hatches, partition walls, and plumbing fixtures constitute the major infiltration/exfiltration paths.

Most of these cracks, gaps, and holes are "built into" the house during its construction. With lower energy prices, few builders felt the need to take specific measures to control air infiltration.

Effects of Air Infiltration

Uncontrolled air infiltration has several effects upon the operation and use of a house. The first and most obvious is increased heating costs. Any air which enters the building, beyond that required for respiration, furnace operation, and humidity/air pollutant control, represents an additional and unnecessary heating load. In almost all older structures, the quantity of outdoor air delivered by air infiltration exceeds that which is required [7], a value generally agreed to be about 0.5 ACH [8]. This explains, for example, why most older homes suffer from dry air during the winter months.

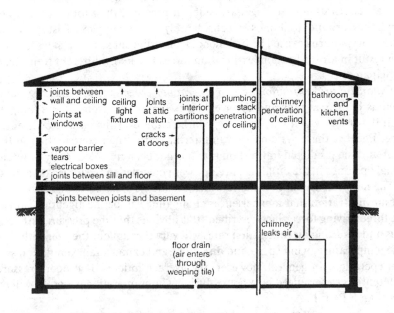

FIG. 1—*Air infiltration locations in a conventional house.*

Air infiltration also can affect the comfort level of the house, as uncontrolled drafts can cause discomfort and chills. Cold drafts also can increase the heating bill beyond that actually necessary to warm outdoor air by causing the occupants to become "thermostat jockies," pushing up the thermostat setting whenever they feel a chill. In extreme cases, air infiltration coupled with a poorly balanced heating system can cause some rooms of a house to become virtually uninhabitable during the winter months. For these reasons, many homeowners regard the degradation of indoor comfort levels as the most serious consequence of air infiltration.

The movement of warm, moisture-laden air outwards through the building shell due to exfiltration forces is responsible for the third major effect. As this air exfiltrates through the (colder) shell, its temperature drops, and condensation can occur [9]. If this moisture is not removed by evaporation or sublimation, it may lead to wetting of insulation and structural elements. Many of the insulations found in older houses are vulnerable to moisture damage, which may cause settling and reduction in their effective thermal resistance [9]. If the moisture content of wood is raised above approximately 20% for extended periods of time (roughly two months) and appropriate temperatures are maintained, wood rot also may occur. Interior finished surfaces, particularly ceilings, also are vulnerable to moisture damage. Ceiling staining caused by moisture accumulation in the attic is common in some houses, and, in extreme cases, complete collapse of large sections of the ceiling can occur within a few years [9].

Although some sources have suggested that many existing homes, even after having been air sealed, are supplied with sufficient outside air for ventilation and combustion purposes through infiltration [7], this mechanism should not be relied upon to supply air required for these purposes. A study [10] of 100 homes across Canada with suspected venting problems revealed that about 40% actually did have problems that required some form of remedial measures. It is possible that these problems could be aggravated if homes are sealed without addressing ventilation and combustion air supply.

In view of the experience level that some air sealing contractors have achieved during the past four or five years, it is recommended that every major combustion appliance be equipped with its own outside air supply, regardless of the amount of air sealing undertaken. An ever-widening range of products is now available [11], and a committee, under the sponsorship of the Canadian General Standards Board (CGSB), has been formed which has been given the responsibility of developing a procedure to permit a contractor to determine what additional ventilation air quantities, if any, are required after a house has been air sealed.[4]

----

[4]Private communication, Bruce Fulcher, ENER-CORP Management, Ltd., April 1964.

Description of the Air Leakage Testing Program

Overview

To evaluate the effectiveness of anti-air infiltration measures, presealing and postsealing air leakage tests were performed upon 82 houses in the Winnipeg or southern Manitoba areas.

Houses were selected from customers obtained in the normal course of business. These customers could be characterized as either homeowners who perceived the need for air sealing or who were convinced of its merits by an energy consultant.

In general these measures included:

1. Weatherstripping of:
   (*a*) Exterior doors.
   (*b*) Windows.
2. Caulking and sealing of:
   (*a*) Exterior doors.
   (*b*) Windows.
   (*c*) Electrical plugs and switches on exterior walls.
   (*d*) Ceiling lights and electrical openings in the attic.
   (*e*) Plumbing stacks, vents, and ducts passing through attics.
   (*f*) Fireplace and furnace chimneys in the attic.
   (*g*) Cracks along interior partitions.
   (*h*) Attic hatch.
   (*i*) Cracks between concrete walls and subfloor.
   (*j*) Floor joist area.
   (*k*) Perimeter or milk, mail, and coal chutes.
   (*l*) General cracks and openings in walls (not including basement walls).

After completion, a second air leakage test was performed.

Air Leakage Test Procedure

The procedure used for conducting the air leakage tests was based upon the draft of a standard specification currently being developed by the CGSB [*3*]. At the time of writing, the standard was in its eighth draft and will be identified on finalization as CAN2-149.10-M84, "Determination of the Equivalent Leakage Area of Buildings by the Fan Depressurization Method."

By depressurizing the house, a negative indoor-to-outdoor pressure differential was created which induced air leakage into the structure. The air leakage test consisted of subjecting the house to a number of different pressure differentials while measuring the rate at which air is exhausted according to the prescribed test procedure [*3*]. Using these data, a characteristic air leakage curve was calculated which described the leakage at any pressure differential. In this manner, changes in the airtightness of the house can be determined by conducting identical leakage tests before and after implementation of any antiinfiltration measures.

It should be noted that the air leakage tests were not always performed in strict conformance with the draft standard [3] largely because many of the tests were carried out prior to release of the draft and because of changes between subsequent drafts. The primary deviation from the draft standard procedure was in the inability of the depressurization apparatus to achieve an induced pressure differential of 50 Pa in some very leaky homes.

Tests in which the flow exponents fell outside of the range of 0.50 to 1.00 and the correlation coefficient was less than 0.9800 were rejected.

Air Leakage Test Results

Data Presentation

Air leakage test results are frequently reported using several different parameters. The one that is most commonly used in Canada and the one that was adopted for this report, as previously explained, is the ELA_{10}.

The ELA_{10} is the size of the equivalent hole, in units of square metres, which would produce the same net leakage as the randomly distributed leakage paths normally found in a house. It is calculated at a pressure differential 10 Pa and is independent of the size of the house.

Air Leakage Test Results—Conventional Houses

Results are separated for the 26 Flora Place units and the remaining 56 conventional houses. A summary of the air leakage test results for the 56 conventional houses is shown in Table 1. A further breakdown of the data, based upon type of house, is given in Table 2. Notice that the ELA_{10}s given in Table 2 are median values.

As is evident from Tables 1 and 2, considerable variation was encountered in both the initial air leakiness of the structures and in the effectiveness of the sealing. However, based upon the 56 houses studied, the median reduction in the ELA_{10} due to the air leakage sealing was 31.6%.

Air Leakage Test Results—Flora Place Houses

A summary of the air leakage test results for the 26 Flora Place houses is shown in Table 3. Once again, considerable variations were encountered in the airtightness of the structures and in the effectiveness of the sealing. This is a rather interesting result since the houses were virtually identical in size, construction, and age. The median reduction in the ELA_{10} due to the air leakage sealing was 42.5% for the 26 houses.

TABLE 1—*Summary of presealing and postsealing air leakage tests—conventional houses.*

House Number	House Type (No. of Stories)	Year of Construction	ELA_{10}, m^2 Presealing	ELA_{10}, m^2 Postsealing	Percentage Reduction in ELA_{10}
1	2	1902	0.07926	0.05526	30.3
2	split level	1926	0.06008	0.04388	27.0
3	2	1925	0.09482	0.07815	17.6
4	2	1916	0.11522	0.10028	13.0
5	1½	1954	0.06346	0.05280	16.8
6	1	1952	0.09517	0.06686	29.7
7	1½	1920	0.12973	0.09581	26.1
8	1½	1948	0.08703	0.06228	28.4
9	1	1955	0.12382	0.08115	34.5
10	split level	1960	0.09138	0.06184	32.3
11	1	1947	0.05473	0.05124	6.4
12	1	1976	0.06196	0.03597	41.9
13	1	1964	0.10304	0.05720	44.5
14	1	1958	0.07486	0.04413	41.1
15	1	1975	0.08843	0.06419	27.4
16	1½	1950	0.04876	0.04070	16.5
17	1	1951	0.14112	0.05475	61.2
18	1	1976	0.06748	0.04280	36.6
19	1	1953	0.09126	0.05345	41.4
20	1	1969	0.09032	0.04803	46.8
21	2	1923	0.14578	0.12032	17.5
22	1	1927	0.19256	0.14243	26.0
23	split level	1973	0.09076	0.06227	31.4
24	2	1970	0.08979	0.05089	43.3
25	split level	1977	0.09755	0.05183	46.8
26	1	1940	0.10971	0.05936	45.9
27	1	1932	0.06247	0.03838	38.6
28	split level	1974	0.04004	0.03619	9.6
29	1	1946	0.04438	0.03178	28.4
30	1½	1947	0.09205	0.06680	27.4
31	1	1966	0.04614	0.01980	57.1
32	split level	1975	0.08016	0.03834	52.2
33	1	1954	0.05668	0.04272	24.6
34	1	1962	0.04440	0.03481	21.6
35	1	1922	0.09711	0.06105	37.1
36	2	1940	0.12632	0.09555	24.4
37	split level	1962	0.10348	0.08031	22.4
38	1½	1953	0.12560	0.05143	59.1
39	split level	1974	0.06718	0.05275	21.5
40	1	1968	0.05869	0.03984	32.1
41	1	1946	0.13322	0.08542	35.9
42	2½	1925	0.25560	0.13084	45.8
43	2	1902	0.26276	0.19217	26.9
44	1½	1950	0.07642	0.04904	27.6
45	2½	1926	0.17859	0.14270	20.2
46	1	1976	0.05120	0.03600	28.0
47	1	1951	0.07973	0.04339	32.6
48	2½	1930	0.30209	0.17236	42.9
49	split level	1980	0.12155	0.10335	15.0
50	split level	1968	0.06501	0.04049	37.7
51	1	1962	0.04621	0.03762	18.6
52	1	1957	0.08765	0.03694	57.9
53	1	1960	0.11005	0.06638	39.7
54	1	1973	0.10964	0.06826	37.8
55	1	1962	0.06513	0.04092	37.1
56	2½	1930	0.25405	0.17340	31.7

TABLE 2—*Equivalent leakage areas [ELA$_{10}$] conventional houses.*

House Type	Sample Size	Median ELA$_{10}$, m^2		Median Percentage Reduction, %
		Presealing	Postsealing[a]	
1 story	28	0.08369	0.05281	36.9%
Split levels	10	0.08546	0.06051	29.2%
1½ story	7	0.08703	0.06318	27.4%
2 story	7	0.11522	0.08714	24.4%
2½ story	4	0.25483	0.15978	37.3%
All houses	56	0.09054	0.06193	31.6%

[a]Calculated by subtracting the median value of the percentage reductions recorded for the individual houses from the median presealing ELA$_{10}$.

TABLE 3—*Summary of presealing and postsealing air leakage tests— Flora Place houses.*[a]

House Number	ELA$_{10}$, m^2		Percentage Reduction, %
	Presealing	Postsealing	
57	0.03088	0.02244	26.9
58	0.03135	0.01789	42.1
59	0.05402	0.02924	45.5
60	0.04097	0.02581	36.2
61	0.06623	0.02414	63.6
62	0.05450	0.03085	41.3
63	0.04564	0.02850	26.9
64	0.04104	0.01837	55.1
65	0.04683	0.03004	35.8
66	0.03848	0.02869	25.1
67	0.03637	0.02698	44.5
68	0.04656	0.02993	36.8
69	0.04048	0.01984	27.2
70	0.04589	0.02490	45.2
71	0.03672	0.01536	58.4
72	0.04172	0.02357	43.6
73	0.05532	0.02358	57.4
74	0.02849	0.02011	29.4
75	0.04232	0.02651	50.2
76	0.04314	0.02594	39.3
77	0.04787	0.02803	44.2
78	0.03922	0.02243	42.8
79	0.03612	0.02146	40.6
80	0.03471	0.02088	39.9
81	0.04047	0.02087	48.7
82	0.07182	0.02162	69.8

[a]All single story with no basement, constructed in 1940.

References

[1] Tamura, G. T., "Measurement of Air Leakage Characteristics of House Enclosures," NRC Publication 14950. National Research Council of Canada, Ottawa, Ontario, 1975.

[2] Roseme, G. D., et al, "Residential Ventilation with Heat Recovery: Improving Indoor Air Quality and Saving Energy," LBL-9749, EEB-Vent 80-10, Lawrence Berkeley Laboratory, Berkeley, CA, May 1980.

[3] "Determination of the Equivalent Leakage Areas of Buildings by the Fan Depressurization Method," CAN2-149.10-M84, 8th draft, Canadian General Standards Board, Ottawa, Canada, Oct. 1984.

[4] Shaw, C. Y., National Research Council of Canada, Ottawa, Ontario, *ASHRAE Transactions* 87, Part 2, 1981, pp. 333–341.

[5] Grimsrud, D. T., et al, "Infiltration & Air Leakage Comparisons—Conventional and Energy Efficient Housing Designs," LBL-9157, EEB-ENV-79-7, Lawrence Berkeley Laboratories, Berkeley, CA, Oct. 1979.

[6] "Energy Efficient Housing, A Prairie Approach," Manitoba Energy & Mines, Energy Division, Winnipeg, Canada, revised 1982.

[7] "Fresh Air and Humidity in a Tighter House," *Factsheet*, Ontario Ministry of Municipal Affairs and Housing, Toronto, Canada, Feb. 1983.

[8] Grimsrud, D. T., et al, "Calculating Infiltration: Implications for a Construction Quality Standard," LBL-9416, Lawrence Berkeley Laboratories, Berkeley, CA, April 1983.

[9] "Air Sealing Homes for Energy Conservation," 2nd draft, Energy, Mines & Resources Canada, Ottawa, Canada, 1984.

[10] Moffatt, S., "Residential Combustion Safety Checklists," Sheltair Scientific Ltd., Vancouver, Canada, Dec. 1984.

[11] "Air Management Manual," Ener-Corp Management, Ltd., Winnipeg, Manitoba, Canada, 1984.

Analysis

Max H. Sherman[1] and Mark P. Modera[1]

Comparison of Measured and Predicted Infiltration Using the LBL Infiltration Model

REFERENCE: Sherman, M. H. and Modera, M. P., **"Comparison of Measured and Predicted Infiltration Using the LBL Infiltration Model,"** *Measured Air Leakage of Buildings, ASTM STP 904*, H. R. Trechsel and P. L. Lagus, Eds., American Society for Testing and Materials, Philadelphia, 1986, pp. 325–347.

ABSTRACT: The Lawrence Berkeley Laboratory (LBL) infiltration model was developed in 1980; since that time many simultaneous measurements of infiltration and weather have been made, allowing comparison of predictions with measured infiltration. This report presents the LBL model as it currently exists and summarizes infiltration measurements and corresponding predictions. These measurements include both long-term and short-term data taken in houses with climates ranging from the mild San Francisco Bay area to the more extreme Midwest. These data also provide a data base for comparison with other infiltration models and provide a starting point for the determination of the accuracy and precision of air infiltration models.

KEY WORDS: infiltration, measurement, prediction, modeling

Nomenclature

$\langle \ldots \rangle$ Indicates a time average of the quantity in arrows

C Generalized shielding coefficient (see Table 1)

C_i Pressure coefficient for a face

C_o Internal pressure coefficient

C_p Heat capacity of air, 1024 W/kg K

H Height, m

H_s Stack height of building (highest-lowest leak), m

H_t Height of weather tower (wind measurement), m

H_w Wind height of building (ceiling height above grade), m

L Effective leakage area, m^2

[1]Staff scientist, Lawrence Berkeley Laboratory, Berkeley, CA 94720.

L_o Total leakage area of envelope, m^2
P Absolute pressure, Pa
Q Airflow (infiltration, ventilation), m^3/s
Q_{50} Airflow at 50 Pa, m^3/s
Q_{bal} Infiltration from balanced mechanical ventilation, m^3/s
Q_s Stack-induced infiltration, m^3/s
Q_{unbal} Infiltration from unbalanced mechanical ventilation, m^3/s
Q_w Wind-induced infiltration, m^3/s
$Q_{weather}$ Natural infiltration, m^3/s
R Fraction of total leakage area in the floor and ceiling
T Absolute (inside) temperature, 295 K
X Difference in ceiling/floor fractional leakage area
α Terrain coefficient (see Table 2)
β Dimensionless height (normalized by stack height of building)
β_o Position of the neutral level
f_s Stack factor
f_w Wind factor
g The acceleration of gravity, $9.8\ m/s^2$
γ Terrain exponent (see Table 2)
n Leakage exponent
q Specific infiltration (ratio of infiltration to leakage area), m/s
q_s Specific stack-induced infiltration, m/s
q_w Specific wind-induced infiltration, m/s
ρ The density of (outside) air, $1.2\ kg/m^3$
v Measured wind speed, m/s
v_* Free stream wind speed, m/s
v_1 Local wind speed, m/s
ΔP Outside-inside pressure difference, Pa
ΔP_o Leakage reference pressure, Pa
ΔT Inside-outside temperature difference, K

Because infiltration is a primary source of energy loss in residences, under-standing the infiltration process is critical to any residential conservation pro-gram. Yet we are far more capable of calculating losses due to conduction than losses due to infiltration. Several explanations for this disparity can be stated. First, conduction losses are calculated more easily because the heat transfer is proportional to the temperature difference and does not depend strongly on any other driving force. Infiltration, on the other hand, depends on the interior-exterior point pressure difference but is not simply propor-tional to it. Furthermore, the driving pressure is caused by uncorrelated phys-ical effects (wind speed and temperature difference). Second, conduction losses can be characterized by means of one parameter, thermal resistance, whereas infiltration, until now, has had no equivalent quantity.

The Lawrence Berkeley Laboratory (LBL) infiltration model was first presented in 1979 [1], and since that time we have been conducting an extensive refinement and validation program that includes both short-term and long-term data from a variety of sources. Our Mobile Infiltration Test Unit (MITU) has spent two successive winters making detailed measurements of weather, surface pressures, and infiltration. In this paper we will use data gathered from MITU and other sources to compare measurements with LBL model predictions.

Theory

The modeling of infiltration involves modeling many different effects. The behavior of air flowing through a leak in the building envelope under known pressures is determined from the fluid dynamics of pipe flow. These pressures, in turn, are a consequence of the interaction of the building and surrounding terrain with the weather. These considerations and others have been examined in great detail in a previous work [2] and will be summarized in the sections to follow.

Leakage Model

Leakage is the fundamental interaction of the envelope with the external pressures. As discussed in Ref 2, the hydrodynamics of air flowing through cracks is quite complex; it involves laminar, transition, and turbulent flow through both rough and smooth paths. Rather than burden our infiltration model with a detailed synthesis of all crack parameters, we have chosen to make the assumption that the flow through a crack can be treated simply. The two simple physical choices are laminar and turbulent flow. As has been demonstrated with a measurement technique called AC pressurization [3], turbulent flow is the better assumption. This leads to an expression for the flow through a crack in terms of the square root of the pressure drop across it.

$$Q = L\sqrt{\frac{2\Delta P}{\rho}} \tag{1}$$

Thus, the quantity that characterizes the leakage has the units of area; we call it the effective leakage area. Leakage area can be thought of as the total amount of open area of a particular leakage site.

Superposition

Although we have a simple expression for the flow through the envelope as a function of pressure, it is not a simple matter to calculate the point pressures on the surface of a building. For weather-driven infiltration, there are two independent driving forces: wind and temperature difference (stack effect). Since, for the most part, the stack and wind effects are uncorrelated, we calculate their effect on infiltration independently; but, because both effects affect the internal pressure, we cannot simply add them to find the total infiltration. A detailed calculation of the total infiltration requires that the pressures be summed at each point and the flow calculated from that summation. We can, however, use our simplified leakage expression to combine the two independent parts; if the flow is proportional to the square root of the pressure, then two flows acting independently must add in quadrature.

$$Q_{weather} = \sqrt{Q_w^2 + Q_s^2} \qquad (2)$$

This same superposition law can be used to combine other flows with the weather-induced flows. Specifically, if there is an exhaust fan operating, it will affect the internal pressure and thus be combined in quadrature. But, if there is a balanced ventilation system (for example, a counter-flow heat exchanger), the internal pressure will not be affected, and the balanced flow will simply add to the rest of the infiltration. Thus, our superposition expression combining both mechanical and naturally induced ventilation is as follows

$$Q = Q_{bal} + \sqrt{Q_{unbal}^2 + Q_w^2 + Q_s^2} \qquad (3)$$

The terms Q_{bal} and Q_{unbal} can be calculated from the known supply and exhaust flows of the mechanical ventilation system.

$$Q_{bal} = \text{minimum of } (Q_{supply}, Q_{exhaust}) \qquad (4.1)$$

$$Q_{unbal} = (Q_{supply} - Q_{exhaust}) \qquad (4.2)$$

Thus, if there is exhaust but no supply, Q_{bal} will be zero and all the mechanical ventilation will be unbalanced.

Stack-Induced Infiltration

The stack effect is caused by the fact that the temperature at the body of air inside the building is different from the outside air temperature. This temperature difference causes a density difference and thus buoyancy, creating a pressure gradient along any vertical boundary. This pressure difference is a function of the temperature difference and the height above the neutral level.

$$\Delta P = \rho g H_s \frac{\Delta T}{T} (\beta_o - \beta) \qquad (5)$$

The neutral level, β_o, is the (dimensionless) height at which the internal pressure and external pressure are equal; as we shall see, it is determined by the requirement that air infiltration must equal air exfiltration. The stack height, H_s, is the height from the lowest leak in the envelope (normally the floor or ground level) and the highest leak in the envelope (normally ceiling level).

This expression gives the pressure at a particular height as a function of the temperatures involved. In a building, however, the leaks are distributed over the entire envelope, requiring a detailed summation. To avoid this level of detail, we have grouped the envelope leakage into three categories: floor, wall, and ceiling leakage area. Within each area we assume that the leakage is evenly distributed. Thus, we have three parameters that describe the leakage distribution: A_o, the total leakage area; R, the fraction of the leakage area in the floor and ceiling; and X, the difference in the fractional floor and ceiling leakage areas.

To calculate the stack infiltration, we must integrate the point pressures that are positive over the entire envelope

$$Q_s^+ = L_o \sqrt{\frac{gH_s}{2} \left| \frac{\Delta T}{T} \right|} \, \beta_o \left(R + X + \frac{4}{3} \beta_o \right) \tag{6.1}$$

and to calculate the exfiltration we must integrate all the negative point pressures

$$Q_s^- = L_o \sqrt{\frac{gH_s}{2} \left| \frac{\Delta T}{T} \right|} \, (1 - \beta_o) \left(R - X + \frac{4}{3} (1 - \beta_o) \right) \tag{6.2}$$

By continuity the infiltration and exfiltration must be equal. Equating these two quantities yields an expression for X in terms of β_o. Eliminating X from Eq 6 gives us one expression for the total stack effect infiltration.

$$Q_s = L_o \sqrt{2gH_s \left| \frac{\Delta T}{T} \right|} \, \frac{2}{3} (1 + R/2) \frac{\sqrt{\beta_o} \sqrt{1 - \beta_o}}{\sqrt{\beta_o} + \sqrt{1 - \beta_o}} \tag{7}$$

For convenience we define the stack factor as follows

$$f_s = \frac{2}{3} (1 + R/2) \frac{\sqrt{2\beta_o(1 - \beta_o)}}{\sqrt{\beta_o} + \sqrt{1 - \beta_o}} \tag{8}$$

In some instances it may be more desirable to use the ceiling-floor fractional leakage difference than the neutral level in the computation of the stack-induced infiltration. In this case we can use an approximate expression that relates the neutral level to the difference, and then the two equations become

$$Q_s = L_o \sqrt{gH_s \left| \frac{\Delta T}{T} \right|} \, \frac{(1 + R/2)}{3} \left(1 - \frac{X^2}{(2 - R)^2} \right)^{3/2} \tag{9}$$

$$f_s = \frac{(1 + R/2)}{3} \left(1 - \frac{X^2}{(2 - R)^2}\right)^{3/2} \tag{10}$$

Wind-Induced Infiltration

When wind impinges on or flows around a solid building, it induces a change in the pressure on the external faces of that building. This change in the surface pressure is proportional to the local wind speed and the shielding coefficient of that face.

$$\frac{dP_i}{dv} = C_i \beta v_1 \tag{11}$$

The pressure coefficient C_i is a function of wind angle and building orientation, and the resulting pressure must be summed over the entire exposed surface. Furthermore, there will be an internal pressure coefficient, C_o, which, like the neutral level for the stack effect, will be determined by requirement of continuity.

From numerical calculations using wind-tunnel data,[2] we have found that the wind-induced infiltration can be described by the following expression

$$Q_w = L_o v_1 C (1 - R)^{1/3} \tag{12}$$

The R dependency stems from the fact that the floor and ceiling are usually much more heavily shielded from the wind than are the walls. The generalized shielding coefficient, C, has been numerically calculated for 5° of obstruction around the building; the values are summarized in Table 1. Boundary layer wind tunnel data for an isolated structure [4] were used to calculate the coefficient for Shielding Class I; subsequent shielding classes were then approximated.

TABLE 1—*Generalized shielding coefficients.*

Shielding Class	C'	Description
I	0.324	no obstructions or local shielding whatsoever
II	0.285	light local shielding with few obstructions
III	0.240	moderate local shielding, some obstructions within two house heights
IV	0.185	heavy shielding, obstructions around most of perimeter
V	0.102	very heavy shielding, large obstruction surrounding perimeter within two house heights

[2] See Ref 2 for details of this numerical procedure.

Although the just-cited expression involves the use of the local wind speed at ceiling height, v_1, most wind data are taken from a weather tower not necessarily in the immediate vicinity. We, therefore, must convert the measured wind speed from a weather station into a local wind speed for our model. One of the standard methods for achieving this is: to convert the wind speed at the weather tower into the invariant velocity that is assumed to exist at the top of the atmospheric boundary layer, some 600 m above the surface; to move to the desired location; and to convert the invariant velocity into the local wind speed. The method we have chosen to use [5] yields essentially the same results but converts the wind speed to a free stream wind speed at 10 m instead

$$v = v_* \alpha \left(\frac{H}{10 \text{ m}} \right)^\gamma \tag{13}$$

The quantities α and γ are terrain-dependent parameters and are listed in Table 2. To convert the local wind speed into the weather tower wind speed, we must use the intermediate of the free stream wind speed.

$$v_1 = v \frac{\alpha_w \left(\dfrac{H_w}{10 \text{ m}} \right)^{\gamma_w}}{\alpha_t \left(\dfrac{H_t}{10 \text{ m}} \right)^{\gamma_t}} \tag{14}$$

Finally, then, we have an expression for the wind-induced infiltration.

$$Q_w = L_o v C (1 - R)^{1/3} \frac{\alpha_w \left(\dfrac{H_w}{10 \text{ m}} \right)^{\gamma_w}}{\alpha_t \left(\dfrac{H_t}{10 \text{ m}} \right)^{\gamma_t}} \tag{15}$$

TABLE 2—*Terrain parameters for standard terrain classes.*

Class	γ	α	Description
I	0.10	1.30	ocean or other body of water with at least 5 km of unrestricted expanse
II	0.15	1.00	flat terrain with some isolated obstacles
III	0.20	0.85	rural areas with low buildings, trees, or other scattered obstacles
IV	0.25	0.67	urban, industrial or forest areas or other built-up area
V	0.35	0.47	center of large city or other heavily built-up area

For convenience we define the wind factor as follows

$$f_w = C(1 - R)^{1/3} \frac{\alpha_w \left(\dfrac{H_w}{10 \text{ m}}\right)^{\gamma_w}}{\alpha_t \left(\dfrac{H_t}{10 \text{ m}}\right)^{\gamma_t}} \qquad (16)$$

Wind direction has not been an explicit part of the model as described. But, if directional effects are judged to be important, they can be included by assigning a shielding class, and perhaps a terrain class, to each directional slice. An alternate measure would be to replace the constant shielding coefficient, C, with a smoothly varying function of angle (for example, $C = C_1 + C_2 \sin \theta$ could be useful for rowhousing). The choice of terrain and shielding classes is one made by inspection; these parameters are not to be treated as adjustable.

Vent-Induced Infiltration

The previous sections have dealt with the calculation of weather-induced infiltration through leaks and other pathways not principally designed for ventilation. In calculating the total ventilation, it is necessary to combine the airflows caused by the HVAC system with the naturally occurring ones. In a previous publication [6], we have shown how this can be done for a few simple mechanical systems; in general, it is necessary to calculate the airflow of the individual component (for example, exhaust vent, furnace flue, fireplace, etc.) and include its value in the total supply or exhaust flows. Superposition then can be used to find the total.

Summary of Model

We summarize the equations just derived.
Superposition

$$Q = Q_{\text{bal}} + \sqrt{Q_{\text{unbal}}^2 + Q_w^2 + Q_s^2} \qquad (17)$$

Balanced (additional) ventilation

$$Q_{\text{bal}} = \text{minimum of } (Q_{\text{supply}}, Q_{\text{exhaust}}) \qquad (18)$$

Unbalanced (additional) ventilation

$$Q_{\text{unbal}} = \text{maximum of } (Q_{\text{supply}}, Q_{\text{exhaust}}) - Q_{\text{bal}} \qquad (19)$$

Stack-induced infiltration

$$Q_s = L_o f_s \sqrt{gH_s \left| \frac{\Delta T}{T} \right|} \tag{20}$$

Wind-induced infiltration

$$Q_w = L_o f_w v \tag{21}$$

Stack-factor

$$f_s = \frac{2}{3} (1 + R/2) \frac{\sqrt{2\beta_o(1 - \beta_o)}}{\sqrt{\beta_o} + \sqrt{1 - \beta_o}} \tag{22.1}$$

$$f_s = \frac{(1 + R/2)}{3} \left(1 - \frac{X^2}{(2 - R)^2} \right)^{3/2} \tag{22.2}$$

Wind factor

$$f_w = C(1 - R)^{1/3} \frac{\alpha_w \left(\dfrac{H_w}{10 \text{ m}} \right)^{\gamma_w}}{\alpha_t \left(\dfrac{H_t}{10 \text{ m}} \right)^{\gamma_t}} \tag{23}$$

Validation

An extensive validation effort was conducted over the course of several years to establish the limits and validity of our single zone model. Included in following paragraphs is a brief description of the validation effort and the results and conclusions thereof.

Short-term Measurements

The most commonly found type of infiltration data are in the form of short-term or spot measurements of leakage, weather, and infiltration. In these data sets, the infiltration usually was measured with a single tracer gas decay, the leakage with a blower door, and the weather with a portable tower. We have extracted from the literature [7–9] 15 different sites spanning the country from old conventional to new, energy-efficient designs and have compared our predicted infiltration to the measured infiltration.

The dashed lines in Fig. 1 represent the experimental error associated with the data; any points within them indicate that the model agrees to within experimental error. Taking the entire set of data, the predicted infiltration was on the average within 2% of the measured infiltration with a standard deviation of about 20%. This indicates that the predictions are quite good and can be expected to yield the correct results to within 20%. (The individual points for a particular house may be taken from different days. Therefore, the scatter of an individual set of measured infiltration values is not significant.)

Time-Series Data

One of the best tests of a physical model is not how well it can reproduce some average quantity from uncorrelated data, but rather how well it mirrors the physical situation and how well it can track changes in the physical quantities involved. In order to study the detailed behavior of infiltration, we built MITU [10], a full-scale test structure equipped with weather-, pressure-, and infiltration-measuring equipment. During the winters of 1981 and 1982, MITU was stationed in Reno, Nevada, and data were recorded.

Figure 2 compares the half-hour infiltration predictions with the measured infiltration as a function of time in MITU. Figure 3 shows data for MITU at the same location but during a more windy time.

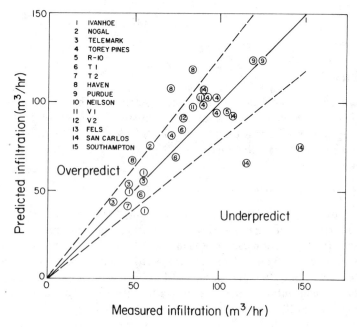

FIG. 1—*Short-term measurements below 150 m³/h.*

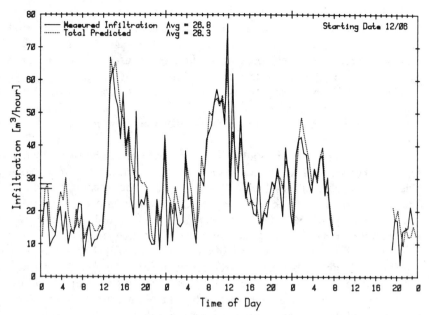

FIG. 2—*Predicted versus measured infiltration for a calm period.*

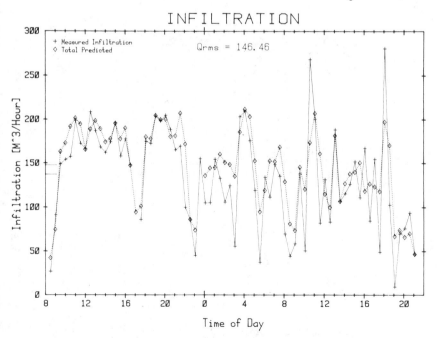

FIG. 3—*Predicted versus measured infiltration for a windy period.*

Both Figs. 2 and 3 show that the model has good tracking ability and can follow increases in infiltration caused by changes in the temperature and wind speed. Furthermore, the measured and predicted averages for the displayed data sets agree very closely; comparing these two figures indicates that the model behaves well over a wide range of infiltration rates.

Because MITU has a very simple, specially built structure, agreement of model predictions with MITU data is insufficient to validate the model. We, therefore, have used long-term data from other sources to help validate our model.

Figure 4 shows a set of data measured in an occupied test house in Rochester, New York [11]. This project was a joint effort with the New York State Energy Research and Development Authority and the Rochester Gas and Electric Company. Even though the predicted infiltration does not agree as well as it did with the MITU data, the model again tracks quite well and gives reasonable results considering the complications of occupancy.

We have used one additional set of long-term data [12] supplied to us by the Owens-Corning Fiberglas research center in Granville, Ohio. It consists of hourly data taken for 1 year on three (A, B, C) similar unoccupied houses.

Except in a very general way, the predicted and measured infiltration do not agree well. A close inspection of the data reveals a periodicity of the measured infiltration that does not match any periodicity of the weather patterns (Fig. 5). This periodicity, however, does match that of the system used to

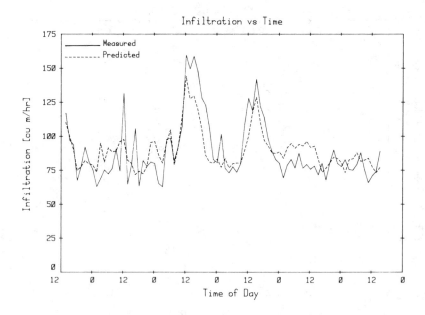

FIG. 4—*Predicted versus measured infiltration for Rochester house.*

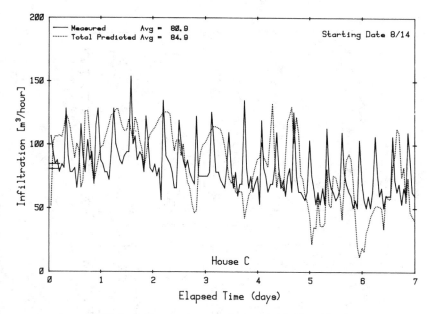

FIG. 5—*Infiltration for a one-week period in House C.*

inject and sample the tracer gas for the infiltration measurements. Unfortunately, this periodicity obscures the time-series behavior and, therefore, is unsuitable for tracking comparison.

Long-term Average

Although the tracking ability of a model is one of the most important validation aspects, the average behavior of the model over the long term can be as important. All the data points shown so far are individual points spaced no more than 1 h apart. In order to compare model behavior as we time average short-term infiltration variations, we group points together into rolling averages and compute the ratio of average predicted to average measured infiltration for different numbers of points. We then can make a histogram of the frequency of occurrence versus the ratio. In Figs. 6 through 9, we show histograms of the MITU data and the three Owens-Corning houses for unaveraged (that is, one point), one-day average, and one-week average data.

Figure 6(top) is a histogram of the half-hour measured points from MITU. The (geometric) mean of the ratio is 1.17, indicating that the mean of the distribution is 17% high. The spread factor of 1.34 indicates that there is a 34% spread around that mean. The shape of the distribution is recognizably Gaussian, indicating that the errors are reasonably random. As we move to longer term averages, the distribution becomes more peaked, indicating that

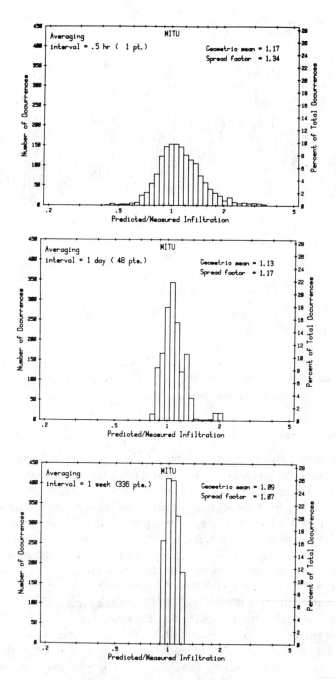

FIG. 6—*Histogram of MITU case.*

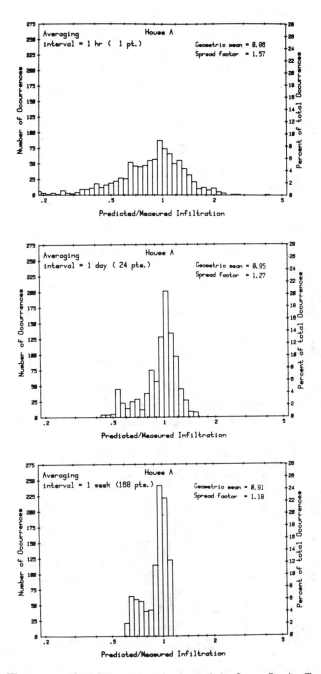

FIG. 7—*Histograms at three different averaging intervals for Owens-Corning Test House A.*

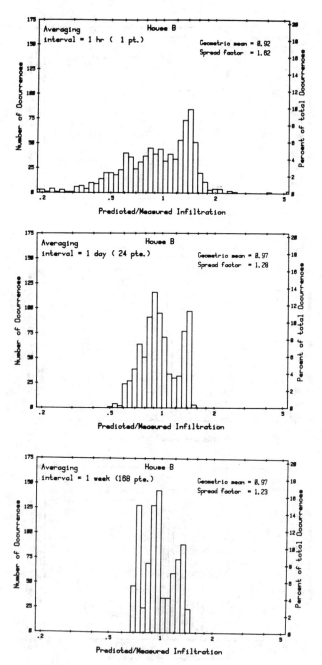

FIG. 8—*Histograms at three different averaging intervals for Owens-Corning Test House B.*

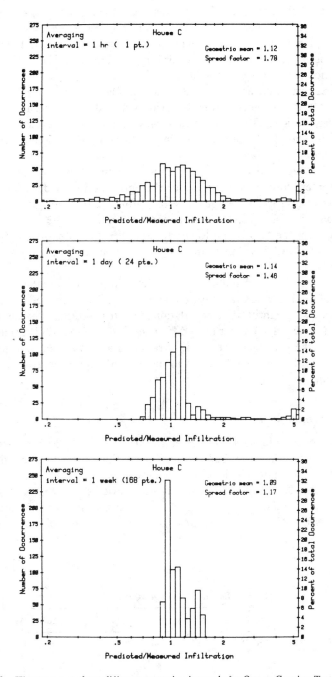

FIG. 9—*Histograms at three different averaging intervals for Owens-Corning Test House C.*

the spread of values is decreasing; furthermore, the mean value is approaching unity, suggesting perfect agreement. For one-week averages, the mean is only 9% high with a 7% spread around it. While it is expected that the distribution should become more peaked for longer averages, it is encouraging to see that the mean error gets smaller.

The next three figures (Figs. 7, 8, 9) are similar histograms for the three houses (A, B, C). In general, their behavior is the same; the spread decreases with longer averages. The mean values, however, are not as close to unity as they were for the MITU case, and (perhaps as a result of the periodicity) their shape is not as Gaussian.

If we take long-term average comparisons to their extreme, we get only one set of numbers to compare—those for the entire period of data taking. In Table 3 we compare the average measured infiltration, the average predicted infiltration, and the predicted average infiltration.

Note that for the MITU and Rochester data the three measures of infiltration agree to about 3%, but in the other three houses there is up to a 15% discrepancy.

The average measured and average predicted infiltration are the numerical averages of the individually measured data points. The predicted average infiltration is a single infiltration calculation made from average weather conditions (that is, average temperature difference and average wind speed). The accuracy of the predicted average infiltration is a measure of how good an estimate of infiltration will be when using only the average weather data for that period.

Detailed Examination

The previous sections have indicated the accuracy of the LBL model in an overall sense. We, however, can extract information about the strengths and weaknesses of the model by looking at a large set of data in great detail; only the MITU data set is both sufficiently large and well-defined. A detailed examination of this data set and comparison with a computer simulation already has been carried out [13], and some of the results will be presented herein.

TABLE 3—*Long-term average infiltration, m^3/h.*

Site	Average Measured	Average Predicted	Predicted Average
MITU	32.5	34.4	32.9
Rochester	89.7	89.4	82.9
House A	74.4	66.9	68.1
House B	72.9	75.7	80.3
House C	87.4	99.4	101.1

The entire MITU data sets from the winters of 1981 and 1982 have been used in this examination. The overall accuracy is given in Table 4.

The mean error is a measure of the bias of the model, that is, how far an average prediction will be from the true value (as given by the measured value). The standard deviation of the errors is a measure of the scatter of the model, or the range of error over which an individual prediction will vary. The smaller the bias, the better the long-term average prediction; thus, if only annual averages are desired, the only criterion for choosing a model would be its bias. The scatter, on the other hand, is a measure of how well the model follows short-term changes (that is, how well the model tracks).

The usefulness of this data set comes from the fact that it can be used to determine some of the sources of error (and, therefore, possible corrections) in the model.

Figure 10 bins all of the data by the measured infiltration value and then finds the mean error for each set of binned data. Any trend would indicate some systematic error in the model that scales with the actual infiltration. Since the infiltration is an indication of the total pressure across the leaks in the structure, any systematic error in the estimation of flow rate as a function of pressure could cause the observed trend. The fact that the trend in the error is downward with increasing infiltration implies that the model overpredicts at low pressures (that is, less than 4 Pa) and underpredicts at high pressures. This is traceable to the fact that the LBL model assumes an exponent of 0.5, and the measured exponent for MITU is 0.65.

Another source of error in a model can come from the calculation of infiltration in different regimes: specifically, stack- and wind-dominated flows. Figure 11 bins the data according to the ratio of stack-induced to wind-induced infiltration: a low value means wind-dominated flow and a high value implies stack-dominated flow. As in the previous figure, there are clear trends to the data. At very low values of the ratio, the model underpredicts; this is traceable to the choice of an average aspect ratio in the model, when, in fact, using the exact aspect ratio would improve the result. At stack/wind ratios

TABLE 4—*Measured infiltration versus LBL model predictions, m^3/h.*

Data Set	1981	1982	Total
Mean of measurements	40.4	45.4	42.7
Standard deviation of measurements	31.3 (77%)	40.9 (90%)	36.1 (85%)
Mean of predictions	45.1	49.1	46.8
Standard deviation of predictions	24.0	31.8	27.8
Mean of errors	4.7 (12%)	3.7 (8%)	4.1 (10%)
Standard deviation of errors	10.0 (25%)	13.5 (30%)	11.8 (28%)

NOTE—All percentages are relative to the mean measured infiltration.

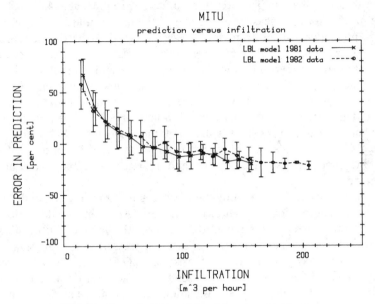

FIG. 10—*Errors in LBL model as a function of infiltration.*

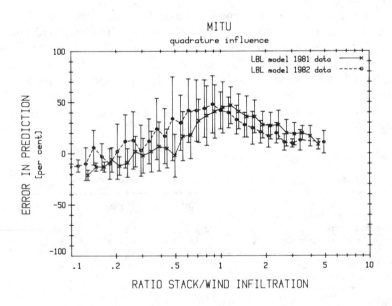

FIG. 11—*Errors in LBL model as a function of stack/wind ratio.*

near unity (that is, where the stack and wind effects are equivalent) the model overpredicts; this is traceable to the empirical method used to combine stack and wind effects (that is, quadrature addition), instead of a point-by-point addition of pressures (which would be impractical for a simplified model).

Wind direction can have a strong effect on the accuracy of any infiltration model. In the LBL model, wind direction is averaged, but the effects of that assumption can be seen by plotting the average error for different wind angle bins. In Fig. 12 we can see that for the simple rectangle of MITU the wind direction dependence is quite similar to the sinusoidal curve that one might estimate from first principles.

Future Work

In addition to defining the current accuracy of the infiltration model, the validation effort has indicated areas for future research. More work is necessary in the area of flow interactions; although each source of ventilation (that is, stack-induced, wind-induced, and mechanically induced supply and exhaust) may affect the pressure across the envelope differently, the LBL model combines them in a simple manner. The accuracy of this procedure should be investigated further, and modifications may be necessary to increase it. As shown in the detailed examination, other areas that could benefit from fur-

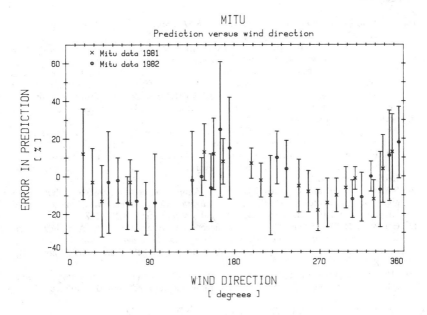

FIG. 12—*Errors in LBL model as a function of wind angle.*

ther study are directional dependence, wind-pressure coefficients, and flow-exponent calculations.

Summary

In this report we have presented the LBL infiltration model and have used field data to validate it. For short-term measurements, the model predicts to within 20% for well-defined environments (for example, the MITU trailer) and slightly higher for other situations. The long-term averages, however, tend to be more accurate. In MITU, the long-term (one week) average infiltration is accurate to 7%; in the Owens-Corning houses the long-term average error increases to up to 15%. A detailed examination of the LBL model using data from the MITU was used to probe the model and to suggest areas for future research.

Acknowledgment

This work was funded by the assistant secretary for Conservation and Community Systems, Buildings Division Office of Buildings and Community Systems, U.S. Department of Energy, under Contract No. DE-AC03-76SF00098.

References

[1] Sherman, M. H. and Grimsrud, D. T., *ASHRAE Transactions*, 86,II, 1980, pp. 778-807 (Lawrence Berkeley Laboratory Report, LBL-10163).
[2] Sherman, M. H., "Air Infiltration in Buildings," Ph.D thesis, University of California, 1980 (Lawrence Berkeley Laboratory Report, LBL-10712).
[3] Sherman, M. H., Grimsrud, D. T., and Sonderegger, R. C., "The Low Pressure Leakage Function of a Building," in *Proceedings of the DOE/ASHRAE Conference on the Thermal Performance Exterior Envelope of Buildings*, ASHRAE SP 28, American Society of Heating, Refrigerating and Air Conditioning Engineers, Atlanta, 1979 (Lawrence Berkeley Laboratory Report, LBL-9162).
[4] Akins, R. E., Peterka, J. A., and Cermak, J. E., in *Proceedings of the Fifth International Conference on Wind Engineering*, Pergamon Press, Elmsford, NY, 1980, pp. 369-380.
[5] "Recommendations for the Calculation of Wind Effects on Buildings and Structures," European Convention for Constructional Steelwork, Technical General Secretariat, Brussels, Belgium, Sept. 1978.
[6] Sherman, M. H. and Grimsrud, D. T., "A Comparison of Alternate Ventilation Strategies," in *Proceedings of the Third Air Infiltration Centre Conference*, London, United Kingdom, Sept. 1982 (Lawrence Berkeley Laboratory Report, LBL-13678).
[7] Grimsrud, D. T., Sherman, M. H., Blomsterberg, A. K., and Rosenfeld, A. H. in *Proceedings of the International Conference on Energy Use Management*, Vol. III, Pergamon Press, Elmsford, NY, 1979, pp. 1351-58, (Lawrence Berkeley Laboratory Report, LBL-9157).
[8] "Demonstration of Energy Conservation through Reduction of Air Infiltration in Electrically-Heated Houses," RP 1351-1, Johns-Mansville Research and Development Center, Denver, CO, 1979.
[9] Tamura, G. T., *ASHRAE Transactions*, 85,I, 1979, pp. 58-71.

[10] Blomsterberg, A. K., Modera, M. P., and Grimsrud, D. T., "The Mobile Infiltration Test Unit—Its Design and Capabilities: Preliminary Experimental Results," LBL-12259, Lawrence Berkeley Laboratory, Berkeley, CA, Jan. 1981.

[11] Sherman, M. H., Modera, M. P., and Grimsrud, D. T. in *Proceedings of the Third International CIB Symposium on Energy Conservation in the Built Environment*, Vol. VI, An Foras Forbartha, Dublin, 1982, pp. 6.A.1–10 (Lawrence Berkeley Laboratory Report, LBL-13520).

[12] Modera, M. P., Sherman, M. H., and Grimsrud, D. T., *ASHRAE Transactions*, 88,I, 1982, pp. 1351–72 (Lawrence Berkeley Laboratory Report, LBL-13509).

[13] Modera, M. P., Sherman, M. H., and Levin, P. A., "A Detailed Examination of the LBL Infiltration Model using the Mobile Infiltration Test Unit," *ASHRAE Transactions*, 89, 1983 (Lawrence Berkeley Laboratory Report, LBL-15636, 1983).

Max H. Sherman, [1] *David J. Wilson,* [2] *and Darwin E. Kiel* [2]

Variability in Residential Air Leakage

REFERENCE: Sherman, M. H., Wilson, D. J., and Kiel, D. E., "**Variability in Residential Air Leakage,**" *Measured Air Leakage of Buildings, ASTM STP 904*, H. R. Trechsel and P. L. Lagus, Eds., American Society for Testing and Materials, Philadelphia, 1986, pp. 349–364.

ABSTRACT: Air leakage is the single most important quantity in the determination of air infiltration in residential structures. Air leakage is most commonly measured using the fan pressurization technique [ASTM Method for Determining Air Leakage Rate by Fan Pressurization Test (E 779-81)]; the data gathered with this method are often used to determine a leakage constant and a flow exponent. In this report, data gathered from the literature are compiled into a list of leakage constants and flow exponents, and the variability of these values over climate and housing types are examined.

KEY WORDS: air leakage measurements

Conventional wisdom holds that infiltration, which is characterized by the process of air leakage, accounts for about one third of the space conditioning load of residential buildings. Over the past several years, researchers have measured the airtightness of many houses using the technique known as fan pressurization [ASTM Method for Determining Air Leakage Rate by Fan Pressurization Test (E 779-81)]. Fan pressurization measurements, often known as blower door measurements, give a quantitative estimate of building tightness, which is independent of climate and weather.

For this report we have gathered all the fan pressurization measurements at our disposal. This large data set is used to draw conclusions based on statistical inference. We have used this data set to compare measurements made on individual houses throughout North America.

[1] Staff scientist, Lawrence Berkeley Laboratory, Berkeley, CA 94720.
[2] Professor and graduate student, respectively, Department of Mechanical Engineering, University of Edmonton, Alberta, Canada.

Data Reduction

In most fan pressurization measurements, the flow through the building is recorded as a function of pressure for several (for example, five) different pressures, typically in the range of 10 to 50 Pa [1.02 to 5.08 mm (0.04 to 0.2 in.) of water]. The measurements are usually made for both pressurization (that is, blowing air through the fan into the house) and depressurization (that is, sucking air through the fan out of the house), although some data are for unidirectional flow only. Empirically it has been found that the data follow a power law expression, and, accordingly, the most common data reduction technique is a least-squares regression to a power law

$$Q = C\Delta p^n \tag{1}$$

On physical grounds we expect the exponent to lie between 0.5 (for orifice flow) and 1.0 (for fully developed/long pipe laminar flow). It is interesting to note that simple power law correlations of blower door tests occasionally yield exponents less than the Bernoulli limit of 0.5. In fact, it is physically possible for such low exponents to occur. For example, flow through orifice meters in pipes at Reynolds numbers greater than 1000 have orifice coefficients which decrease with Reynolds number, leading to a flow-pressure difference exponent less than 0.5.

Although the parameters C and n describe the fan pressurization data, they do not have a simple physical interpretation. For this reason many users prefer to use one simple physical parameter to describe the leakage, even though complete generality is sacrificed. One of the most common single leakage parameters currently in use is the effective leakage area (ELA); we use the symbol A_1 in our equations. It is defined by assuming a Bernoulli equation approximation to Eq 1

$$Q = A_1 \sqrt{\frac{2\Delta p}{\rho}} \tag{2}$$

at a specific reference pressure Δp_{ref}. The ELA of a leak or group of leaks can be thought of as the amount of open area that would allow the same flow at the reference pressure difference. Equating Eqs 1 and 2 at the reference pressure difference gives A_1 in terms of the leakage coefficient and the exponent

$$A_1 = C_1^0 (\Delta p_{ref})^{n-0.5} \tag{3}$$

Because ELA is in more common usage than the leakage coefficient and exponent, all the data presented in following paragraphs are in terms of ELA, with 4 Pa as the reference pressure difference. (Since extrapolations tend to increase the error of the quantity, a measurement at a higher pressure such as

50 Pa would be more precise. Unfortunately, the physical quantity of import is the flow in the natural pressure range around 4 Pa. We, therefore, must sacrifice some precision for physical modeling.)

Because ELA is an extensive property of a building envelope, we will not be able to compare the values for different houses unless we properly normalize the leakage area. Several schemes for normalizing leakage area have been suggested: (1) by volume, (2) by envelope area, and (3) by floor area. Although normalization by envelope area is probably the most physically significant approach, for practicality we have elected to use floor area as our normalization criterion. (Floor area is the most commonly quoted building characteristic.) Furthermore, floor area and envelope area should correlate rather well for single-family buildings. We therefore define the specific leakage as the ratio between the ELA, A_1, and the floor area, A_f.

Data Base of Tested Houses

An initial data base of over 700 houses and over 1000 measurements was extracted from the literature and from unpublished data of research efforts known to the authors over a several year period. Not all the data, however, were used in the final analysis; three criteria had to be met for the data to be accepted in our sample: sufficiency, reliability, and background. The data had to contain both the leakage value (for example, A_1, C, etc.) and the exponent or the data would be rejected. The data had to be reliable in the sense that either all necessary information was in the archival literature or the researchers that took the data were available and able to answer questions. Finally, there had to be sufficient background about the houses, including age, type of construction, etc.

From the large number of reported pressurization tests, a data base was selected for which the physical characteristics of the house were adequately described and for which data were available for both the coefficient C (or the leakage area A_1) and the flow exponent n. Because many investigators fail to report the flow exponent for each house tested when quoting ELA, this requirement limited the size of the data base. Surprisingly, it also was difficult to find data sets which adequately described the construction details of each house tested. While it would seem obvious that air-leakage measurements only can be interpreted if details of the house envelope construction are known, much of the existing data on blower door tests give only a vague real-estate–type description of house construction. In any case where the data appeared insufficient, an attempt was made to contact the appropriate researcher to clarify any insufficiencies.

Although some data were rejected because of the criteria, the authors know of no large data set that was not considered. The final data base selected consisted of 515 houses (about two thirds of the initial set), about two thirds in Canada and one third in the United States. The specific locations of the

TABLE 1—*Data base composition.*

United States			Canada		
	Sample Size			Sample Size	
Location	$-\Delta P^a$	$+\Delta P$	Location	$-\Delta P$	$+\Delta P$
Oroville, CA	56	56	Saskatoon, Sask.	176	...
Rochester, NY	50	50	Ottawa, Ont.	67	...
Davis, CA	32	32	Winnipeg, Man.	51	...
Eugene, OR	24	24	Edmonton, Alta.	11	11
San Francisco, CA	16	16			
Atlanta, GA	7	7			
Waterbury, VT	...	25			
Total	184	210	Total	305	11

$^a-\Delta P$ = depressurization; $+\Delta P$ = pressurization.

houses and sample sizes are listed in Table 1, where the trend to a single depressurization test for Canadian houses clearly is evident. The Canadian data base was assembled using measurements from Dumont et al [1], Beach [2], and unpublished data of Wilson and Kiel. Houses in the United States were tabulated from Lipschutz et al [3], Offermann et al [4], Diamond [5], and Turner et al [6].

Because our goal was to assemble the largest possible data set, no attempt was made to ensure that the data set so gathered would be representative of any particular housing stock. The United States' data are biased towards houses from the warmer West Coast climate, while the reverse was true for the Canadian houses, all of which were located in the cold continental climate of central Canada. As might be expected, this led to dramatic differences between the leakage areas for Canadian and U.S. data sets.

Pressurization Versus Depressurization

Before we compare the leakages of different houses, we can address one issue for an individual house—pressurization versus depressurization. Because of valve action and the presence of wind and stack pressures during the measurement, we expect that the two techniques may yield different results. We can use our data set to estimate both the systematic error (bias) and random error (scatter) associated with using one process instead of both. To examine these differences, the 196 houses with both pressurization and depressurization measurements were analyzed to determine the specific leakage and flow exponent. The results are summarized in Table 2. We see that for this large sample there is no significant difference in either the flow exponent or the leakage area determined from depressurization and pressurization measurements.

TABLE 2—*Comparison of pressurization and depressurization,*
sample size: 196 houses.

	Flow Exponent, n	Leakage Area, cm^2/m^2
Pressurization	0.66 ± 0.09^a	5.9 ± 3.8
Depressurization	0.66 ± 0.08	5.6 ± 3.4

[a]Sample standard deviation.

One of the best methods for quantifying the bias and scatter of the data is to construct a histogram of the ratio of the pressurization leakage area, A_1^+, to depressurization leakage area, A_1^-; Fig. 1A is such a histogram. The mean of this data set indicates the bias between pressurization and depressurization. The fact that the mean is 1.05 indicates that for this data set the pressurization results are 5% higher on average than those from depressurization. Since this bias is small, we can conclude that there is little systematic difference between pressurization or depressurization. Thus, if we are interested in finding the mean leakage area of a large set of data, there are only small differences between using pressurization or depressurization or both; the mean value should be accurate.

Although a mean near unity in Fig. 1A indicates that there is little systematic error, the large standard deviation indicates a significant amount of random error. The data set indicates that for an individual pair of pressurization/depressurization measurements, we can expect a 29% difference between them (direction unknown). Equivalently, a single measurement (either pressurization or depressurization) can be expected to differ by 14% from the average of the two. Thus a single-direction measurement of leakage area has an extra 14% error associated with it. One contributing factor for this scatter is likely to be wind induced.

Figure 1B shows the distribution of the ratio of the pressurization exponent to the depressurization exponent, made in a manner analogous to the just-mentioned distribution. The mean of the exponent distribution of 1.02 indicates that the pressurization exponent is only 2% greater on average than the depressurization exponent—well within measurement error. While smaller than the previous scatter of 29%, the standard deviation in the exponent of 15% is still significant. Thus, the exponent distribution corroborates the conclusion of the previous two paragraphs: that there is no systematic difference between pressurization and depressurization, but that significant uncertainty is associated with an individual measurement.

Data Variability

Because the previous section has shown us that there is no systematic bias between pressurization and depressurization, each of these tests could be con-

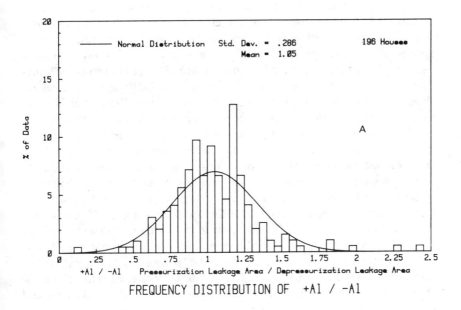

FREQUENCY DISTRIBUTION OF +Al / -Al

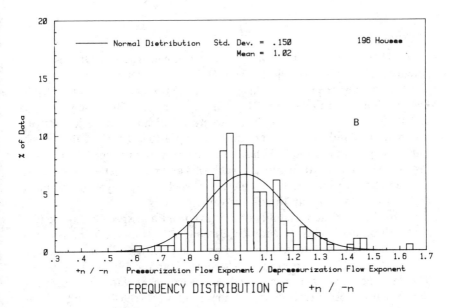

FREQUENCY DISTRIBUTION OF +n / -n

FIG. 1—*Frequency distribution of the ratio of pressurization to depressurization for* (A) *effective leakage area and* (B) *flow exponent.*

sidered as a separate sample point to expand the data base without changing mean values or trends. Furthermore, because a large amount of scatter is associated with single-direction measurements, inclusion of both pressurization and depressurization as independent measurements decreases the random error in the sample. By expanding the data base in this way, we obtain 395 sample measurements for U.S. houses and 316 measurements for Canadian houses. The frequency distribution histograms for these 711 samples are shown in Fig. 2. While the normal Gaussian probability distribution is a reasonably good fit to the variability of flow exponent n, it is clearly inappropriate for the highly-skewed distribution of specific leakage A_1/A_f in Fig. 2.

The mean flow exponent of 0.67 confirms the widely held assumption that a flow exponent near 0.65 is typical of air infiltration leakage sites. On the other hand, the mean and variability of the specific leakage in Fig. 2 is difficult to interpret. With a wide range of construction types, ranging from tight northern Canadian houses to rather loose California housing, and construction dates that range from 1850 for one house in the Vermont sample to 1982 for the Oroville houses, the high variability in specific leakage is not unexpected.

It is clear from an inspection of the specific leakage that in order to understand the cause of the variability, we must disaggregate the sample. Two of the most reasonable (and, fortunately, available) criteria are building age and construction type. In the two sections that follow, we will investigate the effects these two factors have on specific leakage.

Building Age

Of 711 tests, a total of 613 listed the year of construction. Of these measurements, 297 were made in the United States and 316 were made in Canada. The data were sorted into age groups using the system recommended by Dumont, Orr, and Figley in 1981 [1]. This system identified the years 1945 and 1960 as approximate boundaries where significant changes in construction materials and methods were made. For pre-1945 housing, the interior walls were generally lathe and plaster with no air-vapor barrier. In the period 1946 to 1960, a mixture of gypsum wallboard and wax paper vapor retarders were employed, while after 1960 most construction used gypsum wallboard and (when installed) polyethylene air-vapor barriers.

Figure 3 shows the variability of flow exponent and specific leakage (A_1/A_f) for these age groups. In addition, 91 houses (51 from the Winnipeg sample and 40 from Saskatoon) identified as "energy efficient" are shown separately as well as included in the 554 samples from the 1961 to 1983 period. The data show that there is no trend in flow exponent with age of construction. What is most surprising is that houses built between 1961 and 1983 are no tighter than the group from 1946 to 1960. However, with only 26 houses in the 1946 to 1960 sample, it is difficult to be sure of any trend. What is clear is that the Canadian houses classified as energy efficient are much tighter than

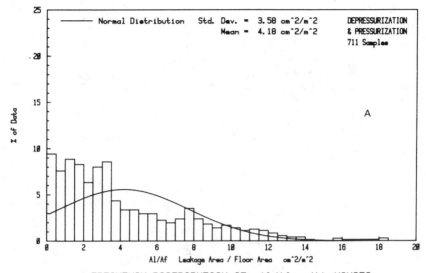

FREQUENCY DISTRIBUTION OF A1/Af : ALL HOUSES

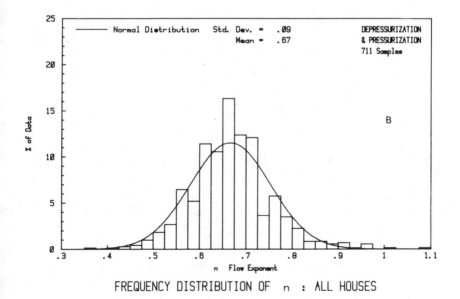

FREQUENCY DISTRIBUTION OF n : ALL HOUSES

FIG. 2—*Frequency distribution of entire sample of houses for* (A) *specific leakage and* (B) *flow exponent.*

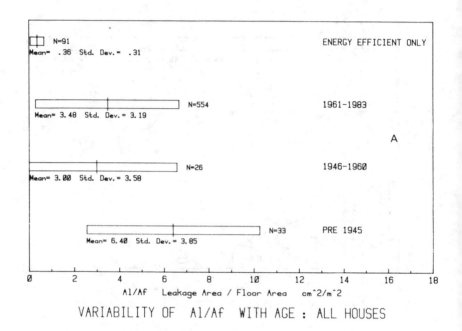

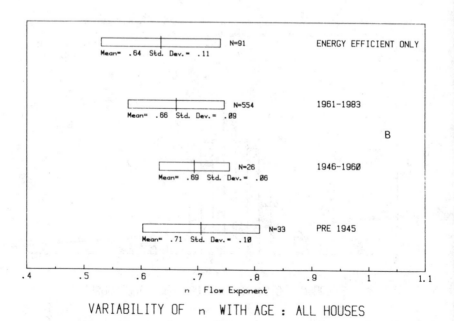

FIG. 3—*Disaggregation for entire sample by age for* (A) *specific leakage and* (B) *flow exponent.*

the general housing stock, with a mean leakage ten times less than the overall average.

The effect of climate on house construction is apparent in Fig. 4, which shows the variability of specific leakage for housing in the United States and Canada. For recent housing, built between 1961 and 1983, Canadian houses are twice as tight as their U.S. counterparts. One interesting point is that blower-door tests in both countries tend to focus on new housing (built after 1961), rather than on older houses that might benefit more from retrofit programs. There is a need to expand the data base by testing a larger proportion of older housing so that the overall sample properly reflects the mix of ages in North American housing.

Construction Type

The second criterion selected for disaggregating the data was construction type. Of the 711 houses in the sample, 519 had wall construction specified. These samples were divided into five construction types, listed below in order of increasing tightness:

1. Walls without integral vapor barriers.
2. Walls with a vapor barrier.
3. Walls with vapor barrier and exterior foam insulation sheathing.
4. Double wall construction.
5. Supertight houses using blower door pressurization during construction.

Figure 5A presents the specific leakage for each of these five categories. It is encouraging that, as expected, the leakage area decreases with improved construction. The most significant reduction in leakage area occurs with the addition of a single interior vapor barrier which reduces the leakage area by more than a factor of three. One surprising result is the effect of adding exterior insulating-foam sheathing, which results in another 40% decrease in leakage area. Finally, the supertight houses demonstrate conclusively that the use of blower door pressurization methods during construction can increase the tightness of a standard air vapor barrier by more than a factor of ten. Given the incentive and a means of measuring their own performance with an on-site blower door, construction crews were able to achieve a remarkable level of quality workmanship.

As shown in the lowest three bars of Fig. 5B, the flow exponent also showed some of the expected trend. As one examines the data from no vapor barrier to a vapor barrier plus sheathing, the exponent increases, as would be expected if the size of the leaks was decreasing. Although the double wall houses are tighter than the vapor barrier plus sheathing house, the flow exponent is about the same or slightly less. A possible explanation for this is that leaks in double wall houses may have to go through a separate leak in each wall. Thus the exponent may not increase even though the flow resistance does. Further-

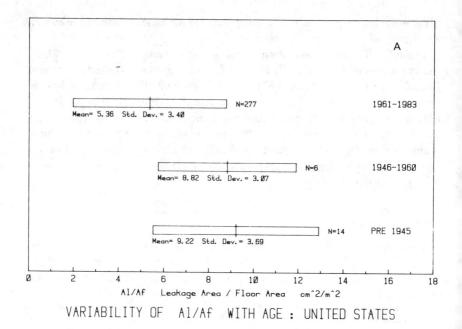

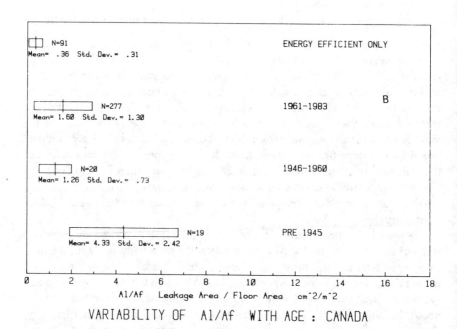

FIG. 4—*Disaggregation of specific leakage by age for* (A) *United States and* (B) *Canada.*

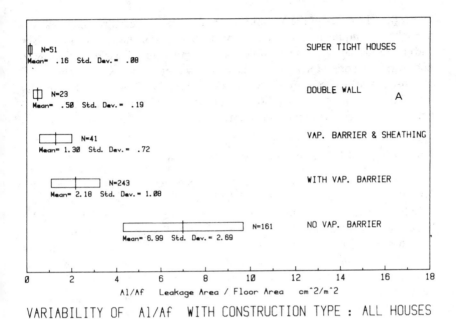

VARIABILITY OF Al/Af WITH CONSTRUCTION TYPE : ALL HOUSES

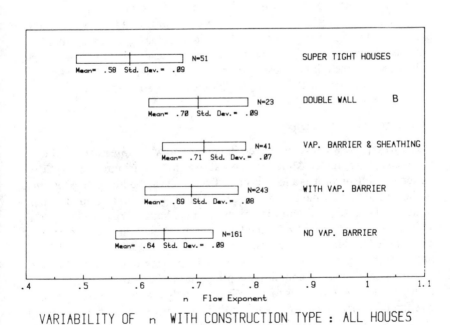

VARIABILITY OF n WITH CONSTRUCTION TYPE : ALL HOUSES

FIG. 5—*Disaggregation of entire sample by construction type for* (A) *specific leakage and* (B) *flow exponent.*

more, the 51 houses in the Winnipeg sample that were constructed using supertight techniques had a mean exponent lower than the very leaky houses with no vapor barrier. One possible reason for this behavior is that the blower door was being operated below its normal flow range. Because the calibration of most blower doors cannot be trusted at these low flow rates, the results must be viewed with some caution. Future studies must be examined to see if either of these effects can be substantiated.

Correlating Specific Leakage and Flow Exponent

If we compare the exponent and specific leakage variability-by-construction plots, we see that there is a slight trend of lower exponents for higher specific leakages. This suggests that loose houses might be dominated by large holes in the building envelope and behave like orifice flow, while very tight houses would be dominated by small cracks and behave like laminar flow. With this in mind, we ought to see a general decrease in flow exponent from 1.0 to 0.5 as specific leakage increases. To investigate this possibility we have plotted the exponent as a function of the specific leakage in Figs. 6A and 6B for all houses. Although the large variability of the flow exponent obscures most of it, this expected trend is visible—with a little imagination.

The only major exception to this trend is the set of supertight homes from Winnipeg. As just mentioned, these 51 Winnipeg houses represent a very special case in which blower door depressurization was used to carry out vapor barrier tightening during the construction of the house while the vapor barrier was still exposed on the inside walls. While it is clear that this is a remarkably successful technique, these houses are so tight that it is difficult to apply any generalizations for the other 464 houses to this specific group.

Summary and Conclusions

In this report, we have used over 500 homes on which pressurization measurements were made. Although the data set has contributed much to the understanding of air leakage, it is not reflective of the building stock because of the type of houses that are measured and recorded and thus cannot be used to define the leakage distribution of the average house. We have shown that while specific leakage (ELA divided by floor area) may vary over an order of magnitude (see Fig. 2A), the flow exponent appears to have a normal distribution with a mean of 0.67 and a standard deviation of 0.09 (see Fig. 2B). The data confirm the common perception that the average flow exponent is between 0.65 and 0.68; this fact can be especially useful when trying to analyze fan pressurization data when insufficient information on the exponent is available.

We used the data to compare pressurization and depressurization; we found that on average there was only a 5% difference between pressurization and depressurization, but for any single measurement there was a 28% difference (see Fig. 1*A*). Since an additional 28% is not usually acceptable, our results suggest that both pressurization and depressurization should be employed whenever any information about an individual structure is desired. For those few occasions when no information about an individual house is desired (for example, to determine the total energy use of a master metered complex), some savings may be realized with no loss of accuracy by using the pressurization technique in only one direction. (Note that ASTM E 779 requires both directions to be used.) Potentially, more research into the cause of random variability of pressurization and depressurization results could allow a single measurement of either to be used in more general circumstances.

In an attempt to categorize the variability of the leakage, we disaggregated the sample by both age and construction type. We found little significant correlation of leakage with age when the age categories used were pre-1945, 1945 to 1960, and post-1960 (see Fig. 3). It is interesting to speculate whether any correlation would develop if the post-1960 data were broken down by decade. Further measurement of new homes (that is, post-1980) would be needed to investigate such a possibility. When we broke down the data by age and country (that is, United States and Canada), we discovered the unsurprising result that in the colder climate the houses are tighter (see Fig. 4).

Some of the observed differences between U.S. and Canadian results might be traceable to the different way in which the tests were made and the different way in which the houses were used. Most of the Canadian measurements were done with all international ventilation sites taped; most of the U.S. tests were done with dampers closed but rarely taped. These differences are a result of the different standard test methods used in the two countries. A contributing effect is that most Canadians have fully conditioned and utilized basements (which tend to have few leaks) while most U.S. housing does not. This difference is especially important when the building volume is being calculated.

The examination of the effect of construction type on the variability produced the expected result; the specific leakage decreased through the five categories (no vapor barrier, vapor barrier, vapor barrier with sheathing, double wall, and supertight). The mean value of these categories can serve as a guideline for designers attempting to design for a certain tightness level (see Fig. 5). With the exception of the two tightest categories, the exponent also behaved as expected. The reason for the unexpected behavior in the two tightest categories is not clear; the two hypotheses are: (1) these tight houses have many cracks in series that do not necessary cause increased flow exponents for tighter configurations; and (2) the blower doors were operating below their valid range, and calibration errors may cause the variability. More accurate measurements of fan pressurization of very tight houses must be done in order to explain this result.

The fact that the exponent generally goes down as the leakage goes up led

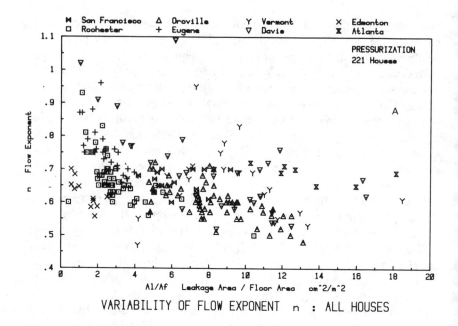

VARIABILITY OF FLOW EXPONENT n : ALL HOUSES

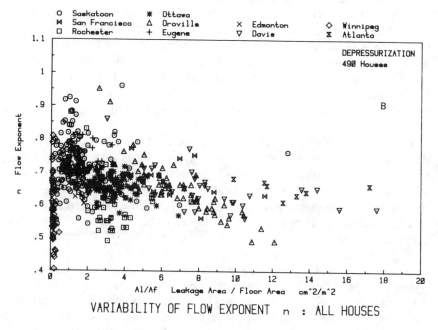

VARIABILITY OF FLOW EXPONENT n : ALL HOUSES

FIG. 6—*Correlation of flow exponent with specific leakage for* (A) *pressurization and* (B) *depressurization.*

us to attempt a simple, qualitative correlation between specific leakage and flow exponent (Figs. 6A, 6B). With the exception of the supertight houses, there does appear to be a correlation, albeit not a strong one (see Figs. 6A, 6B). If a strong correlation existed, auditors or other blower door users would be able to make single point measurements of flow versus pressure and accurately calculate ELA. Because this simplification would speed greatly the process of fan pressurization, the authors plan to investigate the possibility in greater depth.

The amount of data currently available on envelope leaking is still quite small so that the authors view this collection and analysis of leakage data as an on-going and necessary effort. We intend to continue the effort of cataloging and analyzing leakage data and would encourage those with significant data sets to make them available for this effort.

Acknowledgments

This study was supported by research grants from Energy Mines and Resources Canada, Grant EMR-305, and the Natural Sciences and Engineering Research Council of Canada, Grant A8438. Assistance from a Canada Mortgage and Housing Corp. scholarship to Darwin E. Kiel is gratefully acknowledged. Funds from the assistant secretary for conservation and renewable energy, Office of Building Energy Research and Development, Buildings Systems Division of the U.S. Department of Energy under Contract No. DE-AC03-76SF00098 provided joint support.

The cooperation of William Turner of Harvard University, Rick Diamond of Lawrence Berkeley Laboratory, and Gren Yuill of G. K. Yuill Associates Winnipeg, who provided their original data sets, contributed to the success of the study.

References

[1] Dumont, R. S., Orr, H. W., and Figley, D. A., "Air Tightness Measurements of Detached Houses in the Saskatoon Area," Note No. 178, National Research Council of Canada, Division of Building Research, Ottawa, 1981.
[2] Beach, R. K., "Relative Tightness of New Housing in the Ottawa Area," Note No. 149, National Research Council of Canada, Division of Building Research, Ottawa, 1979.
[3] Lipschutz, R. D., Girman, J. R., Dickinson, J. B., Allen, J. R. and Traynor, G. W., "Infiltration and Indoor Air Quality in Energy Efficient Houses in Eugene, Oregon," LBL-12924, Lawrence Berkeley Laboratory, Berkeley, CA, 1981.
[4] Offermann, F. J. et al, "Residential Air Leakage and Indoor Air Quality in Rochester, New York," LBL-13100, Lawrence Berkeley Laboratory, Berkeley, CA, 1982.
[5] Diamond, R. C., "Energy and Housing for the Elderly: Preliminary Observations," EPB Report, Lawrence Berkeley Laboratory, Berkeley, CA, 1983.
[6] Turner, W. A., Treitman, R. D., Bearg, D., Sexton, K., and Spengler, J. D., "Home Energy Efficiency and Indoor/Outdoor Air Pollution in a Predominantly Wood Burning Community," Harvard University Department of Environmental Science and Physiology Report, Cambridge, MA, 1982.

DISCUSSION

D. Saum[1] *(written discussion)*—Some of the variations in the blower door measurements that you show may be due to error sources such as wind. These errors may be limited by averaging pressurization and depressurization measurements, but I am not sure your data can prove this. Would you agree? Also, is there a reference on how to select the values for parameters in the LBL model?

M. H. Sherman, D. J. Wilson, and D. E. Kiel (authors' closure)—The major sources of variation between pressurization and depressurization measurements are the valve action of some leaks and the effects of wind during the measurements. These two effects could be separated by examining the wind conditions during each test. We expect to make this examination in the future. One paper that describes the selection of parameter values in the LBL model is "Calculating Infiltration; Implications for a Construction Quality Standard," by D. T. Grimsrud, M. H. Sherman, and R. C. Sonderegger, *Proceedings*, ASHRAE/DOE conference, Thermal Performance of the Exterior Envelopes of Buildings II, Las Vegas, NV, 6-9 Dec. 1982 (LBL Report LBL-94160, Lawrence Berkeley Laboratory, Berkeley, CA).

[1]Infiltec, Waynesboro, VA.

Mark R. Bassett[1]

Building Site Measurements for Predicting Air Infiltration Rates

REFERENCE: Bassett, M. R., **"Building Site Measurements for Predicting Air Infiltration Rates,"** *Measured Air Leakage of Buildings, ASTM STP 904*, H. R. Trechsel and P. L. Lagus, Eds., American Society for Testing and Materials, Philadelphia, 1986, pp. 365–383.

ABSTRACT: This paper examines the sensitivity of the predicted air infiltration rate to measured building airtightness data and the wind exposure index determined from site inspection. Results of airtightness tests in New Zealand houses are presented to indicate the range of leakage resistance for components (windows, doors, and chimneys, etc.), for solid materials (such as wall and ceiling lining materials), and for cracks separating major components such as the floor and walls. The distribution of leakage opening is discussed in relation to the driving forces of wind- and stack-induced airflows and also in relation to New Zealand styles of house building.

The building site exposure class must be determined in order that standard wind engineering formula can be used to calculate site wind speeds from meteorological weather data recorded some distance away. In the New Zealand situation, with high wind speeds and modest indoor-outdoor temperature differences, predicted natural air infiltration rates are particularly sensitive to site exposure details. Examples of measured and predicted air change rates are given for a number of houses together with comment on the sensitivity to experimental error.

KEY WORDS: air infiltration, airtightness, air leakage in buildings

Air infiltration studies in New Zealand only recently have begun to address two prevalent problems in houses. These problems are:

1. Control of indoor moisture.
2. Winter space heat loss.

The first ranks as the most common reason for unsatisfactory house performance and is likely to be more prominent in comparatively airtight houses where windows are kept closed during colder winter periods. At the opposite

[1]Scientist, Building Research Association of New Zealand, Private Bag, Porirua, New Zealand.

end of the scale are particularly loose houses on wind-exposed sites. One way of identifying houses that could benefit from improved airtightness and those where some form of ventilation assistance is necessary is to estimate the mean air infiltration rate from building airtightness and weather information. This paper is concerned with the provision of airtightness information for New Zealand houses. It places some emphasis on the accuracy of measurements and the resolution necessary for estimates of mean air infiltration rate.

Airtightness Measurements

Test Method

The simplest method of measuring the leakage characteristics of a building employs a fan to hold a steady pressure difference between inside and outside while the leakage rate is measured. Results at a number of pressures then are combined in the form of a leakage function characteristic of the building. The total airflow resistance of the building envelope will be a parallel combination of leakage resistances through many paths, each having a characteristic leakage function that in broad terms will lie between the extremes of orifice or turbulent flow and laminar flow. These flow regimes are represented approximately by the following general equation

$$Q = C(\Delta P)^E$$

$$Q = \frac{1}{R} (\Delta P)^E$$

(1)

where

Q = volume flow, m³/s,
ΔP = pressure difference, Pa,
R = resistance to flow, Ns/m³,
C = flow coefficient, and
E = exponent between 0.5 and 1.0.

The leakage function can be quite complicated in detail, especially in the region where flow and pressure depend strongly on the Reynolds number. Nevertheless, it has become normal practice to use a simple leakage function of the just-cited form to describe the total building leakage.

Equipment

A brief summary is given here of the equipment used for blower door airtightness tests by the Building Research Association of New Zealand. Figure 1 shows the fan and airflow measuring equipment set up in a house. A 380-mm

FIG. 1—Fan and airflow measuring equipment used for airtightness test.

airfoil fan is mounted in an adjustable door panel and fixed in place in an external door opening. It is driven by a lightweight 1600-W, three-phase motor. Synchronous speed control is achieved with a controller, which synthesizes adjustable frequency, three-phase power from a standard 230-V, single-phase outlet. Airflow measurements are made from the static pressure in the throat of a long radius flow nozzle calibrated in the laboratory using ASTM Test for Average Velocity in a Duct (Pitot Tube Method) (D 3154-72). Pressures were measured using a digital manometer calibrated in 0 to 200 and 0 to 2000-Pa ranges. Each test was based on 6 to 9 indoor-outdoor pressure differences in the range 10 to 150 Pa, the lower limit being appreciably above wind pressure measured across the windward wall using an externally mounted pressure tap.

Reproducibility

An assessment has been made of the reproducibility of the blower door method, including the widely used practice of masking leakage openings around doors and windows with tape. Table 1 shows the results of a sequence of airtightness tests carried out on the same house on three separate occasions spaced about a week apart. In this case, the results are expressed as leakage areas at 50 Pa, defined as the area of sharp edge orifice required to pass the same volume flow at 50 Pa.

$$A = \frac{Q}{Cd\left(\frac{2\Delta P}{\rho}\right)^{1/2}} \qquad (2)$$

TABLE 1—*Test of reproducibility.*

Action	Leakage Area at 50 Pa, m²			
	Test A	Test B	Test C	Error
1. House with doors and windows closed	0.152	0.151	0.153	0.007
2. Same as No. 1 with cracks around openable windows and doors taped	0.096	0.096	0.097	0.005
3. Same as No. 2 with shower vent and free standing fire place flue blocked	0.086	0.084	0.086	0.004
4. Leakage area of cracks around openable windows and doors	0.056	0.055	0.056	0.003
5. Leakage area of shower vent and fire place flue	0.010	0.012	0.011	0.003

where

A = leakage area, 50 Pa/m^2,
Q = volume flow, m^3/s,
Cd = discharge coefficient = 0.6,
ρ = density of air, kg/m^3, and
P = pressure difference, Pa.

The errors listed in Table 1 are approximate 95% confidence intervals determined from the residuals of the fit between the model and experimental data points.

It can be seen that the results of three separate measurements agree within the limits of the random error, indicating that the blower door procedure can at least be satisfactorily reproduced. There are systematic errors associated with pressure and airflow measurements that add a further 2% uncertainty to approximately 5% for the random part.

Further examination of the residuals of fitting measurements to the power law equation (Eq 1) has shown that part of the error previously assigned as random is in fact serially correlated to the indoor-outdoor pressure difference.

Figure 2 indicates the size of the serially correlated error and also shows that the power law equation is accurate enough for interpolation within the range of measurement.

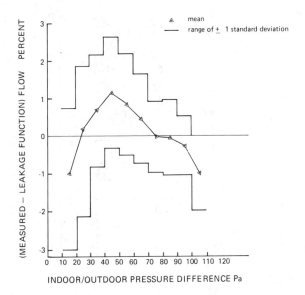

FIG. 2—*Correlation of residuals with pressure. Mean and standard deviation for 50 airtightness tests.*

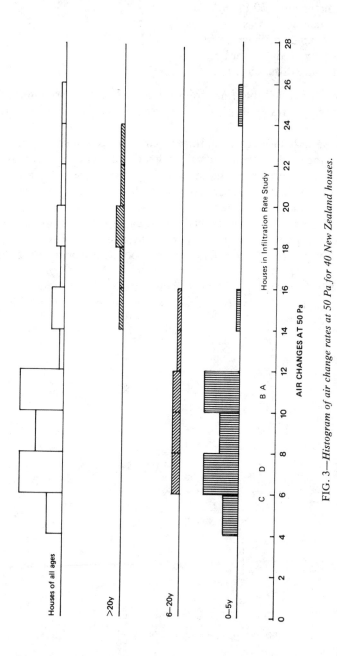

FIG. 3—*Histogram of air change rates at 50 Pa for 40 New Zealand houses.*

House Airtightness Results

A Survey of 40 Houses

A survey of house airtightness was completed in 1982 by Bassett [1]. It used the blower door method to measure the air leakage characteristics of 40 houses of different age and construction type in Wellington.

A histogram of house airtightness expressed in air changes/hour (ACH) is given in Fig. 3. The houses are divided into three age groups, chosen to approximately separate insulated houses into a group less than 5 years old, and those with strip flooring into a group greater than 21 years old. Most results lie in the range of 4 to 26 ACH, with 75% between 4 and 12 ACH. Subdividing by age group shows the 0 to 5 and 6 to 20-year groups to be indistinguishable, but also shows that the 21-plus-year age group, represented by six houses, was less airtight at 16 to 24 ACH.

Airtightness and Design Complexity

Two houses in the 0 to 5-year age group were quite leaky, and it was noted that they both had an unusually complicated shape. This raises the possibility that some design details influence airtightness in a way that can be identified and used at the stage buildings are designed.

In Fig. 4, we attempt to show how the leakage rate at 50-Pa per m^2 shell

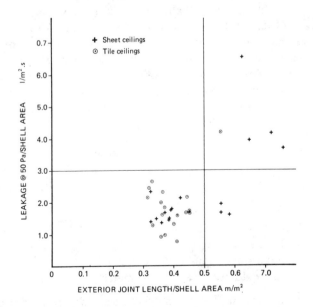

FIG. 4—*Measure of building shell complexity against leakage/shell area at 50 Pa.*

area depends on shell complexity. As a measure of the latter, we add the perimeter length of top and bottom plate, together with vertical lengths of exterior corners, and the boundaries of changes of ceiling pitch. The total is divided by shell area to give a notional measure of shell complexity. Figure 4 shows this variable plotted against the leakage rate at 50 Pa divided once again by shell area. Leakage around doors, windows, and through vents and chimneys also has been subtracted to ensure that the leakage rate is as shape specific as possible.

Figure 4 suggests a subdivision of houses into the following four groups:

1. Average tightness and average shell complexity—23 houses.
2. Below average tightness and average shell complexity—0 houses.
3. Below average tightness and above average shell complexity—5 houses.
4. Average tightness and above average shell complexity—3 houses.

It seems that while some houses of complicated shape can be less airtight than average, this is not always the case. There are eight houses of above average shell complexity; five have higher than average leakage rates, but the other three are about average. It can, however, be said that there is a high degree of association between shape and tightness, since there are no examples of average houses with high leakage rates.

Air Leakage Through Solid Materials

Diffusion of air through the solid components of a building (such as its walls, floor, and ceiling) is potentially important, because these areas are orders of magnitude larger than the size of cracks and joints. Air diffusion resistance measurements were made in the laboratory for a range of interior and exterior lining materials. A summary of the results is given in Table 2, together with a brief physical description of each material. The resolution of the data indicates the range of diffusion resistance for materials of the same description but different batch.

The airflow resistance is defined by Eq 3

$$R = \frac{A \Delta P}{Q} 10^{-6} \quad \frac{\text{MNs}}{\text{m}^3} \tag{3}$$

where

R = leakage resistance, MNs/m^3,
A = area of material, m^2,
Q = volume flow rate of air, m^3/s, and
ΔP = air pressure difference across the material, N/m^2.

As an aid to interpreting Table 2, a reference airflow resistance can be calculated to give a volume flow rate of 2×10^{-5} m^3/m^2 s at 50 Pa. This is 2.5

TABLE 2—*Bulk air flow resistance of common building materials.*

Material	Coating	Density, kg/m^3	Thickness, mm	Order of Magnitude Resistance, MNs/m^3
Flooring grade wood chipboard	none	700	20	10
	varnish	...	...	10^4
Exterior grade plywood asbestos cement board	none	900	4	10
	none	1500	6	10
Paper-coated gypsum, plasterboard	none	750	9.5	10
	alkyd paint system	...	...	>10^7
	acrylic paint system	...	...	10^5
	vinyl wall paper	...	...	10^3
Interior grade wood chipboard (low density)	none	600	10	1
	acrylic paint system	...	...	10^5
Wood fiberboard (low density)	prepainted	330	13	1
Wood fiberboard (high density)	none	1130	5	10
	alkyd paint system	...	...	>10^7
	acrylic paint system	...	...	10^4
	varnish	...	...	10^6
Glass fiber reinforced gypsum plasterboard	none	910	8	1
Melamine formaldehyde laminate for wet areas		1130	5	>10^7
[a]Lapped weatherboards	alkyd paint system		18	10^{-1}
[a]Rusticated weatherboards	none		18	10^{-2}
[a]Wood fiberboard ceiling	none		13	10^{-1}

[a]Includes joints.

MNs/m^3, which is about 1% of the average leakage rate/m^2 of shell area for New Zealand houses less than five years old. A quick scan of the airflow resistances for solid materials in Table 2 shows that only unpainted lining materials are likely to contribute significantly to measured leakage rates. The normal practice of interior decorating by painting greatly increases the airflow resistance to the point where air leakage can be considered insignificant. Samples painted with an alkyd paint system proved to be tighter than our equipment could measure, and a lower limit is recorded in Table 2.

Board or tile materials with joints included in the leakage measurement have lower airflow resistances. However, of the three examples in Table 2, the two outdoor sheathing materials are likely to be fixed in series with a much higher resistance interior lining. This leaves the ceiling tile system as the only lining material in wide use with significant joint system leakage. In a house with average leakage characteristics and a low density wood fiber tile ceiling, leakage through joints in the ceiling could contribute 10% of air leakage under airtightness test. Further reference can be made to Fig. 4, where houses are separated into those with tile ceilings and those with sheet ceilings. In the average tightness–average complexity classification, no significant difference can be attributed to ceiling type. A 10% difference, if present, would be significant at the 80% level.

Component Leakage Information

There are two reasons for surveying the leakage characteristics of joint systems and components of the building envelope. Firstly, it is necessary to know how the leakage opening is distributed in a building in order to calculate the stack- and wind-induced airflows. Secondly, there is the prospect, already demonstrated by Reinhold and Sonderegger [2], that acceptable airtightness estimates might be calculated from plan drawings and tables of leakage resistances so that an estimate of the infiltration rate would be available at the design stage.

Leakage Through Openable Window and Door Joinery

Homeowners are frequently exposed to advertising for draft-stopping materials for windows and doors. This may give them the impression that the bulk of air leakage originates from these sources, but a recent survey of 20 houses by Bassett [1] in New Zealand showed that these sources are unlikely to exceed 25% of the total leakage area.

Window and door leakage measurements were completed using the technique of masking joints and remeasuring the total house leakage rate. Windows and doors of all types were masked together and statistical methods used to resolve differences attributed to joinery type. The most important difference is that between aluminum and wood-framed joinery with the following leakage rate and 95% confidence interval applying at 50-Pa pressure difference.

Window and Door Joinery Type	Leakage/m at 50 Pa, $L/s \cdot m$
Aluminum extrusion	0.5 ± 0.5
Wood molding	4 ± 1

Figure 5 summarizes window leakage measurements and shows the sample of older New Zealand wooden windows to be similar to those measured by Tamura [3] in Canada and comparable with average data given in the IHVE guide [4] and the "ASHRAE Handbook of Fundamentals" [5]. Also of note is

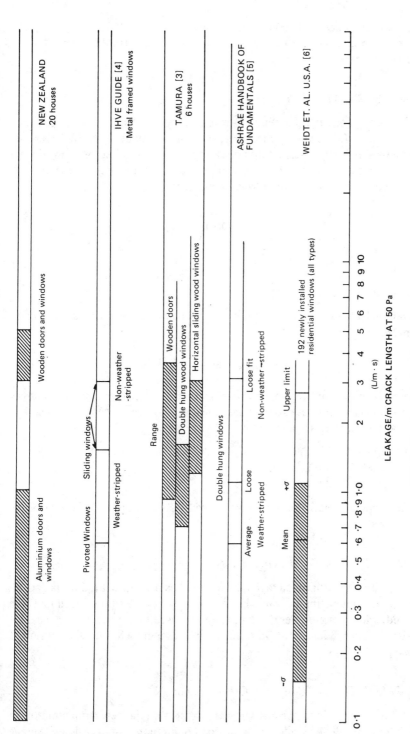

FIG. 5—*Results of window/door leakage tests.*

the similarity between leakage rates for aluminum joinery in this country and the measurements of Weidt et al [6] for newly installed residential windows in the United States.

Standards for Window Air Leakage

There are standards for window airtightness giving leakage rates at a range of pressures. Often the applied pressure is much higher than the reference 50 Pa used in airtightness studies because of the need to test for frame distortion at peak wind speeds. For comparative purposes, Fig. 6 gives flow rates at 50 Pa converted using the following equation

$$Q_{50} = Q(n)\left(\frac{n}{50}\right)^{0.65}$$

where

n = standard pressure, Pa.

Where leakage rates are given on an area basis, the following approximate conversion is used

$$1(L/m^2 \cdot s) \text{ equivalent to } \frac{1}{4}(L/m \cdot s)$$

The New Zealand Standard, Specifications for Performance of Windows (NZS 4211) [7], defines three grades of leakage. When converted to a leakage rate at 50 Pa, they are as follows:

1. Grade A—0.3 L/s · m.
2. Grade B—1.0 L/s · m.
3. Grade C—2.0 L/s · m.

Leakage rates at 50 Pa are shown in Fig. 6 from a number of standards for comparison.

Leakage Through Construction Joints

A limited amount of leakage information has been measured for construction joints in new timber frame houses. These data are summarized in Table 3, and, while not sufficiently complete to be used to predict leakage characteristics of new houses, the data can be used as a guide to the distribution of leakage openings.

Leakage At Services Entry and Other Openings

While a house is under airtightness test, it is a relatively simple matter to look for major leaks by detecting drafts. On a number of occasions, leakage

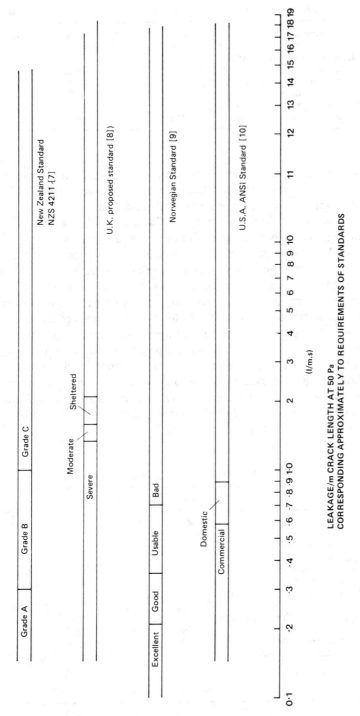

FIG. 6—*Standards for window air leakage.*

TABLE 3—*Measured construction joint leakage rates at 50 Pa pressure in two new houses.*

Joint	Max	Min	Mean	Units
Bottom plate: wood chipboard prelaid floor, gypsum plaster board wall	0.1	0.03	0.08	L/s · m
Top plate: gypsum plaster board wall, low density wood fiberboard ceiling	0.4	0.3	0.3	L/s · m
Window architraves: gypsum plaster wall board overlapped by wood architrave	0.8	0.7	0.7	L/s · m

openings discovered this way were blocked and a new tightness test performed to measure the improvement. It is helpful to compare the size of some of these leaks with chimneys and other common vents and with the house envelope leakage. Table 4 shows the relative sizes of leakage openings around electrical and plumbing service entry together with chimneys and some of the most extreme examples of workmanship defect. Because there is great variety in the types and sizes of leakage openings, these openings should be considered as examples rather than statistically secure mean values and ranges.

Of immediate note is the relatively small leakage area of chimneys and workmanship defects compared with the total envelope leakage area. It was found to be quite difficult to make major improvements to houses in this test sample within the practical constraints of taping over accessible cracks. For example, blocking the cracks around openable windows and doors to simulate a weather-stripping operation reduced the overall leakage by between 17 and 23%. This indicates that a large variety of leakage openings contribute to the total and that the location and size of many of these openings are not yet known for New Zealand houses.

TABLE 4—*Specified leakage openings.*

Location and Description	Max	Min	Mean	Units
Leakage in L/s at 50 Pa Applied Pressure				
Average 100-m² house in survey sample less than 5 years old	. . .	. . .	620	L/s
Wood frame external door, ten cases	80	24	43	L/s
Aluminum ranch slider doors	2.6	. . .	. . .	L/s · m
Louver windows, leakage per louver (50 louvers)	4.5	. . .	. . .	L/s · louver
Plumbing to bath with bath enclosed, three cases	71	11	38	L/s
Most severe workmanship defect	43	. . .	. . .	L/s
Manhole cover-access to roof space, one case	10	. . .	. . .	L/s
Brick chimney and open fire place, one case	120	. . .	. . .	L/s

Airtightness Requirements for Infiltration Rate Prediction

Infiltration Prediction Models

There are a number of simplified procedures for calculating air infiltration rates. Three categories of input data are generally necessary, and these categories can be listed as follows:

1. Airtightness data to characterize the building.
2. Weather office records of wind and temperature.
3. Site exposure details to transform wind records from the weather office into wind speeds at the building site.

The simplified infiltration model developed at Lawrence Berkeley Laboratories (LBL) by Sherman and Grimsrud [11] is used here to calculate infiltration rates in four houses. The results are then compared with measured infiltration rates, and an assessment is made of the accuracy in airtightness information worth striving for.

The LBL Model

The basic form of the air infiltration model is

$$Q = L\sqrt{f_s^2 \Delta T + f_w^2 V^2}$$

where

Q = infiltration, m³/s,
L = effective leakage area, m²,
ΔT = indoor-outdoor temperature difference, K,
f_s = stack parameter, m/s/ $K^{1/2}$,
V = wind speed, m/s, and
f_w = wind parameter.

The stack and wind parameters take the following form

$$f_s = \frac{(1 + R/2)}{3} \left(1 - \frac{X^2}{(2 - R)^2}\right)^{3/2} \sqrt{\frac{gH}{T}}$$

$$f_w = C'(1 - R)^{1/3} \left(\frac{\alpha(H/10)^\gamma}{\alpha'(H'/10)^{\gamma'}}\right)$$

where R and X are leakage area distribution parameters

$$R = \frac{L_c + L_f}{L} \quad \text{and} \quad X = \left|\frac{L_c - L_f}{L}\right|$$

where

C' = shielding class coefficient,
α,γ = the coefficients describing terrain class near the building,
α',γ' = coefficients describing terrain class near the weather tower,
H,H' = heights of the building and the weather tower, respectively,
L_c = ceiling leakage area, m², and
L_f = floor leakage area, m².

Airtightness Measurements for Four Houses

Air infiltration rate, wind speed, and temperature measurements are available for four of the houses in the airtightness survey. Three of the houses (A, B, and C) are similar in type, size, and sheathing materials. They are detached, single-story houses with about 100 m² of floor area, suspended particleboard floors, and similar interior lining materials. House D is semidetached with a concrete block party wall. It is split level, has a basement underneath, and has a skillion roof lined with particleboard.

Airtightness data for the four houses is marked on Fig. 3. House C is rather tighter than A, B, and D, which in terms of leakage rate at 50 Pa/shell surface area are quite similar.

Blower door airtightness data and information from Tables 3 and 4 were used to calculate values for R and X. These values appear in Table 5, together with values calculated on the basis of leakage distributed uniformly over the shell.

Finally, the infiltration rates are calculated for a range of wind speeds and compared with measured infiltration rates in Fig. 7. With low indoor-outdoor temperature differences and wind speeds above 2 m/s, the leakage rate is a linear function of wind speed and can be expressed in terms of air changes/kilometre wind run.

TABLE 5—*Building airtightness information for four houses.*

Building	Calculated Leakage Distribution		Uniform Leakage Distribution	
	R	X	R	X
A	0.52	0.17	0.62	0
B	0.48	0.12	0.61	0
C	0.44	0.00	0.64	0
D	0.64	0.04	0.63	0

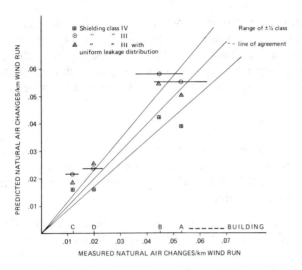

FIG. 7—*Correlation of infiltration rate predictions using LBL model with experiment.*

Infiltration Rate Measurements for Four Houses

Air infiltration rate, wind speed, and temperature measurements are available for houses A, B, C, and D. The measurements were made by Clarkson [12] using the tracer gas decay method and SF_6 as a tracer material. On-site, wind-speed measurements were made above roof height and were similar in strength to wind speeds measured at a meteorological station less than 10 km away. The work was completed in the summer when indoor-outdoor temperature differences were less than 3°C. Air infiltration rates, at three wind speeds between 2 and 10 m/s, were found within experimental error to form a linear relationship with wind speed. A series of 16 measurements had been made in two similarly sited houses and found to be largely independent of wind direction, which at house level generally bore no relation to wind directions measured in the free air stream.

In Fig. 7, three calculated infiltration rates/kilometre wind run are plotted against the measured value. For Shielding Class III, two similar results are calculated, one using detailed air leakage data and the other assuming the leakage is distributed uniformly over wall, floor, and roof areas. Also shown in Fig. 7 is the effect of changing the exposure class from Class III to IV, indicating that for wind-dominated infiltration it is more important to know the wind exposure class than to have accurate knowledge of the leakage distribution. The authors of the LBL model recommend that major leakage openings be assigned to wall, roof, or floor locations and the balance of house leakage be assigned according to component area.

In winter, when indoor-outdoor temperature differences are higher than those measured in this study, the stack-induced leakage becomes more important. For the four buildings in this study located in Wellington, it still remains more important to have the site exposure class correctly assigned than it is to take proper account of the distribution of leakage openings.

Conclusions

The material gathered in this paper summarizes the house airtightness information now available in New Zealand and also shows more clearly the detail of airtightness information needed for predicting season air infiltration rates. The conclusions are:

1. House airtightness expressed either as leakage area or leakage rate at 50 Pa can be determined from blower door results with a total error of less than 10%.

2. Taping over leakage openings as a way of subtracting the leakage component from the whole house leakage has been shown to be reproducible.

3. Leakage through solid interior lining materials should contribute less than a few percent to whole house leakage and much less when painted. The bulk of air leakage, therefore, must flow through cracks and construction joints.

4. A simple model of airtightness in terms of building complexity shows that high leakage can be associated with complicated shell detail, yet on its own the model is insufficiently accurate for predicting airtightness.

5. Infiltration rates calculated using the LBL model for four different houses agree with the experiment to the limit of our ability to assign wind exposure factors.

6. The uncertain inputs into the calculated season infiltration rate can be ranked in order of importance as follows:

   (a) Site exposure index.
   (b) Whole house airtightness.
   (c) The distribution of leakage openings.

References

[1] Bassett, M. R., "Preliminary Survey of Air Tightness Levels in New Zealand Houses" in *Transactions*, Institution of Professional Engineers, Wellington, New Zealand, July 1984.
[2] Reinhold, C. and Sonderegger, R. in *Proceedings*, Fourth Air Infiltration Centre Conference, Elm, Switzerland, Sept. 1983, pp. 16.1–16.30.
[3] Tamura, G. T., *ASHRAE Transactions*, Vol. 81, Pt. 1, 1975, pp. 202–211.
[4] "IHVE Guide Book A," The Institution of Heating and Ventilating Engineers, London, 1970.
[5] "ASHRAE Handbook of Fundamentals," American Society of Heating, Refrigeration, and Air Conditioning Engineers, New York, 1981.
[6] Weidt, J. L., Weidt, J., and Selkowitz, S. in *Proceedings*, ASHRAE-DOE Conference on Thermal Performance of the Exterior Envelopes of Buildings, Florida, Dec. 1979, ASHRAE, Atlanta, pp. 149–159.

[7] "Specification for Performance of Windows," NZS 4211, New Zealand Standards Association, Wellington, 1979.

[8] "Recommendations for the Grading of Windows. Resistance to Wind Loads, Air Infiltration and Water Penetration, and with Notes on Window Security," DD 4, British Standards Institution, London, 1971.

[9] "Norwegian Performance Test Methods for Wind and Rain Penetration Through Windows," Document 0-2801, Norwegian Building Research Institute, Oslo, 1969.

[10] "American Standard Specification for Aluminium Windows," ANSI A134.1, American Standards Association, Chicago, 1966.

[11] Sherman, M. H. and Grimsrud, D. T., *ASHRAE Transactions*, Vol. 86, 1980, pp. 778-806.

[12] Clarkson, T. S., "Preliminary Investigation of Air Infiltration into Typical New Zealand Timber Frame Dwellings," Technical Information Circular No. 182, New Zealand Meteorological Service, Wellington, 1981.

Åke Blomsterberg[1] and Leif Lundin[1]

Natural and Mechanical Ventilation in Tight Swedish Homes— Measurements and Modelling

REFERENCE: Blomsterberg, Å. and Lundin, L., **"Natural and Mechanical Ventilation in Tight Swedish Homes—Measurements and Modelling,"** *Measured Air Leakage of Buildings, ASTM STP 904*, H. R. Trechsel and P. L. Lagus, Eds., American Society for Testing and Materials, Philadelphia, 1986, pp. 384–398.

ABSTRACT: Air infiltration, an important energy loss mechanism in buildings, has been studied in a number of tight homes in Sweden. Two methods of measurement have been used: the fan pressurization technique was used for measuring the airtightness of the building envelope and the tracer gas technique was used for measuring the natural and mechanical ventilation. An automated air infiltration measurement system was developed. The system works on the principle of keeping a constant concentration of a tracer gas. Pressurization is used routinely for checking dwellings in Sweden. This technique does not give the air infiltration as a direct result.

A previously developed model correlating airtightness and air infiltration was used for evaluating the performance of the tested houses. The original model was developed at Lawrence Berkeley Laboratory for American homes and has now been modified for Swedish homes.

The results show that it is difficult to model air infiltration, and that it is difficult to achieve the recommended minimum ventilation rate as given in the Swedish Building Code if you are to rely only on natural ventilation in a tight home. Most new Swedish homes meet the airtightness requirement of the Swedish Building Code and are equipped with mechanical ventilation.

The paper presents results from measurements in Swedish homes using the tracer gas technique and the pressurization technique. The techniques are described. The results from the measurements are compared with predictions using a model correlating airtightness and air infiltration.

KEY WORDS: air infiltration, air leakage, measurements, modelling, pressurization, tracer gas, ventilation

Air infiltration typically accounts for one third of the energy loss in a heated building. The driving forces for natural air infiltration are weather, that is,

---

[1]Research engineer, National Testing Institute, Borås, Sweden S-50115.

wind forces and temperature differences. For a given combination of weather conditions, the size of the air infiltration is determined by the character of the building envelope, the main property being the airtightness. A promising technique to characterize this housing quality is air leakage measurements. An air leakage standard for new construction has existed since 1977 in Sweden. Pressurization, that is, measurement of the air leakage, is performed routinely for checking new Swedish dwellings.

Long-term measurements of air infiltration have been made possible with the constant concentration tracer gas technique. An automated system working on that principle has been developed at the National Testing Institute. This paper, a previous paper by Åke Blomsterberg et al [1], and a report by Max Sherman [2] support the idea that results from air leakage measurements can be used to predict air infiltration for an entire building. Results from constant concentration tracer gas measurements and fan pressurization measurements in three houses are evaluated, and the ventilation rates for longer time periods are predicted using a model originally developed at Lawrence Berkeley Laboratory (LBL).

Test Methods

In order to perform the measurements necessary for this paper, two methods were used: the pressurization technique and the tracer gas technique [2,3].

The pressurization technique is used for testing airtightness of building envelopes for entire buildings. The procedure is the following: a fan is mounted into the building envelope. Using this fan, the entire house is first pressurized and then depressurized (that is, a differential pressure is established between the inside and the outside of the house). All vents are sealed off during the test. The air flow through the fan is determined using a flowmeter. It is assumed that this air flow is equal to the air flow through the building envelope at the same time. Within a short period of time, a pressure flow rate profile is established for the house.

The tracer gas technique is used for measuring air infiltration for natural running conditions in a building. Tracer gas, a gas normally not present in the structure, is injected into the house and the concentration is measured— from that the air infiltration can be derived. A completely automated constant concentration tracer gas technique [4] has been used.

The measurement system maintains a constant concentration of a tracer gas in nine rooms simultaneously. Tracer gas is injected into each room, and the concentration is measured in each room. A target concentration is maintained. The result of the measurements is the supply of fresh air to each room, that is, the fresh air that comes directly to the room without passing through another room. The result is given in cubic metres per hour directly without any estimation of the effective volume.

Long-term measurements can be made. The technique requires accurate measurements of the absolute concentration of a tracer gas and of the tracer gas flow. The concentration must remain constant the entire measuring period.

Description of the Model

The original model was developed at LBL [2,5]. The primary input to the model is the air leakage of the entire building envelope, which is given as an effective leakage area

$$L = Q \sqrt{\frac{\rho}{2\Delta P}} \tag{1}$$

where

Q = air flow, m³/s,
ΔP = pressure drop across the building envelope, Pa,
L = effective leakage area, m², and
ρ = density of air, kg/m³.

Because the pressures driving infiltration are normally within a limited range (1 to 10 Pa), the effective leakage area is calculated for a pressure difference of 4 Pa.

The forces that drive infiltration are pressure differences across the building envelope caused by wind forces and by indoor-outdoor temperature differences. The stack-induced infiltration is calculated as follows

$$Q_s = L f_s \sqrt{\Delta T} \tag{2}$$

where

Q_s = stack-induced infiltration, m³/s,
f_s = stack parameter, m/(sK$^{1/2}$), and
ΔT = inside-outside temperature difference, K.

The stack parameter is given by the following expression

$$f_s = \frac{(1 + R/2)}{3} \left| 1 - \frac{X^2}{(2 - R)^2} \right|^{3/2} \sqrt{\frac{gH}{T}} \tag{3}$$

where

$$R = \frac{L_{\text{floor}} + L_{\text{ceiling}}}{L_{\text{tot}}}$$

$$X = \frac{L_{\text{ceiling}} - L_{\text{floor}}}{L_{\text{tot}}}$$

g = acceleration of gravity, m/s^2,
H = inside height of the structure, m, and
T = inside temperature, K.

The wind-induced infiltration is calculated by

$$Q_w = Lf_w v \qquad (4)$$

where

Q_w = wind-induced infiltration, m^3/s,
f_w = wind parameter, dimensionless, and
v = wind speed, m/s.

The wind parameter is given by

$$f_w = C' \left| (1 - R)^{1/3} \right| \left(\frac{\alpha \left(\dfrac{H}{10}\right)^{\gamma}}{\alpha' \left(\dfrac{H'}{10}\right)^{\gamma'}} \right) \qquad (5)$$

where

C' = generalized shielding coefficient (see Table 1),
α, γ = terrain parameters (see Table 2) at the structure,
α', γ' = terrain parameters at the site of the wind measurements,
H = inside height of the structure, m, and
H' = height of the wind measurement, m.

The air flow resulting from the two driving forces must be combined to arrive at the total infiltration. If the expressions for wind- and stack-induced

TABLE 1—*Generalized shielding coefficients.*

Shielding Class	C'	Description
I	0.324	no obstructions or local shielding whatsoever
II	0.285	light local shielding with few obstructions
III	0.240	moderate local shielding; some obstructions within two house heights
IV	0.185	heavy shielding; obstructions around most of perimeter
V	0.102	very heavy shielding; large obstruction surrounding perimeter within two house heights

TABLE 2—*Terrain parameters for standard terrain classes.*

Class	γ	α	Description
I	0.10	1.30	ocean or other body of water with at least 5 km of unrestricted expanse
II	0.15	1.00	flat terrain with some isolated obstacles
III	0.20	0.85	rural areas with low buildings, trees, or other scattered obstacles
IV	0.25	0.67	urban, industrial, or forest areas or other built-up area
V	0.35	0.47	center of large city or other heavily built-up area

infiltration are interpreted as effective pressure differences across the leakage area of the structure, the total infiltration can be determined by adding these pressures. If the flow is proportional to the square root of the pressure, then two flows acting independently must add as follows

$$Q_{tot} = \sqrt{Q_w^2 + Q_s^2} \tag{6}$$

This equation is useful for a structure without any specially designed ventilation system. Most Swedish one-family houses do, however, have unpowered vents or a mechanical ventilation system. Unpowered vents protrude beyond the envelope and therefore should not be included into the total leakage area. Their ventilation should be calculated separately [6]. The flow through an unpowered vent will have the same form as the infiltration through the envelope

$$Q_{vent} = L_v \sqrt{C_v V_v + \frac{gH_v \Delta T}{2T}} \tag{7}$$

where

L_v = effective leakage area of the vent, m^2,
C_v = vent shielding coefficient,
V_v = wind speed at the top of the vent, m/s, and
H_v = height of the vent, m.

The ventilation through the vents should be combined with the other flows using superposition

$$Q_{tot} = \sqrt{Q_w^2 + Q_s^2 + Q_{vent}^2} \tag{8}$$

If the house is equipped with an exhaust fan, the same discussion as for an unpowered vent applies, that is

$$Q_{vent} = Q_{exhaust\ fan} \tag{9}$$

where $Q_{exhaust\ fan}$ is the rating of the fan, m^3/s.

A balanced ventilation system should not affect the pressure drop across the envelope caused by natural driving forces. The fan flow therefore simply can be added to the natural ventilation

$$Q_{tot} = Q_{fan} + \sqrt{Q_w^2 + Q_s^2 + Q_{vent}^2} \qquad (10)$$

where

Q_{fan} = rating of the exhaust fan, m^3/s.
Q_{vent} = Q_{fan} minus rating of the supply fan.

Results and Discussion

In this section, the results from three houses will be presented. Each house represents a very common type of building and ventilation system in Sweden. These types are:

1. *Svaneholm*—a one-family house built during the early 1960s. It is a one-story building with full basement. The external walls are made of elements (0.3 to 1.2 m wide; 2.4 m high). The element itself is made of a wood frame filled with cellulose filament. This kind of structure has a large number of vertical joints. The facade is made of bricks. The vapor barrier consists of a tar board. The heating system is a hydronic system with an oil-fired boiler. The furnace room was sealed off from the rest of the house during the tests. The house is ventilated by unpowered vents.

2. *Lanna*—a one and one-half story, one-family house with crawl space. It has a modern design with a well-insulated timber frame and a plastic air/vapor barrier. The house is heated by electric baseboard heaters. The ventilation system has an exhaust fan and air inlets above the windows.

3. *Skultorp*—a one-story, one-family house built in 1982. It has no basement but has a crawl space. It has a heavily insulated timber frame structure with a plastic air/vapor barrier. The ventilation system has both supply and exhaust fans. The house is heated by a warm air system.

The airtightness of the three houses is very close to the results obtained from a survey made in 1976 [7,8] as is shown in Table 3.

TABLE 3—*Comparison of airtightness, number of air changes.*

	Built 1965 to 1975 (6 Houses)	Built 1975 to 1976 (39 Houses)	Built in 1962, Svaneholm	Built in 1981, Lanna	Built in 1982, Skultorp
Pressurization at 50 Pa, h^{-1}	5.5 ± 3.0	3.8 ± 1.9	5.0	2.6	1.1

For all three houses, the ventilation rate of each individual room was monitored. There is quite a variation between different rooms for the Svaneholm house (Fig. 1), that is, fresh air coming directly into the room without passing through another room. The basement seems to have the best ventilation.

In the Lanna house, most rooms have a fairly constant ventilation (Fig. 2). The living room and the hallway have a ventilation rate which changes with time. The kitchen seem to be very poorly ventilated, that is, hardly any fresh air comes directly into the kitchen. The total average ventilation rate of 0.16

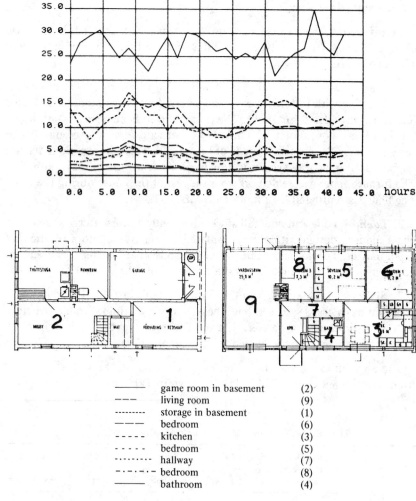

	game room in basement	(2)
— — —	living room	(9)
·········	storage in basement	(1)
— — —	bedroom	(6)
- - - - -	kitchen	(3)
- - - - -	bedroom	(5)
··········	hallway	(7)
- · - · - · -	bedroom	(8)
———	bathroom	(4)

FIG. 1—*Measured ventilation rates for individual rooms in the Svaneholm house (air infiltration plus unpowered vent ventilation).*

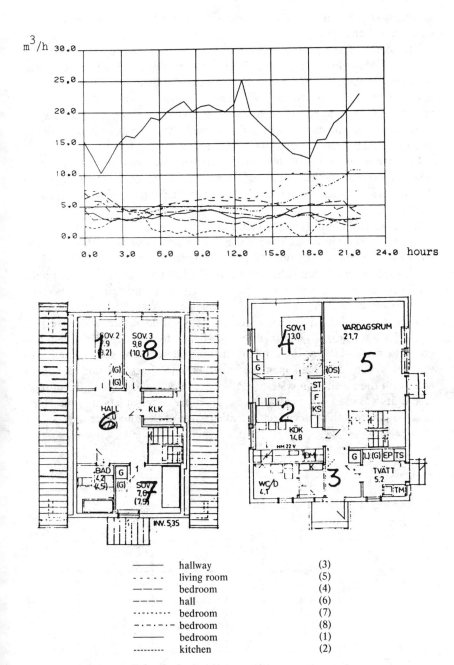

———————	hallway	(3)
- - - - -	living room	(5)
——— ———	bedroom	(4)
— — — —	hall	(6)
··········	bedroom	(7)
— · — · — · —	bedroom	(8)
———————	bedroom	(1)
--------	kitchen	(2)

FIG. 2—*Measured ventilation rates for individual rooms in the Lanna house (air infiltration plus exhaust fan ventilation). The average wind speed was 1.8 m/s, and the average temperature was +7.7°C.*

air changes per hour (ACH) (47 m³/h) is too low (Fig. 3), due to a poorly adjusted exhaust fan.

The Skultorp house has a ventilation rate that is almost constant with time (Fig. 4). This is because the ventilation system is coupled with a very tight building envelope. As to the ventilation rate of individual rooms, it all depends on how well the ventilation system is adjusted. The ventilation rates of individual rooms are not presented here, as one tracer gas injection value got caught in the open position during the measurements. In one room, we therefore were inadvertently using the constant flow technique.

In order to get an idea as to how these three houses would perform during a year, they were modelled using the LBL model. The model was first applied to the houses for the same weather conditions as during the tracer gas measurements.

In Table 4, the inputs to the LBL model are shown.

The results for the Svaneholm house show a very close correlation between measurements and predictions (Fig. 5). The average measured value is 70.7 m³/h, and the predicted value is 71.5 m³/h. For the test period, the model tracks the measured ventilation rate very well. The calculations were made with the effective leakage area of the envelope separated from the effective leakage area of the unpowered vents. If this is not done, the model overpredicts with a factor of 2. The shielding coefficient for the unpowered vent was given the value of 0.2 as the wind effect is considered to be small. The top of the vent is covered with an open hood in order to minimize the interference by wind with the ventilation system. Half of the effective leakage of the unpowered vents was used in the calculations. There are supply inlets at ground level that amount to half of the effective leakage area of the unpowered vents. The

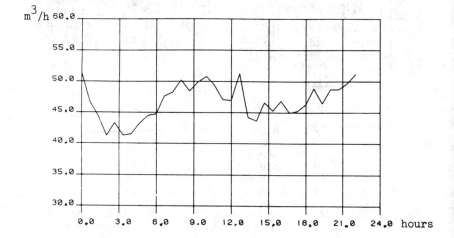

FIG. 3—*Measured total ventilation rate for the Lanna house.*

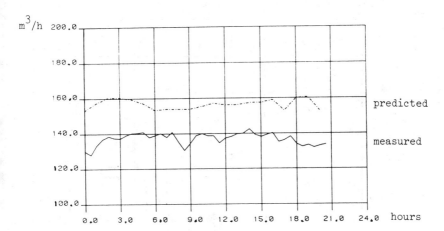

FIG. 4—*Measured total ventilation rate versus predicted ventilation rate for the Skultorp house (air infiltration plus balanced ventilation). The average wind speed was 2.8 m/s, and the average temperature was −1.1°C.*

TABLE 4—*Parameter values used in the LBL model.*

House	Svaneholm	Lanna	Skultorp
$L_{ceiling}$, cm^2	125	117	30
L_{floor}, cm^2	0	0	30
L_{tot}, cm^2	250	217	89
L_v, cm^2	300/2	. . .	. . .
α	0.85	0.85	1.0
γ	0.20	0.20	0.15
α'	0.85	0.85	1.0
γ'	0.20	0.20	0.15
C'	0.185	0.285	0.24
C_v	0.2	. . .	. . .
H', m	7.5	9	10
H, m	3.0	5.2	2.4
H_v, m	4.0	. . .	. . .
T, °C	22	21	20
Q_{vent}, m^3/h	. . .	. . .	20
Q_{fan}, m^3/h	. . .	. . .	126

model was not used on the Lanna house because the exhaust fan wasn't working properly.

For the Skultorp house, the LBL model overpredicts by 15% (see Fig. 4). This could be explained with the results from the Mobile Infiltration Test Unit, which say that the LBL model overpredicts the total infiltration when the magnitudes of the wind-induced and the stack-induced infiltration rates are comparable [4]. Adding to the uncertainty is the inaccuracy in the mea-

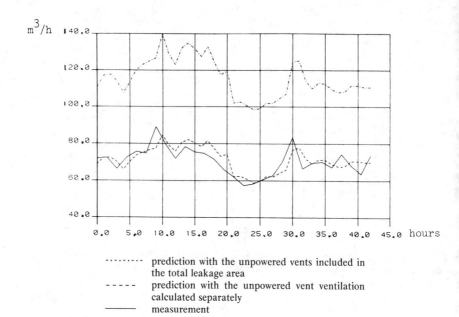

FIG. 5—*Measured total ventilation rates versus predicted ventilation rates for the Svaneholm house (air infiltration plus unpowered vent ventilation). The average wind speed was 2.2 m/s, and the average temperature was +0.8°C.*

surement of the air flow (Q_{fan} and $Q_{exhaust\ fan}$) through the fan ($\pm 10\%$). It also might be that the air flow through the fan is not constant.

For the Svaneholm house, the model was used to predict the ventilation rate during one year (Table 5 and Fig. 6). Hourly weather data for Stockholm was used. With no occupants in the house, the house never reached the required minimum ventilation rate of 0.5 ACH (155 m³/h). The monthly average ventilation rate varies very much, the highest ventilation rate being for November and the lowest for July. This is reasonable as November is very windy and cold, while July is moderately windy and warm. The air infiltration (through the envelope) seems to be quite important compared to the ventilation through the unpowered vents.

For the Skultorp house, there is no need to make a long-term prediction. The air infiltration is very small. As long as the mechanical ventilation system works properly, there won't be any problems.

Conclusions

Three typical Swedish one-family houses have been examined, each representing a different kind of ventilation system. With doors and windows closed, the one-family house with unpowered vents was inadequately venti-

TABLE 5—*Predicted ventilation rates for Svaneholm, monthly averages.*

	Wind, m/s	Temperature, °C	Q_{tot}, m³/h	Q_s, m³/h	Q_w, m³/h	Q_{vent}, m³/h
Jan.	4.1	−0.9	90	47	47	61
Feb.	4.3	−1.4	92	48	50	77
March	3.7	−2.1	88	48	42	44
April	3.6	3.5	78	42	41	44
May	3.8	11.5	66	31	44	22
June	3.3	14.9	55	26	38	28
July	3.4	17.7	52	21	39	13
Aug.	3.4	16.5	53	23	39	24
Sept.	3.1	10.7	61	33	36	30
Oct.	4.1	7.3	77	38	47	39
Nov.	4.9	1.0	94	45	56	46
Dec.	4.1	1.0	87	45	46	58

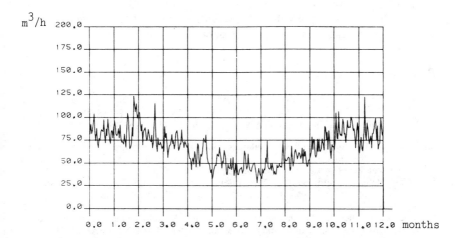

FIG. 6—*Predicted total ventilation rate for one year for the Svaneholm house, daily averages.*

lated all year around, although the house was not as tight as is required in the Swedish Building Code. The ventilation rate for the summer case was very low. This is, however, no major problem as people this time of the year can be expected to open their windows to get fresh air. Airing during the rest of the year means an additional energy consumption that is hard to control.

The test results show that the best way of both supplying adequate ventilation and conserving energy is to make sure that the building envelope is sufficiently tight and then to install a mechanical ventilation system. If this is done, it will be possible to control the ventilation rate all year around and to avoid excessive or too small ventilation. The only question would be how constant the air flow through the fan will be. The system should either be of the balanced type or the exhaust air type with special vents to the outside for supplying fresh air.

In order to conserve energy, the first system can be combined with a heat exchanger and the second system with an exhaust air heat pump for heating domestic hot water.

In this paper, it was shown that it is possible to correlate fan pressurization measurements and infiltration rates. Improvements in this technique are necessary and are clearly possible. Relying on only natural ventilation for the ventilation of low leakage houses clearly is not possible. The solution is to install a ventilation system where adequate ventilation rates can be guaranteed 12 months a year and where energy losses caused by ventilation can be recovered. A ventilation system will work well only in a tight dwelling. When ventilating a house, attention has to be paid to each individual room. Every room should have a supply of fresh air sufficient for its usage. This was shown not always to be the case.

In the future, we will monitor and evaluate an additional number of houses using the techniques described in this paper.

References

[1] Blomsterberg, Å., Sherman, M., and Grimsrud, D., "A Model Correlating Air Tightness and Air Infiltration in Houses," presented at Conference on Thermal Performance of the Exterior Envelopes of Buildings, Orlando, FL, 1979, LBL-9625, Lawrence Berkeley Laboratory, Berkeley, CA.

[2] Sherman, M., "Air Infiltration in Buildings," LBL-10712, Ph.D. thesis, Lawrence Berkeley Laboratory, Berkeley, CA, 1980.

[3] "Determination of Airtightness in Buildings, SS 02 15 51," Swedish standard, 1980.

[4] Blomsterberg, Å. and Lundin, L., "An Automated Air Infiltration Measurement System— Its Design and Capabilities. Preliminary Experimental Results," Air Infiltration Review, Vol. 4, No. 1, 1982.

[5] Modera, M., Sherman, M., and Levin, P., "A Detailed Examination of the LBL Infiltration Model Using the Mobile Infiltration Test Unit," presented at the 1983 ASHRAE annual meeting, Washington, DC, ASHRAE, New York, NY.

[6] Sherman, M., Sonderegger, R., and Grimsrud, D., "The LBL Infiltration Model," Lawrence Berkeley Laboratory, Berkeley, CA, 1982, unpublished.

[7] Hildingson, O. and Holmgren, S., "Air Tightness in Buildings—Investigation and Development of Measuring Techniques," Master's thesis, Lund Institute of Technology, Lund, Sweden, 1976.

[8] Blomsterberg, Å., "Air Tightness vs. Air Infiltration for Swedish Homes—Measurements and Modelling," in Proceedings of the CIB W-67 Third International Symposium on Energy Conservation in the Built Environment, Vol. VI, An Foras Forbartha, Dublin, Ireland, 1982.

DISCUSSION

D. Saum[1] *(written discussion)*—(1) How is compliance with the 3-ACH standard administered? (2) How many houses are measured? (3) How many pass? (4) And, what happens if they fail?

Å. Blomsterberg and L. Lundin *(authors' closure)*—(1) Usually the customer requires that the standard is met and that someone runs a test using standard testing procedure. (2) Roughly one out of ten houses is tested. (3) In general, modern Swedish housing meets the requirement. (4) It depends upon what kind of agreement there is between the contractor and the customer.

E. Krutson[2] *(written discussion)*—(1) Are the 3-ACH (at 50 Pa) and the 0.5-ACH infiltration separate standards in Sweden? When was each introduced? (2) Can you state briefly why you prefer the constant concentration method of measuring air infiltration?

Å. Blomsterberg and L. Lundin *(authors' closure)*—(1) The 3 ACH (at 50 Pa) is an airtightness requirement for the envelope of a building, and the 0.5 ACH is the minimum required ventilation rate. The first requirement was introduced in 1977. A 4.5-ACH standard was introduced in 1975. The second requirement was introduced in the late 1960s. (2) The constant concentration technique we use for long-term measurements and for simultaneously monitoring individual rooms, because that is the method which gives the most accurate results under those conditions. The decay technique is useful for one-time tests of the overall house ventilation rate.

E. Krutson *(written discussion)*—Did you say that Parameter I is dimensionless? From its definition ACH/$\sqrt{\Delta T}$ geometric factor, it seems to have the dimension $s^{-1}\,°C^{-1/2}$. (2) You said that the best reference pressure for fan pressurization is the indoor pressure *before* testing. How is this done?

Å. Blomsterberg and L. Lundin *(authors' closure)*—I do not recognize any of these statements. I think they concern the paper by Boman and Lyberg.

R. A. Grot[3] *(written discussion)*—Can you give some details on the combustion of the mechanical ventilation rates to explain the uneven ventilation rates in each room?

Å. Blomsterberg and L. Lundin *(authors' closure)*—I am not quite sure that I understand the question. The uneven ventilation rates in each room in a house have different explanations depending upon the mechanical ventilation system. A house with an exhaust fan will have low ventilation rates in rooms with tight exterior walls, assuming the outlets to be located in the middle of the house and that the whole house is slightly depressurized. A tight house

[1]Infiltec, Waynesboro, VA.
[2]U.S. Department of Energy, New York, NY 10014.
[3]National Bureau of Standards, Gaithersburg, MD.

with a balanced ventilation system, where fresh air is supplied to each room, will have an uneven ventilation rate if the system is not well adjusted. The leakier the house, the larger the natural air infiltration will be.

P. Giesbrecht[4] *(written discussion)*—(1) Does the recommended Swedish ventilation rate of 0.5 ACH include the unintentional leakage through the envelope? (2) Are heat recovery units common in new Swedish homes?

Å. Blomsterberg and L. Lundin (authors' closure)—(1) Yes, the 0.5 ACH includes infiltration as well as mechanical ventilation. (2) Very common in new homes.

[4]Ener-Corp Management, Ltd., Winnipeg, Manitoba, Canada R3L 0KS.

Carl A. Boman[1] and Mats D. Lyberg[1]

Analysis of Air Change Rates in Swedish Residential Buildings

REFERENCE: Boman, C. A. and Lyberg, M. D., "Analysis of Air Change Rates in Swedish Residential Buildings," *Measured Air Leakage of Buildings, ASTM STP 904*, H. R. Trechsel and P. L. Lagus, Eds., American Society for Testing and Materials, Philadelphia, 1986, pp. 399–406.

ABSTRACT: Measurements of the rate of air exchange in residential buildings have been carried out by the Swedish Institute for Building Research since 1970. The results of an analysis of these measurements are presented in this paper for about 500 buildings not having mechanical ventilation.

The studied buildings include one- and two-story, detached, single-family houses, row houses, and multifamily residential buildings built between 1900 and 1982 and of various design. In some cases, the buildings have been retrofitted by improving the insulation of the attic or the exterior walls. The building sites vary from freely exposed to a sheltered urban environment.

Tracer gas measurements using the decay technique have been used for the determination of the rate of air exchange. In about 300 cases, the measurement of air change rates has been complemented by measurements using pressurization techniques. Data on 50 other parameters also have been collected. These parameters describe the building geometry, the building design, and the meteorological conditions at the time of measurement. The measurements have been performed with the outdoor temperature varying from −15 to +25°C and for wind speeds from 0 to 10 m/s.

The calculation model used for the analysis includes two dimensionless variables and two parameters. The dependent variable is given by the measured air change rate and the geometric properties of the building, while the other variable is defined as the ratio of the aeromotive force to the buoyancy force. The two parameters of the model represent the degree of wind shelter and the leakage area of the building, respectively.

For the analysis, the buildings have been divided into classes according to the building environment, the year of construction, and the type of building.

KEY WORDS: air change rate, infiltration model, leakage area, pressure coefficient, pressurization, tracer gas

In this paper we report results from an analysis of data on the rate of air change and volume flow rate in pressurization of residential buildings. The

[1]Research officer and project manager, The Swedish Institute for Building Research, Gävle, Sweden.

data have been collected by the Swedish Institute for Building Research (SIB) from 1974 to 1982. These data have been collected for various research projects having different purposes, like determination of the energy status of buildings, assessment of the indoor air quality in buildings, investigation of buildings with radon content in the air, diagnosis of building damages caused by moisture, etc. Data from measurements in about 1200 buildings are now being transferred to a data file.

The results given in this report are based on data from 500 buildings not having mechanical ventilation, representing one- and two-story detached homes, two story row houses, and three-story apartment buildings situated in different parts of Sweden. Measured rates of air change that include buildings with mechanical ventilation have been reported elsewhere [1]. Measurements have been carried out in buildings of various designs, but the data analyzed in this paper emanate mainly from buildings of a light structure. During the measurements, climate variables such as indoor and outdoor air temperature, the wind speed and direction at the building site, etc. have been recorded.

The rate of air change has been determined by measurement of the decay of tracer gas [nitrous oxide (N_2O)] concentration in the air [2] from an initial concentration of 30 to 100 ppm. Fans have been placed in every room of the house or apartment to ensure mixing of the air.

The pressurization measurements have been performed according to the Swedish standard for measurements of this kind (The National Swedish Authority for Testing, Inspection and Metrology: Standard Method Description SP 1977:1). The buildings have been subjected to an over- and underpressure in steps until a pressure difference of at least 50 Pa has been attained. The flow rate of the supplied or extracted air volume has been recorded.

To make a comparison between measurements performed under different climatic conditions, it is necessary to use some model to reduce as far as possible the influence of the temperature difference, the wind, and the building shape on the results. The results from the measurements have been analyzed using a simple model of the mechanisms producing the airflow through the building envelope. The use of a similar, but simpler, model has been reported elsewhere [3]. The model used here has the following characteristics:

1. The air leaks are assumed to be uniformly distributed over the exposed parts of the building's exterior walls and ceiling.

2. The airflow across the building envelope is produced by buoyancy forces and aeromotive forces.

3. Exterior walls are exposed to buoyancy as well as aeromotive forces, while the ceiling is exposed only to buoyancy forces (Fig. 1).

4. In the model, exterior walls are divided into two surfaces having the same area, the windward and the leeward surfaces, both associated with a uniformly distributed pressure difference that is caused by aeromotive forces

relative to the building interior and that is of equal magnitude but of different sign.

5. The model contains two parameters. One parameter, the relative leakage area, is defined as the ratio of the total area of the air leaks, as determined from the model, to the area of the building envelope. The other parameter, the pressure difference coefficient across the building envelope, describes the wind-driven difference in pressure just mentioned. The value of the former parameter is to be determined.

6. The value of the pressure difference coefficient is fixed in the model if the wind exposure of the building site and the geometry of the building are known. In practice, we make a distinction only between exposed and sheltered building sites and between buildings having an approximately square

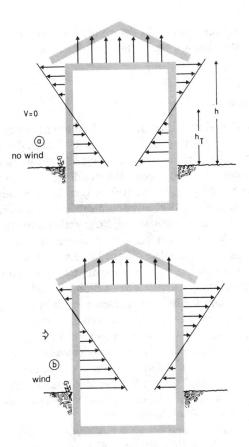

FIG. 1—*The pressure across the building envelope assumed in the model. The height* h *is the height of the building interior above the ground, and* h_T *is the height at which the buoyancy force is equal to zero. (a) No wind present; (b) wind present.*

main floor (for example, detached homes) and those having a rectangular floor (for example, row houses or rectangular apartment buildings). For these building categories, the numeric value of the pressure difference coefficient has been determined by use of information from wind-tunnel studies of the pressure distribution over the building for buildings of different shape and wind exposure [4].

7. The required input data to the model consist of geometrical properties of the building, such as the volume, the height of the building interior above the ground, the ceiling area, and the area of the building facades, and of measured variables, such as the rate of air exchange (for tracer gas measurements), the volume flow rate for a given over- or underpressure (for pressurization measurements), the wind speed at a height equal to that of the top of the building, the wind direction, and the internal and external air temperature.

This model has been applied to determine the relative leakage area of a building using data from a tracer gas measurement or from a pressurization measurement.

Results and Discussion

To determine the relative leakage area of buildings, we have mainly used data from tracer gas measurements. Buildings have been divided into various categories described by variables such as single-family dwellings (SFD) versus multifamily dwellings (MFD); age of the building; features of the building exterior, such as buildings with an envelope consisting mainly of wood, concrete, light concrete, or bricks, in addition to the insulating material; the foundation of the building, such as buildings with a basement versus buildings erected on a slab; prefabricated buildings versus buildings erected on site; and buildings with a fireplace versus buildings without one, etc.

It has been found that the most important factor determining the relative leakage area of a building is whether the building is prefabricated or built on site. Another important factor is the presence or absence of a fire place, but the importance of this factor is greatly reduced if the slide valve is closed. The age of the building also should be an important factor, but its effect is reduced because many of the old buildings where measurements have been performed already have been retrofitted or weather-stripped. The influence of the other factors just listed cannot be seen because of experimental errors, errors stemming from the method of analysis, and the actual differences between nominally identical buildings.

Regarding the classification of buildings according to their age, this is a rather straightforward procedure for Swedish buildings if one assumes that they have been built according to the prescriptions of the building code in force when the building was designed. One building code has been valid from 1940 to 1960, another from 1960 to 1975, and the present one from 1975.

TABLE 1—Relative leakage area for some building categories calculated using data from tracer gas measurements and the average recorded air change rate, ACH, wind speed, v, and temperature difference, ΔT.

Building Category	Period	Sample Size	Relative Leakage Area, cm²/m²	Average ACH, h⁻¹	Average Wind Speed, v, m/s	Average Temperature Difference, ΔT, K
3-story MFD with fireplace	1940 to 1960	30	7.2 ± 3.1	0.78	2.4	16
3-story MFD, no fireplace	1940 to 1960	35	3.9 ± 1.1	0.49	1.7	25
3-story MFD	1960 to 1975	85	3.0 ± 0.9	0.35	2.3	22
Detached SFD	1940 to 1960					
Nonretrofitted		15	2.5 ± 1.0	0.35	2.0	21
Retrofitted		35	2.7 ± 2.0	0.42	2.0	22
Detached SFD and row houses	1960 to 1975					
Sheltered site		190	3.0 ± 1.4	0.31	2.4	16
Exposed site		40	3.2 ± 1.3	0.33	2.9	19
Detached SFD on slab prefabricated	1970 to 1975	20	1.2 ± 0.5	0.17	1.4	18
Detached SFD and row houses	1975 and later	16	1.4 ± 0.6	0.20	2.1	20

Results for which statistically significant data are available are presented in Table 1. The spread within each category is typically on the order of 40%. The experimental error can be estimated to be 10 to 15%, and the error caused by the simplifications made in the construction of the model is estimated to be of the same magnitude. The resulting error in the calculated relative leakage area then can be expected to be between 15 and 20%. The model error should not be important when the model is applied to a group of nominally identical buildings constructed by the same company and erected by the same workers. However, under these circumstances, the variation in relative leakage area for such a group of buildings has been found to be between 20 and 40%.

If data from tracer gas measurements and pressurization measurements are to be used to calculate the relative leakage area, it is important to verify that both methods lead to the same result. To do this, the relative leakage area has been calculated for those detached homes where tracer gas measurements, as well as pressurization measurements down to a pressure difference of about 5 Pa, have been carried out.

The procedure followed for this calculation is as follows. First, the data for the under- and the overpressure have been corrected to take away the influence from the pressure differences caused by buoyancy and aeromotive forces on the resulting volume air flow, so that the data points from the under- and the overpressurization fall approximately on the same curve. Examples of the result of such a correction are presented in Fig. 2. After this step, the resulting relative leakage area has been determined, using a linear extrapolation, for the average pressure difference across the building envelope at hand when the tracer gas measurement was performed.

The results of the just-mentioned calculation are presented in Fig. 3. There is a rather good agreement between the relative leakage area calculated using data from tracer gas measurements and data from pressurization measurements for the case when no openings have been sealed. The actual error is of the same magnitude as the expected experimental error; that is, there seems to be strong evidence that the two methods yield the same result. However, the number of studied buildings is too small for any definite conclusions to be drawn. This question will be studied in more detail in the near future.

Conclusions

The relative leakage area of buildings has been calculated for some building categories using data from tracer gas measurements. The results show that the most important factor determining the relative leakage area of a building is whether the building has been prefabricated or erected on site. Otherwise, buildings of the same age have about the same relative leakage area, independent of the design, provided there is no fireplace.

A method has been employed to study the correlation between the calcu-

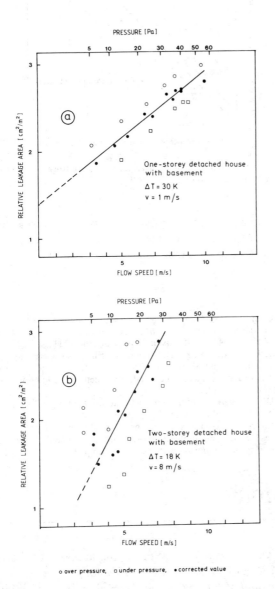

o over pressure,   □ under pressure,   • corrected value

FIG. 2—*Examples of the correction of over- and underpressurization data. The relative leakage area, obtained from pressurization measurements, is plotted verus the average air flow velocity.*

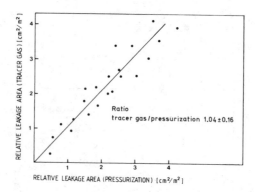

FIG. 3—*The value of the relative leakage area obtained from tracer gas measurements versus the value obtained from pressurization.*

lated relative leakage area, using data from tracer gas measurements, and data from pressurization measurements. There is evidence that both experimental methods lead to the same result.

References

[1] Boman, C. A. and Lyberg, M. D., "Measured and Building Code Values of Air Change Rates in Residential Buildings," *Proceedings*, 5th Air Infiltration Centre (AIC) Conference, Reno, NV, 1-4 Oct. 1984, AIC, Berkshire, Great Britain, 1984.
[2] Fracastoro, G. V. and Lyberg, M. D., "Guiding Principles Concerning Design of Experiments, Instrumentation and Measuring Techniques," Chapter IIIa, International Energy Agency (IEA) Task III document, The Swedish Council for Building Research, Document D11:1983, Stockholm, 1983.
[3] Lyberg, M. D., "Models of Infiltration and Natural Ventilation," Report M83:23, The Swedish Institute for Building Research, Stockholm, 1983.
[4] Wirén, B., "Effects of Surrounding Buildings on Wind Pressure Distributions and Ventilative Heat Losses for a Single-Family House—A Wind Tunnel Study," *Journal of Wind Engineering and Industrial Aerodynamics*, Vol. 15, 1983, pp. 15-26.

DISCUSSION

R. Grot (written discussion)—What is the accuracy of the leakage area measurement? You quote an error of +15% for tracer gas.

C. A. Boman and M. D. Lyberg (authors' closure)—Assuming an error of 10 to 15% for a tracer gas or pressurization measurement and, in addition, an error of 15% because a rather simple model is used, the resulting error for the determination of the leakage area should be about 20%.

¹U.S. Department of Energy, New York, NY 10014.

Martin W. Liddament[1]

A Review of European Research into Airtightness and Air Infiltration Measurement Techniques

REFERENCE: Liddament, M. W., "**A Review of European Research into Airtightness and Air Infiltration Measurement Techniques,**" *Measured Air Leakage of Buildings, ASTM STP 904*, H. R. Trechsel and P. L. Lagus, Eds., American Society for Testing and Materials, Philadelphia, 1986, pp. 407–415.

ABSTRACT: An important function of the Air Infiltration Centre, Bracknell, Berkshire, Great Britain, is to keep research organizations informed of on-going research into air infiltration in buildings. To fulfill this need, the Centre regularly undertakes a worldwide survey of current research. In this report, the results of the Centre's most recent survey, completed in 1983, are used to provide a background to present European airtightness and air infiltration measurement practices. A wide range of research activities are summarized involving the use of both pressurization and tracer gas techniques. In addition, the increasing effort being devoted to the measurement of air infiltration in nondomestic buildings is emphasized. Other topics covered include ventilation efficiency measurements and multitracer air movement studies.

KEY WORDS: review, airtightness, air infiltration, measurement methods, dwellings, nondomestic buildings

An important function of the Air Infiltration Centre (AIC) is to maintain a current awareness of air infiltration research. The Centre endeavors to fulfill this commitment in a number of ways, the most important of which is to undertake a regular worldwide survey of on-going research into air infiltration in buildings [1]. Since the inception of the AIC in June 1979, the results of three such surveys have been published. The first, in Oct. 1980, contained an analysis of 65 projects based on information received from organizations in 14 countries. This was followed in Dec. 1981 by an analysis of 126 new projects. The results of the most recent survey were published in Nov. 1983 and were based on an analysis of 187 projects in 22 countries. In recognition of the

[1]Head, Air Infiltration Centre, Bracknell, Berkshire, RG12 4AH, United Kingdom.

growing importance being attached to the influence of fresh air exchange rates on indoor air quality, the scope of this latest survey was specifically extended to include this topic.

Approximately one third of the respondents to the survey cited indoor air quality as a specific objective, with measurement techniques taking second place with a 25% response. The remaining most widely cited objectives included mathematical modeling, airtightness construction and retrofit methods, studies into the cost-effectiveness of airtightness measures, and investigations into the performance of heating, ventilation, and heat recovery systems.

Almost 50% of the projects reported were based on research summaries received from Europe; these projects include a number of entries from the Eastern European countries of Czechoslovakia, Hungary, Poland, and Yugoslavia. Of the remaining entries, 25% came from the United States, 20% from Canada, and 5% from other countries. A full list of countries is given in Table 1. It is the purpose of this report to focus on the European aspects of this survey, with particular emphasis on measurement methods. In preparing this report, other sources of research information also were used, including the International Council for Building Research (CIB) "Heating and Climiti-

TABLE 1—*Survey of research—contributing countries.*

Country	Number of Replies
Australia	1
Belgium	2
Canada	37
Czechoslovakia	1
Denmark	4
Finland	4
France	1
Germany	8
Hungary	1
Italy	2
Japan	6
Netherlands	18
New Zealand	1
Norway	2
Papua New Guinea	1
Poland	2
South Africa	1
Sweden	10
Switzerland	6
United Kingdom	31
United States of America	47
Yugoslavia	1

zation Review of Research" [2] and details of the Commission of the European Communities research program into building energy conservation [3].

Basis for European Research

The significance of air infiltration research cannot be overemphasized; on the one hand, air infiltration can account for a substantial proportion of the heat loss from a building, while, on the other hand, excessive levels of airtightness can result in a serious deterioration in indoor air quality. These apparently conflicting needs have formed the basis behind much of the research effort in Europe over several decades. In the United Kingdom, as early as 1942, for example, the Egerton Committee on Heating and Ventilation [4] recommended minimum standards for ventilation in dwellings based on the need to keep occupied spaces free from noticeable odors. It was further stated that ". . . . the standards recommended, which are minimal for winter conditions, should not be much exceeded in winter otherwise the cost of heating will be significantly increased." During the intervening period, energy resources became more plentiful with the result that reduced consideration was given to the need for energy conservation. More recently, however, the unreliability of imported energy supplies has been vividly demonstrated, thus providing renewed impetus for further research. This is particularly true of Sweden, where indigenous energy resources are limited and the winter climate is severe. Consequently, the Swedish government is placing substantial emphasis on the conservation of energy in buildings, with the intention of reducing energy consumption in the existing building stock by 30% [5]. In pursuance of this aim, much effort has been concentrated on the reduction of air infiltration and on the introduction of ventilation heat recovery systems. Stringent airtightness regulations for new buildings also have been introduced [6]. To support these actions, a substantial research program is in progress. In other parts of Europe, the oil crisis of 1973 also resulted in the initiation of energy conservation research.

Buildings Investigated

The majority of buildings referenced in the Centre's survey of research are dwellings, although, increasingly, other varieties of building are being considered. In the 1980 survey, for example, the ratio of dwellings to other buildings was approximately 3:1, whereas in the 1983 analysis this ratio had reduced to 2:1. The remaining buildings include commercial premises, industrial buildings, schools, and hospitals. Measurements in both occupied and unoccupied buildings are being performed, with simulated occupancy also being a fairly popular approach. Unlike North America, very few buildings (especially dwellings) are air-conditioned, thus energy conservation studies tend to concentrate on space heating needs rather than cooling loads.

Measurement Methods

Air Leakage Measurements (Pressurization Testing)

Dwellings—Airtightness standards for new dwellings were introduced in Sweden in 1980 [6]. The statutory maximum leakages of 3 ACH at 50 Pa for single-family dwellings, 2 ACH for other two-story dwellings, and 1 ACH for high-rise apartment buildings put an obligation on builders and the local building inspectorate to ensure that new housing conformed to these standards. Whole building pressurization test measurements are, therefore, a common procedure in Sweden, and suitable instrumentation for measurements in dwellings is available from several manufacturers. Test conditions are very precise [7] and it is important to recognize that it is the "fabric" leakage that is measured; all purpose-provided openings and slot air vents, etc., are sealed for the duration of the test. Norway has proposed similar but slightly less stringent airtightness requirements [8], with the result that pressurization testing is becoming a common practice in this country. Elsewhere in Europe, whole-house, air-leakage testing is restricted very much to the research sector, and commercially produced instrumentation such as the "blower door" is not available.

Industrial Buildings—The maximum volume of enclosure that may be pressurized is governed by the overall airtightness of the building and the size of the available fan. In the past, these conditions have restricted the size of the building in which pressurization measurements could be made. More recently, however, tests have been made in large industrial-type premises. Lundin [9] describes such a technique used by the Swedish National Testing Institute, where air leakage measurements have been made in buildings with gross volumes in excess of 60 000 m^3.

Component Leakage—Component pressurization leakage testing appears to be much more widely reported in Europe than elsewhere. Many of these investigations are being performed to improve the theoretical understanding of air leakage sites in buildings and to quantify component leakage values. Components of interest include windows, doors, facades, and party walls. This technique also is being used in the United Kingdom by Ward [10] to assess the potential and performance of retrofit measures. European countries reporting component pressurization testing in the AIC survey include Belgium, Finland, France, Italy, Poland, Sweden, Switzerland, and the United Kingdom.

Tracer Gas Measurements

The tracer gas technique is well established, and basic concentration decay measurements are commonplace throughout Europe. The most significant difference between European and American tracer gas testing is the widespread use in Europe of nitrous oxide, which now appears to be little used in the United States and Canada. Recent tracer gas developments have concentrated on automatic methods for multizone monitoring and on multitracer air movement studies. Other important studies are focusing on ventilation efficiency measurements and on the measurement of air infiltration in large enclosed spaces. Each of these aspects is covered in further detail in paragraphs that follow.

Automatic Instrumentation for Multizone Monitoring—Instrumentation for multizone monitoring has been developed in Denmark [*11*], Sweden [*12*], and the United Kingdom [*13*] and also is currently in the course of development at the Federal Institute of Technology in Lausanne, Switzerland. The Danish instrumentation has been used to continuously monitor air change rates within an occupied dwelling over a period of many months. The system comprises a microcomputer, which is used to monitor the rate of tracer gas injection and to sample tracer gas in up to 10 rooms. The tracer gas is sampled in each room sequentially, and any drift in concentration from a nominal value of 50 ppm is restored by adjustments to the tracer gas injection rate. The fresh air exchange rate in each room is therefore directly proportional to the tracer gas injection rate. In its original form, the instrumentation was designed to operate using nitrous oxide tracer gas but subsequently has been modified to use sulfur hexafluoride.

Similar operating principles are used in the instrumentation developed at the National Testing Institute in Sweden [*12*] and at British Gas in the United Kingdom [*13*]. The British Gas system also has been designed to accommodate a secondary tracer gas for use in air movement studies.

The main problem with these methods is that instability in tracer gas concentrations tends to arise as a result of a step change in conditions, as occurs, for example, when windows or external doors are opened or closed. Thus, when developing the software to operate multizone constant concentration systems, it is essential to ensure that step changes do not give rise to excessive or harmful increases in tracer gas concentration. The principal advantage of the multizone method is that it enables individual room air change rates to be quickly measured. This has proved invaluable in assessing the influence of various design features on both individual room and whole house air change rates. In particular, such problems as insufficient ventilation rates can be rapidly identified.

Measurements of Air Movement—Air movement studies have become an important aspect of air infiltration research and a number of measurement systems recently have been developed for this purpose. One such system, based on a multitracer concentration decay technique, has been developed at the Polytechnic of Central London in the United Kingdom [*14*]. The system can accommodate up to four perfluoro tracer compound gases, which may be released at various points in the building. The mixture of gases may be sampled at any number of positions in the building as a function of time since release. The samples are collected using adsorption tubes and subsequently are analyzed in the laboratory. From the analysis, the concentration of each gas at discrete time intervals and at each location can be determined. The entire sampling process is controlled by means of a microcomputer.

A variation of this technique has been developed at Sheffield University, also in the United Kingdom [15]. This system is capable of measuring the concentrations of up to three fluoro tracer gases simultaneously, using a directly linked gas chromatograph with electron capture. Each gas may be released into one of three distinct zones within the building and, by measuring the variations in concentration of the gases over a period of 2 to 3 h, the ventilation rate and interzone air movement may be determined. A similar approach for determining interzone air movement within a large office building (with a gross volume of 1860 m³) has been developed at the U.K. Building Research Establishment [16]. The building is subdivided into three zones, each of which is seeded with either carbon dioxide, sulfur hexafluoride, or nitrous oxide. An automatic sampling system is used to monitor the concentrations of each of these gases in each zone. As with the previous methods, the resultant gas concentrations are used to determine the interzone airflow patterns.

Ventilation Efficiency—Measurements into the efficiency of ventilation strategies have had important significance in Sweden, where the implementation of airtightness regulations for dwellings has resulted in the widespread introduction of mechanical ventilation systems in domestic buildings. The fundamental aim of current investigations is to develop design guidelines for establishing efficient ventilation in multiroom applications [17]. Of particular concern is the optimum location of inlet and exhaust terminals to ensure adequate ventilation. Measurements are being made in an indoor full-scale test house with one facade exposed to the outdoor environment. The performance of both mechanical extract and combined supply/extract systems are being assessed. Ventilation efficiency is being measured using both the concentration decay and constant emission tracer gas techniques. In both instances, the tracer gas concentration is continuously recorded at different locations within the building, from which the local ventilation rate and hence the ventilation efficiency is determined.

Tracer Gas Measurements in Industrial Buildings—The success of the tracer gas method is dependent on the perfect mixing of the gas. Adequate mixing normally can be achieved in dwellings by placing small mixing fans at each internal doorway or by injecting the gas directly into the air distribution plenum of warm air heating systems. Furthermore, small deficiencies in mixing often can be overcome by paying careful attention to the sampling method. Very often multipoint sampling is used, in which each location is either linked via an equal length tube to a manifold or is sampled sequentially and averaged. Other detection methods rely on single-point sampling from a central location or on sampling the tracer gas concentration in the return air duct of warm air systems. Unfortunately, the tendency for internal air circulation and stratification to resist mixing tends to place an upper limit on the size of enclosure in which conventional tracer gas measurements may be made. It is partly for this reason that so much effort has been devoted to dwellings and very little to other varieties of buildings. Recently, however, consideration has been given to the excessive air infiltration heat loss from large single cell industrial structures, with particular emphasis on warehouses. These buildings are frequently very leaky and, unlike factories, have no waste process heat available to satisfy space heating requirements.

Although gasketing options are normally available, occupiers are very often unwilling to pay the additional premium because there is no reliable information on payback periods. As a consequence, a number of researchers have begun to devote their attention to this problem. The position regarding airtightness measurements in warehouses already has been touched upon [9], but new techniques involving the use of tracer gas are being introduced. Two such approaches were described at the Air Infiltration Centre's 4th Annual Conference, held in Elm, Switzerland [18,19]. While in some respects the methods adopted are contrasting, the underlying philosophy of each is very similar. Firstly, it was agreed that it is unwise to attempt to overcome, by means of artificial mixing, the naturally occurring stratification and air movement patterns in these buildings. Apart from the extreme difficulty of implementing such a measure, it is argued that the conditions under which air infiltration ordinarily occurs would be destroyed and that, therefore, such an approach would yield a meaningless result. Both methods therefore are based on the assumption that imperfect mixing is likely, and that the measurement of air infiltration rates should take account of this. The approaches also are similar in that multipoint injection and sampling techniques are used.

The method developed by Dewsbury [2,18] incorporates three infrared gas analyzers, each linked to ten sampling tubes via computer-operated valves. The network has been designed to automatically sample the tracer gas concentration at 30 locations within a 5-min period. Nitrous oxide tracer gas is initially injected throughout the building, and the local concentration decay rate at each measurement site is recorded over a period of several hours. The apparatus is currently being verified by comparing results against a known induced air change rate in a warehouse having an approximate volume of 7 000 m³. The system also is being verified against various patterns of imperfect internal mixing.

Freeman [19] uses discrete injection and sampling units, each of identical design and comprising a sealed gas bag and a peristaltic pump. The injection units are initially filled with sulfur hexafluoride, while the sample units are empty. Tracer gas is released at a constant rate of emission and locally mixed using small fans to ensure no layering of the tracer gas due to density differences. Samples are taken some distance from the injection points by drawing air into the sampling units. The flow rate can be adjusted to collect samples over periods ranging from 0.5 to 14 days. Many samples can be collected simultaneously at different heights and positions in the zone being investigated. The performance of this technique has been compared with conventional decay and constant concentration techniques in test volumes of up to 630 m³, this being the volume limit for the conventional approaches.

Further studies on tracer gas measurements in naturally ventilated large enclosures are being carried out in France at the Centre Technique des Industries and in the United Kingdom at Coventry Polytechnic.

Discussion

From the viewpoints of both energy conservation and indoor air quality considerations, there is an urgent need to ensure that design and retrofit approaches are well planned and are conducted in conjunction with a coordinated program of measurements. It is, therefore, encouraging to note that a diverse range of air infiltration and airtightness measurement techniques are being developed and used, not only in Europe but also throughout the world. In addition to the widespread use of basic pressurization and tracer gas measurement methods, a move towards air infiltration studies in nondomestic buildings has resulted in a strengthening of research into multicell applications and air movement measurements. In particular, an understanding of air flow patterns in tight buildings is vital in order to maximize ventilation efficiency at low air exchange rates. Many of these new areas of study still require further development, especially in the interpretation of results.

Measurement methods still are confined largely to the research sector, with no complete tracer gas system being commercially available in Europe. This tends to hamper progress and limits the number of buildings in which air infiltration measurements are being made. It is hoped that future developments, perhaps in the field of passive tracer gas techniques, will overcome this problem.

It is thought that a continuing need to conserve energy, especially in the industrial and commercial sectors where individual space heating demands can be large, will provide a foundation for further development in measurement techniques.

References

[1] Liddament, M. W., "1983 Survey of Current Research into Air Infiltration and Related Air Quality Problems in Buildings," Air Infiltration Centre, Bracknell, Berkshire, Great Britain, Nov. 1982.
[2] "Heating and Climatization Review of Research," International Council for Building Research, Steering Group S-17, Rotterdam, 1981.
[3] "New Ways to Save Energy—System Simulation in Buildings," Proceedings, European Economic Community International Conference, Liege, Belgium, Dec. 1983, Commission of the European Communities, Luxembourg.
[4] Egerton Committee, "Heating and Ventilation of Dwellings," Post War Building Studies No. 19, Her Majesty's Stationery Office, London, England, 1945.

[5] Olofsdotter, B., "Energy and the Built Environment," D9, in English, Swedish Council for Building Research, Stockholm, 1982.

[6] Swedish Building Regulations, SBN 1980, with comments, Statens Planverk, Stockholm, Sweden.

[7] Kronvall, J., "Airtightness—Measurements and Measurement Methods," D6, Swedish Council for Building Research, Stockholm, Sweden, 1980.

[8] "Thermal Insulation and Airtightness," Norwegian Building Regulations of 1 Aug. 1969, revised 1980, Ministry of Local Government and Labour, Oslo, Norway.

[9] Lundin, L. in *Proceedings*, 4th AIC Conference on Air Infiltration Reduction in Existing Buildings, Elm, Switzerland, Sept. 1983, Air Infiltration Centre, Bracknell, Berkshire, Great Britain, pp. 6.1–6.8.

[10] Ward, I. in *Proceedings*, 4th AIC Conference on Air Infiltration Reduction in Existing Buildings, Elm, Switzerland, Sept. 1983, Air Infiltration Centre, Bracknell, Berkshire, Great Britain, Supplement pp. 1–26.

[11] Collet, P. F. in *Proceedings*, 2nd AIC Conference on Building Design for Minimum Air Infiltration, Stockholm, Sweden, Sept. 1981, Air Infiltration Centre, Bracknell, Berkshire, Great Britain, pp. 147–160.

[12] Lundin, L. and Blomsterberg, A., "An Automated Air Infiltration Measurement System—Its Design and Capabilities—Preliminary Results," *Air Infiltration Review*, Vol. 4, No. 1, Nov. 1982.

[13] Alexander, D. K., Etheridge, D. W., and Gale, R. in *Proceedings*, 1st AIC Conference on Air Infiltration Instrumentation and Measurement Techniques, Windsor, England, Oct. 1980, Air Infiltration Centre, Bracknell, Berkshire, Great Britain, pp. 45–71.

[14] Prior, J., Littler, J., and Adlard, M., "Development of a Multi-tracer Gas Technique for Observing Air Flow in Buildings," *Air Infiltration Review*, Vol. 4, No. 3, May 1983.

[15] Howarth, A. T., Irwin, C., and Edwards, R. E., "An Improved Multi-tracer Gas Technique for the Calculation of Air Movement in Buildings," *Air Infiltration Review*, Vol. 5, No. 2, Feb. 1984.

[16] Perera, M., Walker, R. R., and Oglesby, O. D. in *Proceedings*, 4th AIC Conference on Air Infiltration Reduction in Existing Buildings, Elm, Switzerland, Sept. 1983, Air Infiltration Centre, Bracknell, Berkshire, Great Britain, pp. 12.1–12.13.

[17] Sandberg, M., "Ventilation Efficiency as a Guide to Design," *ASHRAE Transactions*, Vol. 89, Pt. 2, 1983.

[18] Potter, N., Dewsbury, J., and Jones, T. in *Proceedings*, 4th AIC Conference on Air Infiltration Reduction in Existing Buildings, Elm, Switzerland, Sept. 1983, Air Infiltration Centre, Bracknell, Berkshire, Great Britain, pp. 147–160.

[19] Freeman, J., Gale, R., and Lilly, J. P. in *Proceedings*, 4th AIC Conference on Air Infiltration Reduction in Existing Buildings, Elm, Switzerland, Air Infiltration Centre, Bracknell, Berkshire, Great Britain, pp. 5.1–5.14.

Summary

The session on measured air infiltration rates in residences showed that the situation has changed drastically since the first symposium on air infiltration in 1978. Whereas in 1978 little measured data existed on air infiltration in residential buildings, today there are probably more than a thousand dwellings on which air infiltration data or pressurization data, or both, exist. This session contained excellent papers that summarized the state of the existing data on air infiltration.

Lagus and King discussed air infiltration and induced pressurization in duplexes and row apartments at two naval bases. Data were collected in both the winter and summer. They calculated the leakage areas in these dwellings using both air infiltration data and fan pressurization data. The directional nature of the dependence of air infiltration on wind speed is shown in some of the data.

The paper by Shaw gives a detailed study of the seasonal variation of air leakage in two Canadian houses. The data show as much as a 20% seasonal variation in the airtightness of the houses and that there is a good correlation of this variation to the relative humidity.

Nagda et al. presented the results of a 2-year detailed study of air infiltration and indoor air quality in two houses, one of which was retrofitted to reduce its air infiltration. The effect of installing an air-to-air heat exchanger also was studied. Though the retrofitting reduced the air leakage by 40%, the reduction in air infiltration due to the retrofit was overwhelmed by the reduction in infiltration rates due to the changes in weather conditions, the absolute differences between the two houses remaining surprisingly identical before and after retrofit. The air-to-air heat exchanger increased the ventilation rate of the house by about 0.3 to 0.4 air changes per hour.

Persily presented the results of air infiltration and pressurization measurements on about 70 passive solar buildings. Though it has been believed that houses of passive solar design were tighter than typical construction, the data in this paper show that passive solar buildings are no tighter than typical new construction. The paper also presents several models to relate the measured air infiltration as a function of temperature and wind speed to the building tightness.

Gammage et al. presented data on air infiltration and airtightness in 31 East Tennessee homes. In these homes the duct system was a major source of air leakage and added about 0.3 air changes per house to the air infiltration rate. Some of these houses have return air ducts that run through the garage, and this was a source of infusion of contaminants into the houses.

Goldschmidt presented an extensive review of the existing data on air infiltration worldwide with the purpose of trying to determine the effectiveness of the operation of gas furnaces on the air infiltration in homes. He concludes that the existing data support an 0.1 to 0.2 additional air exchange per hour due to the existence of gas furnaces. This paper is a good source for reference to the data on air infiltration.

The purpose of the commercial and industrial session was to present the state of the art of air leakage measurement techniques as they relate to nonresidential buildings. For the past several years many researchers have been working on residential infiltration, specifically single-family structures. Since the largest number of residential buildings in North America are single-family, this effort has been properly placed. In the last few years, however, much has been learned in these structures, and many researchers are beginning to turn their attention to nonresidential structures.

The Lundin paper discussed pressurization tests of nine moderately sized industrial buildings by fan pressurization. The buildings ranged in floor area from 1025 to 6524 m^2, with envelope areas (walls and roofs) from 2100 to 9876 m^2. The buildings included both steel frames with attached sheet metal wall elements and precast concrete frames with light-weight concrete wall elements. Because of the high airflow rate, conventional means for its measurement were not appropriate, and tracer gas was used for determining actual flow rates. This method proved effective and accurate. Airflow rates per square meter of building envelope, measured at a pressure difference of 50 Pa, ranged from 2.0 to 8.0 m^3/h. There was no obvious and significant difference between the steel and concrete buildings.

The paper by Waters and Simons and the paper by Ashley and Lagus dealt with the problems of making tracer gas measurements in large, single-cell, industrial-type buildings. The problem of mixing was deemed paramount; problems related to mixing included injection, sampling, and control. The paper by Waters and Simons described how multipoint sampling may be helpful in understanding the mixing problems and internal flows. The paper by Ashley and Lagus described many of the practical problems associated with making measurements in structures as large as airplane hangers.

The papers by Hunt, Grot and Persily, and Persily and Grot dealt with making fan pressurization and tracer gas measurements on mid- to high-rise office buildings. The paper by Hunt was concerned with making differential measurements on subsections of these buildings. As it turned out, the fan used for the zone measurements was relatively undersized, and Hunt went into detail about how one can extract useful information from such results and what kind of accuracies one can expect.

The Grot and Persily papers concerned almost the same set of buildings; Grot described the results of tracer gas measurements made in these buildings with the HVAC system both on and off, while Persily discussed the pressurization measurements made with the buildings' HVAC system. The tracer measurements indicated that it is important to consider a large building's infiltration rate (that is, ventilation when the mechanical system is off) and ventilation when operating the outside-air intakes; the results suggest that in many cases the building can get sufficient outside air with the outside-air damper fully closed. The leakage studies used the HVAC system to pressurize or depressurize the building and to determine the tightness characteristics. Interesting comparisons were made between these buildings and typical residential ones. Since large buildings have a much smaller surface-to-volume ratio, it was concluded that air changes per hour at a specified pressure difference was not a good method for comparing buildings of different sizes. Preliminary results using the Shaw model for correlating the pressurization results to the tracer gas results were disappointing, but Grot and Persily indicated that more work would be done in this area.

All papers in this session were excellent contributions to the literature and opened a new field of infiltration research. For those who wish to extend their knowledge of the work that has been done in this area, I recommend that they review the proceedings of the 4th Air Infiltration Centre (AIC) conference that took place in Elm, Switzerland in September 1983. The proceedings and other infiltration research is available directly from the AIC in Bracknell, Great Britain.

The coming of age of the perfluorocarbon tracer (PFT) methods, developed at Brookhaven National Labs, was apparent in the opening presentation (Dietz et al.) in the session on Techniques for Measurements and Infiltration Reduction. Not only has the method proved to be successful in relatively long-term average ventilation measurement, but short-term and multizone measurements have been achieved also using the PFT approach. In multizone measurements, three distinct perfluorocarbon tracers allow the research team to quantify interzone airflows in a three-zone structure. A fourth tracer is currently under investigation.

The paper presented by Jacobson et al. compared air leakage reduction from house retrofits as measured by pressurization and tracer gas measurements. The lack of a strong correlation between these two quantities indicates the difficulty of using pressurization data in estimating air infiltration energy savings.

On-site measurements in family housing using a streamlined testing procedure, which included fan depressurization only, was described by Verschoor and Collins of Manville Research and Development Center. Key to the testing was the extremes in tightness encountered in the housing, clearly pointing out that certain housing needs no further tightening.

Treating all of the outer wall surfaces, other than windows, Luebs and Weimar from NAHB Research Foundation and DuPont reported on the success using an air barrier just under the exterior sheathing. This approach eliminates air penetration but allows trapped moisture to escape. The heating season savings measured in a test house were greater than 25%, of which about half could be attributed to the reduction of air infiltration.

Throughout the session it was very evident that our field measurements of house airtightness have greatly increased over the past few years. The techniques for measurement have continued to be refined, but that technique directly interpreting air infiltration from pressurization measurements alone comes with a sizeable error band. Component leakage values fulfill a useful purpose in placing tightening goals in perspective, but testing the building as completed is the final proof that the desired airtightness level has been achieved. Such airtightness quantification allows one to point out where mechanical ventilation is desirable or necessary or both. Standards for the testing methods must be well-specified, and calibration methods for test equipment must not be overlooked.

The paper by Giesbrecht and Proskiw discussed a field study on the effectiveness of air leakage sealing techniques on 82 houses located in Winnipeg and Southern Manitoba, Canada. Air leaks were detected using negative pressure and smoke pencils. Air sealing measures included the weather-stripping of windows and doors and the caulking of other leakages as indicated. Before and after retrofit, fan pressurization tests (negative pressure only) indicated median equivalent leakage area reductions of 31.6% at 10 Pa. The greatest reduction was in single story houses with 36.9%. In two-story houses, the reduction averaged only 24.4%.

During a panel discussion at the 1978 symposium "Building Air Change Rate and Infiltration Measurements" hosted by ASTM Committee E-06, one gentleman asked a detailed question about the prediction of infiltration rates under a wide variety of meteorological and building conditions. There was, at that time, a lot of interest and pressure from, for instance, various regulatory agencies at the local, state, and (to a somewhat lesser degree) federal levels. At that time, the committee was being asked to run a four-minute mile while, in fact, we were just at the stage where we were learning to crawl. In the intervening 6 years, it appears that we have learned to walk—and, occasionally, to run. However, listening to papers presented in the Analysis Session, as well as the ensuing discussion, the situation can be likened to Friday rush hour in Manhattan's Penn Station.

The paper by Sherman and Modera basically outlined the continuing work at Lawrence Berkeley Laboratory on an infiltration model designed to predict natural air infiltration from fan pressurization measurements. The model, itself, deals with two parts: the first, with the weather and local environment; the second, with the leakage distribution of an individual structure. In order to arrive at a physically tractable model, a large number of assumptions regarding uniformity of leakage, wind profile, shielding, temperature profile, wind directions, and a linear flow envelope have been made. In addition, linear superposition of thermal and wind effects has been posited. Four key assumptions regarding the model are: (1) orifice flow, (2) flow superposition, (3) averaging over aspect ratio, and (4) averaging over wind directions. Extensive calculational analysis shows that errors due to wind-direction averaging could be as much as 60% for some cases. Errors due to aspect-ratio averaging could be as much as 20%. The model itself, however, seems to predict average behavior of a large number of structures under diverse meteorological conditions. As such, it provides a powerful analytical constraint on measured data, as well as on other calculational models.

The paper by Sherman et al. draws a distinction between air leakage and infiltration. Air leakage is being measured by fan pressurization. However, infiltration is the quantity of interest in, for instance, energy conservation and indoor air pollution studies. The primary thrust of this paper was to study the effects of changes in the value of the leakage constant and the pressure exponent. It is well-demonstrated that if in doubt "n" should be somewhat larger than 0.5, implying that flow is not quite true turbulent flow. A pressure exponent of 0.67 is a good choice in the absence of any other data. One interesting fact that emerged from this study is that for a large sample of houses it doesn't matter whether leakage area is calculated using positive pressurization, negative pressurization, or the average of both. Approximately the same calculated infiltration rates resulted. However, for any one house, the error could be almost 30%. This same magnitude of variability is seen in the leakage area and the exponent "n."

A striking feature of data presented in both of the Sherman papers is the log-normal frequency distribution of infiltration values. This distribution also is seen in Grot's (NBS) community weatherization program data. However, for any given structure or climate, the variability in the pressure exponent and the leakage area precludes simple a priori predictions with great precision.

The paper by Bassett elucidates the adaptation of an infiltration model in a mild climate. In this paper, he points out that it is possible to correlate, in a loose fashion, airtightness data and a wind exposure index determined from site examination. For the New Zealand structures presented, it is apparent that a model appropriate for infiltration calculations in this region is primarily a wind-driven model possessing little sensitivity to temperature.

The papers by Blomsterberg and Lundin and Boman and Lyberg discuss at length various adaptations of the LBL model to Swedish homes. In the Blomsterberg and Lundin paper, extensive discussion is presented for a few homes that are extremely tight by U.S. standards. These houses show 3 ACH at 50 Pa pressurization. The model, itself, is an LBL model that was modified by adding a term for forced ventilation and for an exhaust fan. Mechanical ventilation is necessary since the Swedish homes are generally so tight that an acceptable air quality cannot be maintained by natural infiltration alone. The data presented also show the variations in infiltration from room to room throughout a single structure. These data are notable since they demonstrate graphically that while the *average* air infiltration for a structure may be high enough from an indoor air quality standpoint, several rooms within that same structure may, in fact, fall well below a minimum recommended ventilation rate.

The paper by Boman and Lyberg discusses the results of measurements in 1200 houses in Sweden. The buildings studied include all types of houses within Sweden—including single-family, multi-family, row-housing, one and two-story detached—all of which were built between 1900 and 1982. Natural infiltration was measured using a tracer gas decay technique. A fraction of the homes—approximately 25%—also had air leakage rates determined by a pressurization technique. The data, again, show the importance of the local weather conditions and, particularly, shielding on measured and predicted air infiltration rates.

Both of these Swedish papers demonstrate that it is possible to construct a very tight residential structure. The models used are variants of the Lawrence Berkeley model. This model has permeated the analysis and calculational approaches of the energy—which seems to have permeated the analysis and modeling thinking of the energy conservation community to date.

Liddament discussed a recent survey on air infiltration research. The survey was conducted by the Air Infiltration Centre in Bracknell, Berkshire, United Kingdom. The survey results are used as background for European airtightness and infiltration-measurement practices. Although past and current research emphasizes dwellings, increasing efforts are being devoted to other building types. The survey covered measurement technology, both pressurization and tracer gas (including multitracer air movement studies), airtightness, ventilation efficiency, indoor air quality, and air movement within buildings. The survey included countries in West and East Europe, North America, South Africa, the Far East, Australia, and New Zealand. The results indicate that the conflicting concerns of indoor air quality and of energy conservation through airtightness is being considered worldwide. However, it was noted also that measurements of air infiltration and airtightness still are confined largely to research activities.

It was disappointing that no papers were received discussing other models for infiltration in residences, namely, the Institute for Gas Technology model or the Shaw-Tamura model. While neither of these models has been as widely discussed as the LBL model, they certainly possess validity for at least a limited set of data. At a future symposium, one would hope that a presentation of the rudiments of these models would be presented. Such a presentation would afford a better appreciation and an understanding of the advantages and limitations of the infiltration/air leakage models that have been proposed.

There has been great progress over the last 6 years in the area of air infiltration modelling. However, much of the effort has been devoted strictly to single-cell type models which are appropriate to single-family residential structures. Now that a start has been made for these structures, it is hoped that models appropriate to row housing, apartment buildings, industrial and commercial buildings, and large office buildings will begin to appear. Such models will be required to obtain a detailed understanding of the performance characteristics of these structures, as well as to provide an analytical framework within which to interpret the increasing body of experimental data relative to infiltration, air leakage, and mechanical ventilation.

R. A. Grot

National Bureau of Standards, Washington, DC; symposium cochairman

M. H. Sherman

Lawrence Berkeley Laboratories, Berkeley, CA; symposium cochairman

D. T. Harrje

Princeton University, Princeton, NJ; symposium cochairman

P. L. Lagus

S-Cubed, La Jolla, CA; symposium cochairman and coeditor

Author Index

S

Shaw, C. Y., 17
Sherman, M. H., 325, 348, 422
Simons, M. W., 106
Socolow, R. H., 265

V

Verschoor, J. D., 294

W

Waters, J. R., 106
Wieser, R. F., 203
Wilson, D. J., 348
White, D. A., 61

Subject Index

A

ACH (Air changes per hour) (*see* Air exchange measurements)

Air exchange (*see also* Air exchange measurement, Air leakage measurements), 36, 61–69, 70–97, 399, 400

Following retrofit, 42–43 (Table 3, Fig. 5), 86, 265–267

Retrofit, Navy family housing, Mechanics manual, 296, 297 (Fig. 1)

Swedish standard SP1977:1, National Swedish Authority for Testing Inspection and Metrology: Standard method description, 400

Air exchange measurements (*see also* Perfluorocarbon tracer system), 399–405

Air changes per hour (ACH), 240 (Equation 14), 295

Equations (15–22), 246–247

In high-rise office buildings, 137 (Fig. 1), 138, 139 (Figs. 2–3), 148, 149

In passive perfluorocarbon tracer system, 203, 220–221

Results and discussion, 222–226 (Fig. 6, Tables 5–8)

In pressurization testing, 275–277 (Table 5)

Infiltration and exfiltration, 71, 240 (Equation 14—ACH), 247–249 (Fig. 13, Table 21)

Mechanics' handbook, Navy family housing, 296

Air exchange rates (*see* Air exchange measurements, Air infiltration measurement, Air leakage measurement)

Air filtration (*see* Air infiltration)

Airflow measurement (*see* Air exchange measurement)

Airflow resistance

Of common building materials, 373 (Table 1)

Air-handling equipment, large federal buildings, 185

Air infiltration/exfiltration (*see also* Air leakage, Airtightness, Infiltration, Pressurization/depressurization, Perfluorocarbon tracer systems), 33, 61–69, 315

BNL classic comparison house, 308 (Table 1)

Caused by exhaust fan/ventilation system operation, 315

Central duct fan, 62

Effects on energy use, 70, 316

HVAC systems, 62

In large federal buildings, 184, 195 (Fig. 4)

Infiltration models (PFT systems) (*see also* Air infiltration measurement), 260–261

Infiltration reduction, 265

In military aircraft hangers, 121

In high-rise office buildings, 151

425